Comparison and Oscillation Theory of Linear Differential Equations

This is Volume 48 in
MATHEMATICS IN SCIENCE AND ENGINEERING
A series of monographs and textbooks
Edited by RICHARD BELLMAN, *University of Southern California*

A complete list of the books in this series appears at the end of this volume.

Comparison and Oscillation Theory of Linear Differential Equations

C. A. SWANSON

DEPARTMENT OF MATHEMATICS
THE UNIVERSITY OF BRITISH COLUMBIA
VANCOUVER, BRITISH COLUMBIA
CANADA

 ACADEMIC PRESS   New York and London   1968

ACADEMIC PRESS INC.
111 Fifth Avenue, New York, New York 10003

United Kingdom Edition published by
ACADEMIC PRESS INC. (LONDON) LTD.
Berkeley Square House, London W.1

LIBRARY OF CONGRESS CATALOG CARD NUMBER: 68-23477

PRINTED IN THE UNITED STATES OF AMERICA

Preface

This book is concerned primarily with the zeros of solutions of linear differential equations: second order ordinary equations in Chapters 1 and 2, fourth order ordinary equations in Chapter 3, other ordinary equations and systems of differential equations in Chapter 4, and partial differential equations in Chapter 5. The term "comparison theorem" originated with Sturm's classical theorem (Theorem 1.1) but is now used in the following more general sense: If a solution of a differential equation 1 has a property P, here generally connected with its oscillatory behavior, then the solutions of a second differential equation 2 have property P or some related property under some stated connection between 1 and 2. Sturm's classical theorem and many modern analogs of it state roughly this: If 1 has a nontrivial solution with zeros, then every solution of 2 has zeros provided the coefficients of 2 majorize those of 1.

Chapter 1 deals with comparison theorems for second order equations and related topics. Chapter 2 treats oscillation and nonoscillation theorems for second order equations; i.e., conditions (either necessary ones or sufficient ones or both) for the solutions to have (or not to have) an infinite number of zeros in the interval $(0, \infty)$. Although Kneser [95] found some oscillation criteria as early as 1893, completely satisfactory theorems were not provided until the work of Hartman [69–78], Hille [81], Leighton [112–115], Nehari [143], Wintner [69–78, 211–213] and others in the period 1947–1957.

No significant analog of Sturm's theory for higher order equations was found until Birkhoff's paper [21] on third order equations in 1911. Reynolds [173] extended some of Birkhoff's work to nth order equations in 1921, and Fite [45] also gave some early results for higher order equations in 1917. The theory of Morse [136,137] dealing with variational methods gave considerable impetus to the modern theory, and the subject started to grow quickly in the late 1940's. The third order theory has been developed largely since 1955 by Greguš [52–57], Hanan [61], Lazer [111], Ráb [159–162], Švec [187–189], Villari [203,204], and Zlamal [222]. These results are summarized in Chapter 4.

The fourth order theory received a considerable unification with the definitive paper of Leighton and Nehari [117] in 1958. Later contributions were made by Howard [84], Barrett [8–12], Kreith [104], and others. Separation, comparison, and oscillation theorems for fourth order equations are included in Chapter 3.

v

The nth order case was hardly studied at all from the time of Reynolds until recently, when a number of mathematicians [1,2,5,6,32,42,50,60,94,96, 99–102,119,120] began studying the general case and generalizing some of the results obtained by Hille, Wintner, Leighton, and others already mentioned. The general case is considered in Chapter 4, Sections 5 and 6.

Reid [169–172] and Sternberg [183] extended the theory to systems of second order equations, again using some of the ideas developed by Morse [136], Bliss and Schoenberg [23]. Earlier, Whyburn [210] had considered a special system which is equivalent to a single fourth order equation. These results are described briefly in Chapter 4, Sections 7 and 8.

The first analog of a Sturm–type comparison theorem for an elliptic partial differential equation was obtained by Hartman and Wintner [79] in 1955. Various recent extensions of this result and related theorems are covered in Chapter 5.

It has not been possible to give complete proofs of all results: in general, the proofs are included in Chapters 1, 2, and 5, partially included in Chapter 3, but largely excluded in Chapter 4. Most of the detailed results have appeared in the journals since 1947, although a few of the older results also are included. Some of the results in Chapters 1 and 5 are new. The writer has attempted to trace all results to their original author(s); however, a certain amount of overlapping of authorship occurs on account of the constant generalization in recent years. Any errors or omissions in this regard will be gratefully received by the undersigned.

This book is about *linear* differential equations although, curiously, nonlinear methods are used and seem to be indispensable in some cases; e.g., Chapter 2, Section 5 and Chapter 4, Section 7. In particular, the strongest results in some sections of Chapter 2 are based on the Riccati equation. Eigenvalue problems are thoroughly connected with the theory of oscillation, as recognized by Barrett, Nehari, and others, and accordingly Courant's minimax principle has an important position in the theory of all even order equations. Some properties of eigenvalues and eigenfunctions are presented in Chapter 1, Section 5, and similar results are scattered throughout the sequel.

A large part of the book can be read profitably by a college senior or beginning graduate student well-acquainted with advanced calculus, complex analysis, linear algebra, and linear differential equations. It is hoped also that the book will be helpful to mathematicians working in this subject. Most of the material has never appeared in book form.

Exercises are given after many sections both to test the material and to extend the results. Some of the exercises are large projects which involve consultation of the references given. The bibliography is meant to be fairly complete since 1950, although some of the earlier references are omitted.

C. A. Swanson

Vancouver
April, 1968

Contents

PREFACE   v

Chapter 1. **Sturm-Type Theorems for Second Order Ordinary Equations**

  1. Comparison Theorems for Self-Adjoint Equations   1
  2. Additional Results of Leighton   8
  3. Extension to General Second Order Equations   10
  4. Comparison Theorems for Singular Equations   16
  5. Comparison Theorems for Eigenfunctions   20
  6. Reid's Comparison Theorems on Focal Points   29
  7. Levin's Comparison Theorems   33
  8. The Order of Zeros   38

Chapter 2. **Oscillation and Nonoscillation Theorems for Second Order Ordinary Equations**

  1. The Oscillation Criteria of Hille and Nehari   44
  2. Conditionally Oscillatory Equations   52
  3. Nehari's Comparison Theorems   56
  4. The Hille–Wintner Comparison Theorem   60
  5. Hille's Necessary and Sufficient Conditions for Nonoscillatory
      Equations   68
  6. Leighton's Oscillation Criteria   70
  7. Potter's Oscillation Criteria   76
  8. Hille's Kneser-Type Oscillation Criteria   85
  9. Nonoscillation Theorems of Hartman and Wintner   88
 10. Asymptotic Estimates for the Number of Zeros of a Solution of
      (1.1) or (2.1)   95
 11. Nonoscillation Criteria for Hill's Equation   104
 12. Nonoscillation Criteria for Complex Equations   109

vii

Chapter 3. **Fourth Order Ordinary Equations**

1. Introduction   113
2. Separation Theorems   114
3. Comparison Theorems for (3.2) and (3.3)   122
4. Comparison Theorems for Other Fourth Order Equations   127
5. Comparison Theorems for Eigenfunctions   132
6. Nonoscillation Theorems   135
7. Leighton and Nehari's Sufficient Conditions for Nonoscillatory
   Equations   140
8. Comparison Theorems for Nonoscillation   142
9. Howard's Comparison Theorems for Eigenvalue Problems   145

Chapter 4. **Third Order Ordinary Equations, nth Order
Ordinary Equations and Systems**

1. Introduction   149
2. Separation Theorems for Third Order Equations   150
3. Comparison Theorems for Third Order Equations   156
4. Oscillation Criteria for Third Order Equations   160
5. Separation and Comparison Theorems for nth Order Equations   165
6. General Oscillation Theorems   168
7. Nonoscillation Theorems for Systems of Differential Equations   177
8. Whyburn's Second Order System   183

Chapter 5. **Partial Differential Equations**

1. Introduction   186
2. Comparison Theorems for Self-Adjoint Equations in Bounded   187
   Domains
3. Comparison Theorems for General Second Order Elliptic
   Equations   191
4. Comparison Theorems on Unbounded Domains   194
5. Extension to Complex-Valued Solutions and Subsolutions   198
6. Lower Bounds for Eigenvalues   203
7. Oscillation Theorems   205
8. Comparison Theorems for Eigenfunctions   208

Bibliography   213

AUTHOR INDEX   223
SUBJECT INDEX   226

Chapter 1

Sturm-Type Theorems for Second Order Ordinary Equations

1. Comparison Theorems for Self-Adjoint Equations

The existence and location of the zeros of the solutions of ordinary differential equations are of central importance in the theory of boundary value problems for such equations, and accordingly an immense literature on this subject has arisen during the past century. The first important result was the celebrated comparison theorem of Sturm [184], dealing with the second order self-adjoint equations

$$lu \equiv \frac{d}{dx}\left[a(x)\frac{du}{dx}\right] + c(x)u = 0, \tag{1.1}$$

$$Lv \equiv \frac{d}{dx}\left[A(x)\frac{dv}{dx}\right] + C(x)v = 0 \tag{1.2}$$

on a bounded open interval $\alpha < x < \beta$, where a, c, A, and C are real-valued continuous functions and $a(x) > 0$, $A(x) > 0$ on $[\alpha, \beta]$. These equations define the *differential operators,* l, L, i.e., mappings whose domains consist roughly of twice differentiable functions. Specifically, the domain $\mathfrak{D}_l$ of l is defined as the set of all real-valued functions $u \in \mathscr{C}^1[\alpha, \beta]$ such that† $au' \in \mathscr{C}^1(\alpha, \beta)$, and $\mathfrak{D}_L$ is the analog of $\mathfrak{D}_l$ with A replacing a. A "solution" of (1.1) is a function $u \in \mathfrak{D}_l$ satisfying $lu = 0$ at every point in (α, β). It is not necessary that a' and A' be continuous or even exist at every point, but if $a \in \mathscr{C}^1(\alpha, \beta)$ (or $A \in \mathscr{C}^1(\alpha, \beta)$) the above definition requires only that a solution of $lu = 0$ (or $Lu = 0$) be of

† A prime on a function denotes differentiation with respect to the argument of the function.

1

class $\mathscr{C}^1[\alpha, \beta] \cap \mathscr{C}^2(\alpha, \beta)$. In what follows, we shall exclude "trivial" solutions, i.e., solutions which are identically zero on the interval under consideration. Sturm's original theorem can be stated as follows:

Sturm's Comparison Theorem 1.1   *Suppose* $a(x) = A(x)$ *and* $c(x) < C(x)$ *in the bounded interval* $\alpha < x < \beta$. *If there exists a nontrivial real solution* u *of* $lu = 0$ *such that* $u(\alpha) = u(\beta) = 0$, *then every real solution of* $Lv = 0$ *has at least one zero in* (α, β).

Proof   Suppose to the contrary that v does not vanish in (α, β). It may be supposed without loss of generality that $v(x) > 0$ and also $u(x) > 0$ in (α, β). Multiplication of (1.1) by v, (1.2) by u, subtraction of the resulting equations, and integration over (α, β) yields

$$\int_\alpha^\beta [(au')'v - (av')'u]\, dx = \int_\alpha^\beta (C - c)uv\, dx. \tag{1.3}$$

Since the integrand on the left side is the derivative of $a(u'v - uv')$ and $C(x) - c(x) > 0$ by hypothesis, it follows that

$$\left[a(x)(u'(x)v(x) - u(x)v'(x)) \right]_\alpha^\beta > 0. \tag{1.4}$$

However, $u(\alpha) = u(\beta) = 0$ by hypothesis, and since $u(x) > 0$ in (α, β), $u'(\alpha) > 0$ and $u'(\beta) < 0$. Thus the left member of (1.4) is negative, which is a contradiction.

Sturm obtained Theorem 1.1 in 1836 [184] but it was not until 1909 that Picone [149] disposed of the case $a(x) \neq A(x)$. The modification due to Picone is as follows:

Sturm–Picone Comparison Theorem 1.2   *Suppose* $a(x) > A(x)$ *and* $c(x) < C(x)$ *in the interval* $\alpha < x < \beta$. *Then the conclusion of Theorem 1.1 is valid.*

The proof will be deferred since this is a special case of a theorem of Leighton (Theorem 1.4) to be proved later. The original proof of Picone made use of a modification of the formula (1.3) [90].

A significant improvement of the Sturm–Picone theorem was obtained by Leighton in 1962 [116] from a variational lemma depending only on an elementary identity. This lemma will be stated in terms of the quadratic functional defined by the equation

$$J[u] = \int_\alpha^\beta (Au'^2 - Cu^2)\, dx. \tag{1.5}$$

The domain $\mathfrak{D}$ of J is defined to be the set of all real-valued functions $u \in \mathscr{C}^1[\alpha, \beta]$ such that $u(\alpha) = u(\beta) = 0$. A standard integration by parts yields Green's first formula

$$\int_\alpha^\beta uLu \, dx + J[u] = \left[A(x)u(x)u'(x) \right]_\alpha^\beta \qquad (1.6)$$

for $u \in \mathfrak{D}_L$, or even under less stringent conditions which ensure the meaningfulness of the formula. The following lemma is similar to a theorem from the calculus of variations [24].

Lemma 1.3   *If there exists a function $u \in \mathfrak{D}$, not identically zero, such that $J[u] \le 0$, then every real solution of $Lv = 0$ except a constant multiple of u vanishes at some point of (α, β).*

Proof   Suppose to the contrary that there exists a solution $v \neq 0$ in (α, β). For all such v and all $u \in \mathfrak{D}$, the following identity is valid in (α, β):

$$Av^2\left[\left(\frac{u}{v}\right)'\right]^2 + \left(\frac{Au^2v'}{v}\right)' = Au'^2 - Cu^2 + \frac{u^2}{v} Lv. \qquad (1.7)$$

Indeed, the left member is equal to

$$A \frac{(vu' - uv')^2}{v^2} + \frac{2Auu'v'}{v} + \frac{u^2}{v^2}\left[v(Av')' - Av'^2\right]$$

$$= Au'^2 - Cu^2 + \frac{u^2}{v}\left[(Av')' + Cv\right].$$

Since $Lv = 0$ in (α, β), integration of (1.7) gives

$$\int_y^z (Au'^2 - Cu^2) \, dx = \int_y^z A\left[v\left(\frac{u}{v}\right)'\right]^2 dx + \left[\frac{Au^2v'}{v}\right]_y^z, \qquad (1.8)$$

for arbitrary y and z satisfying $\alpha < y < z < \beta$.

If $v(\alpha) \neq 0$ and $v(\beta) \neq 0$, it follows from (1.5) and the hypotheses $u(\alpha) = u(\beta) = 0$ that

$$J[u] = \int_\alpha^\beta A[v(u/v)']^2 \, dx. \qquad (1.9)$$

Since $A > 0$, $J[u] \ge 0$, equality if and only if $(u/v)'$ is identically zero, i.e., u is a constant multiple of v. The latter cannot occur since $u(\alpha) = 0$ and $v(\alpha) \neq 0$, and hence $J[u] > 0$. The contradiction shows that v must have a zero in (α, β) in the case $v(\alpha) \neq 0$, $v(\beta) \neq 0$.

Now consider the case $v(\alpha) = v(\beta) = 0$. Since the solutions of second order ordinary linear differential equations have only simple zeros [35], $v'(\alpha) \neq 0$ and

$v'(\beta) \neq 0$. Then an application of l'Hospital's rule yields

$$\lim_{y \to \alpha+} \frac{A(y)u^2(y)v'(y)}{v(y)} = \lim_{y \to \alpha+} \frac{2A(y)u(y)u'(y)v'(y) - C(y)u^2(y)v(y)}{v'(y)}$$

$$= 0,$$

where the hypothesis that v satisfies (1.2) has been used. Likewise

$$\lim_{z \to \beta-} \frac{A(z)u^2(z)v'(z)}{v(z)} = 0.$$

It then follows from (1.8) in the limit $y, z \to \alpha, \beta$ that (1.9) is still valid, and $J[u] \geq 0$. Hence we obtain the contradiction $J[u] > 0$ unless v is a constant multiple of u.

In the mixed cases $v(\alpha) = 0, v(\beta) \neq 0$ and $v(\alpha) \neq 0, v(\beta) = 0$, it is clear from the foregoing proof that (1.9) still holds and accordingly that v has a zero in (α, β). This completes the proof of Lemma 1.3.

Lemma 1.3 extends Leighton's result [116] slightly by weakening the hypothesis $J[u] < 0$ to $J[u] \leq 0$.

In addition to (1.5) consider the quadratic functional defined by

$$j[u] = \int_\alpha^\beta (au'^2 - cu^2)\, dx, \qquad u \in \mathfrak{D}, \tag{1.10}$$

which is related to the differential operator l by Green's formula (the analog of (1.6))

$$\int_\alpha^\beta ulu\, dx + j[u] = \left[a(x)u(x)u'(x) \right]_\alpha^\beta \tag{1.11}$$

for $u \in \mathfrak{D}_1$. The *variation* of $j[u]$ is defined as $V[u] = j[u] - J[u]$, that is

$$V[u] = \int_\alpha^\beta [(a - A)u'^2 + (C - c)u^2]\, dx \tag{1.12}$$

with domain $\mathfrak{D}$.

Theorem 1.4   (Leighton)   *If there exists a nontrivial real solution u of $lu = 0$ in (α, β) such that $u(\alpha) = u(\beta) = 0$ and $V[u] > 0$, then every real solution of $Lv = 0$ has at least one zero in (α, β).*

In the following result the hypothesis $V[u] > 0$ is weakened to $V[u] \geq 0$.

Theorem 1.5   *If there exists a nontrivial real solution u of $lu = 0$ in (α, β) such that $u(\alpha) = u(\beta) = 0$ and $V[u] \geq 0$, then every real solution of $Lv = 0$ has one of* *the following properties*: (1) *v has at least one zero in* (α, β), *or* (2) *v is a constant multiple of u.*

Proof Since $u(\alpha) = u(\beta) = 0$ and $lu = 0$, it follows from Green's formula (1.11) that $j[u] = 0$. The hypothesis $V[u] \geq 0$ of Theorem 1.5 is equivalent to $J[u] \leq j[u]$. Hence the hypothesis $J[u] \leq 0$ of Lemma 1.3 is fulfilled, and v vanishes at least once in (α, β) unless v is a constant multiple of u.

Under the hypothesis $V[u] > 0$ of Theorem 1.4, alternative (2) of Theorem 1.5 implies $J[u] = 0$ by (1.9), and hence $V[u] = 0$. The contradiction establishes Theorem 1.4.

The Sturm–Picone theorem 1.2 follows immediately from Theorem 1.4 since the hypotheses $a(x) > A(x)$ and $c(x) < C(x)$ of the former imply that $V[u] > 0$. Likewise the following improvement of Theorem 1.2 is an immediate consequence of Theorem 1.5.

Theorem 1.6   *Suppose* $a(x) \geq A(x)$ *and* $c(x) \leq C(x)$ *in the interval* $\alpha < x < \beta$. *If there exists a nontrivial real solution u of lu = 0 such that* $u(\alpha) = u(\beta) = 0$, *then every real solution of Lv = 0 except a constant multiple of u has at least one zero in* (α, β).

The next result requires the slightly stronger hypothesis that L is a "strict Sturmian majorant" of l. This means, in addition to the conditions $a(x) \geq A(x)$ and $c(x) \leq C(x)$, that either (1) $c(x) \neq C(x)$ for some x in (α, β), or (2) (if $c(x) \equiv C(x)$) that $a(x) > A(x)$ and $c(x) \neq 0$ for some x.

Theorem 1.7   *Suppose that L is a strict Sturmian majorant of l. Then if there exists a nontrivial real solution of lu = 0 satisfying* $u(\alpha) = u(\beta) = 0$, *every real solution of Lv = 0 has a zero in* (α, β).

This follows from Theorem 1.4 since $V[u] > 0$ is a consequence of the strict Sturmian hypothesis.

In the special case that the differential equations (1.1) and (1.2) coincide, we obtain the classical Sturm separation theorem as a special case of Theorem 1.6.

Sturm Separation Theorem 1.8   *The zeros of linearly independent solutions of* (1.1) *separate each other.*

The following example given by Leighton [116] illustrates that Theorem 1.4 (or Theorem 1.5) is stronger than the Sturm–Picone theorem 1.2 (and also Theorems 1.6 and 1.7).

Example 1   In the case that $a(x) = A(x) = c(x) = 1$ and $C(x) = x + 1 - k$, $0 < k < \pi/2$, on $0 \le x \le \pi$, the differential equations (1.1), (1.2) become

$$u'' + u = 0, \tag{1.13}$$
$$v'' + (x + 1 - k)v = 0, \tag{1.14}$$

respectively. The solution $u = \sin x$ of (1.13) satisfies $u(0) = u(\pi) = 0$. The variation (1.12) reduces to

$$V[u] = \int_0^\pi (x - k) \sin^2 x \, dx,$$

and an easy calculation yields

$$V[u] = \frac{\pi}{2}\left(\frac{\pi}{2} - k\right) > 0.$$

According to Theorem 1.4, every solution of (1.14) has a zero in $(0, \pi)$. This cannot be concluded from the Sturm–Picone theorem 1.2 (or from Theorems 1.6 and 1.7) since the condition $c(x) \le C(x)$ does not hold throughout the interval $0 < x < \pi$.

Example 2   It will be shown that every solution of Airy's equation

$$v'' + xv = 0 \tag{1.15}$$

has an infinite sequence of positive zeros x_n $(n = 1, 2, \ldots)$ with no finite accumulation point.

The result will be obtained by applying Sturm's classical theorem 1.1 to the differential equations (1.13) and (1.15). In this case, $a(x) = A(x) = 1$, and $c(x) = 1 < x = C(x)$ on every interval $[n\pi, (n + 1)\pi]$ $(n = 1, 2, \ldots)$. Since the solution $u(x) = \sin x$ satisfies $u(n\pi) = u((n + 1)\pi) = 0$, every real solution of (1.15) has a zero in $(n\pi, (n + 1)\pi)$. Finally, it is a general property of linear differential equations that the zeros of a solution cannot have a finite accumulation point [90, p. 223].

The material of this section has some connections with the theory of differential inequalities. In particular, Theorems 1.4–1.7 are still valid when the differential equation $Lv = 0$ is replaced by the differential inequality $Lv \le 0$; the proofs are relegated to the exercises below. Another result, in the case $C(x) \le 0$, is that the inequality $Lu(x) \le 0$ $(u \in \mathfrak{D})$ on $[\alpha, \beta]$ implies $u(x) \ge 0$ on this interval; in fact, if u were negative at any point in (α, β), there would exist numbers α' and β' $(\alpha \le \alpha' < \beta' \le \beta)$ such that $u(\alpha') = u(\beta') = 0$ and $u(x) < 0$ in $\alpha' < x < \beta'$. Then Green's identity (1.6) applied to the interval (α', β') would yield a contradiction. In the special case of the operator L defined by

$$Lu = \frac{d^2u}{dx^2} + C(x)u, \qquad 0 \le x \le \beta,$$

the same result has been proved by Bellman [18, 13, p. 141] under the weaker hypothesis $C(x) \leq (\pi^2/\beta^2) - \delta$ on $[0, \beta]$ for some $\delta > 0$.

Under the hypotheses stated above, the differential inequality $-L(x) \geq 0$ on $[\alpha, \beta]$ $(u \in \mathfrak{D})$ implies that $u(x) \geq 0$ on $[\alpha, \beta]$, and the operator $-L$ is said to be *inverse-positive* on $\mathfrak{D}$. The reader is referred to the excellent accounts of inverse-positive differential operators given by Beckenbach and Bellman [13, Chapter 4], Szarski [197], and Schröder [179]. In particular, Beckenbach and Bellman describe analogs of the result above for systems of first order linear differential equations and applications to stability theory.

Connections between inverse-positive operators and existence and uniqueness theorems have been given by Bihari [20], Langenhop [109], Lax [110], Nemyckii and Stepanov [144]. Szarski's book [197] contains an extensive treatment of the theory of differential inequalities with applications to both ordinary and partial differential equations, as originated by Čaplygin [27] and developed by Haar [59], Kamke [93], Nagumo [139], Redheffer [167], Szarski [195, 196], Ważewski [205], and Westphal [208].

Exercises

1. Show that Theorem 1.6 is a consequence of Theorem 1.5.
2. Give the details of the proof of Theorem 1.7.
3. Show that Theorem 1.1 is a special case of Theorem 1.7.
4. Prove the Sturm separation theorem 1.8.
5. Use Theorem 1.5 to obtain the conclusion of Example 1 even if $k = \pi/2$.
6. Show that every solution of the extended Airy equation $v'' + x^n v = 0$, where n is a positive integer, has an infinite sequence of positive zeros. If n is even, show that in addition every solution has an infinite sequence of negative zeros.
7. Show that the substitution $y = x^{-1/2}z$ reduces Bessel's equation of order α

$$x^2 y'' + xy' + (x^2 - \alpha^2)y = 0$$

to the form

$$z'' + (x^2 + \tfrac{1}{4} - \alpha^2)x^{-2}z = 0.$$

Hence show that every solution of Bessel's equation has an infinite sequence of zeros on the positive x-axis.

8. An *L-subsolution* (*-supersolution*) is a function $u \in \mathfrak{D}_L$ satisfying the inequality $Lu \leq 0$ $(Lu \geq 0)$ at every point in the interval under consideration. Prove the following generalization of Lemma 1.3: If there exists a function $u \in \mathfrak{D}$ not identically zero such that $J[u] \leq 0$, then every positive *L*-subsolution or negative *L*-supersolution has a zero in (α, β) unless it is a constant multiple of *u*.

9. Prove the following generalization of Theorem 1.5: If there exists a positive *l*-supersolution *u* in (α, β) vanishing at the endpoints such that $V[u] \geq 0$, then every positive *L*-subsolution has a zero in (α, β) unless it is a constant multiple of *u*.

10. State and prove analogs of Theorems 1.6 and 1.7 for subsolutions and supersolutions.

11. Prove that the zeros of linearly independent solutions of the general second order linear equation

$$p(x)u'' + q(x)u' + r(x)u = 0$$

are interlaced, i.e., the Sturm separation theorem is still valid. Assume that *p*, *q*, and *r* are continuous and $p(x) > 0$ on the interval under consideration. *Hint:* Transform the differential equation to the form (1.1) by multiplying it by

$$M(x) = \exp\left\{ \int [q(x)/p(x)] \, dx \right\}.$$

2. Additional Results of Leighton

The following comparison theorem was obtained by Leighton in 1962 [116] as an alternative to Theorem 1.4.

Theorem 1.9 *Suppose in addition to the above hypotheses on a, c, A, and C (stated below* (1.2)) *that $a \in \mathscr{C}^1(\alpha, \beta)$ and $A \in \mathscr{C}^1(\alpha, \beta)$. Then if there exists a nontrivial real solution of lu = 0 in (α, β) such that $u(\alpha) = u(\beta) = 0$ and*

$$\int_\alpha^\beta \left[\left(C - \frac{A}{a} c \right) u^2 + auu' \left(\frac{A}{a} \right)' \right] dx > 0, \qquad (1.16)$$

every real solution of Lv = 0 has at least one zero in (α, β).

Proof For $u \in \mathfrak{D}_L$ it follows from (1.1) and (1.2) that

$$Lu = (Au')' + Cu$$

$$= \left(\frac{A}{a} au' \right)' + Cu$$

$$= \frac{A}{a} (au')' + au' \left(\frac{A}{a} \right)' + Cu$$

$$= \left(C - \frac{A}{a} c \right) u + au' \left(\frac{A}{a} \right)'$$

since $lu = (au')' + cu = 0$ in (α, β). Hence by Green's formula (1.6) the left member of (1.16) is equal to

$$\int_{\alpha}^{\beta} uLu \, dx = -J[u].$$

The hypothesis (1.16) then implies that $J[u] < 0$. By Lemma 1.3, every solution v of $Lv = 0$ vanishes at some point of (α, β) unless v is a constant multiple of u. However, the latter implies that $J[u] = 0$ by (1.9), which is a contradiction. This completes the proof of Theorem 1.9.

The following converse of Lemma 1.3 is equivalent to the necessity of the Jacobi condition in the calculus of variations [22].

Theorem 1.10. *If there exists a nontrivial solution of $Lv = 0$ such that $v(\alpha) = v(\gamma) = 0$, where $\alpha < \gamma < \beta$, then there exists a nontrivial function $u \in \mathfrak{D}$ such that $J[u] \leq 0$.*

Proof Suppose to the contrary that $J[u] > 0$ for all nontrivial $u \in \mathfrak{D}$. Consider the functional

$$J_t[u] = \int_{\alpha}^{\beta} [(tA(x) + 1 - t)u'^2 - tC(x)u^2] \, dx,$$

which is positive for all nontrivial $u \in \mathfrak{D}$ and all t on $[0, 1]$. The corresponding differential equation (1.2) (the Euler equation) is $[(tA(x) + 1 - t)u']'$ $+ tC(x)u = 0$. Let $u = u(x, t)$ be a solution satisfying the initial conditions $u(\alpha, t) = 0$, $u_x(\alpha, t) = 1$ for all t, $0 \leq t \leq 1$. For $t = 0$, this must reduce to $u(x, 0) = x - \alpha$. Note that the condition $u(x, t) = 0$ at some point (x, t) implies that $u_x(x, t) \neq 0$, for otherwise $u(x, t)$ would be identically zero by the uniqueness theorem for linear differential equations [35], contradicting $u_x(\alpha, t) = 1$ for all t on $[0, 1]$.

Consider the set of all points (x, t) in the rectangle $R: \alpha \leq x \leq \beta, 0 \leq t \leq 1$ satisfying $u(x, t) = 0$. This set represents a curve in the xt-plane since $u_x(x, t) \neq 0$ at each point where $u(x, t) = 0$, by the implicit function theorem, and by hypothesis $(\gamma, 1)$ lies on the curve. By examining the rectangle R, one easily verifies that such a continuous curve cannot exist, and the contradiction establishes Theorem 1.10.

Leighton also stated the nonoscillation theorem below, relative to the differential operators l and l_λ, where

$$l_\lambda v \equiv \frac{d}{dx}\left[a(\lambda x)\frac{dv}{dx}\right] + \lambda^2 c(\lambda x)v. \tag{1.17}$$

Suppose that the functions a and c in (1.1) are continuous and $a(x) > 0$ on an interval $\alpha \leq x < \beta$ ($\alpha > 0$) and that l is a strict Sturmian majorant of l_λ on this *interval for every number λ in an open interval $(1, 1 + \delta)$, $\delta > 0$. Then every nontrivial real solution u of* (1.1) *for which* $u(\alpha) = 0$, $u'(\alpha) \neq 0$ *has at most one zero in* (α, β).

This result is false, as shown by the example $\alpha = \frac{1}{2}$, $\beta = 2$, and

$$lu \equiv \frac{d}{dx}\left(\frac{x^2}{2\pi}\frac{du}{dx}\right) + \frac{2\pi}{x^2}u = 0, \tag{1.18}$$

in which

$$a(x) = x^2/2\pi, \ c(x) = 2\pi/x^2.$$

Then

$$a(\lambda x) = \lambda^2 a(x) > a(x) \qquad \text{for all} \quad \lambda > 1,$$

and

$$c(x) = \lambda^2 c(\lambda x).$$

Thus l is a strict Sturmian majorant of l_λ. (Compare (1.1) with (1.17). The solution $u(x) = \sin 2\pi/x$ has zeros at $x = \frac{1}{2}, \frac{2}{3}, 1$, and 2 (in particular).

3. Extension to General Second Order Equations

Comparison theorems analogous to those of Section 1 will be obtained for the differential equations

$$lu \equiv \frac{d}{dx}\left[a(x)\frac{du}{dx}\right] + b(x)\frac{du}{dx} + c(x)u = 0 \tag{1.19}$$

and

$$Lv \equiv \frac{d}{dx}\left[A(x)\frac{dv}{dx}\right] + B(x)\frac{dv}{dx} + C(x)v = 0 \tag{1.20}$$

on a bounded open interval (α, β), under the assumptions given below (1.2) and the additional assumptions that b and B are real-valued continuous functions on $[\alpha, \beta]$. For some theorems it will be required that b and B be differentiable as well.

Although (1.19) can be put in the form (1.1) by multiplication by

$$\exp\left\{\int_{x_0}^x \frac{a'(t) + b(t)}{a(t)}\,dt\right\} \tag{1.21}$$

over intervals where a, a', and b are continuous and $a(t) > 0$, there are advantages in obtaining direct comparison theorems for solutions of (1.19) and (1.20): besides the obvious practical advantage of eliminating the need for the "integrating factor" (1.21), there is incentive in developing methods which will generalize to n-dimensions (i.e., partial differential equations, which will be treated in Chapter 5). In the sequel a "solution" will be understood in the same sense as in Section 1, so that the case that a' is not everywhere continuous (or even does not everywhere exist) can be included, provided all quantities involved in (1.19) and (1.20) exist and are continuous.

Let $Q[z]$ be the quadratic form in 2 variables z_1, z_2 defined by

$$Q[z] = Az_1{}^2 - 2Bz_1z_2 + Gz_2{}^2, \tag{1.22}$$

where G is a continuous function satisfying

$$G \geq B^2/A. \tag{1.23}$$

The form $Q[z]$ is said to be positive semidefinite [48] whenever $Q[z] \geq 0$ for all real pairs (z_1, z_2). Evidently a necessary and sufficient condition for $Q[z]$ to be positive semidefinite is that the discriminant be nonpositive, which is equivalent to (1.23).

The analog of the quadratic functional (1.5) is

$$J[u] = \int_\alpha^\beta F[u] \, dx, \qquad u \in \mathcal{D} \tag{1.24}$$

where

$$F[u] = Au'^2 - 2Buu' + (G - C)u^2. \tag{1.25}$$

The domain $\mathcal{D}$ is the same as that defined below (1.5).

Lemma 1.11 *Suppose $G \geq B^2/A$ in (α, β). If there exists $u \in \mathcal{D}$, not identically zero, such that $J[u] < 0$, then every solution of $Lv = 0$ has a zero in (α, β).*

Proof Suppose to the contrary that there exists a solution $v \neq 0$ in (α, β). For all such v and all $u \in \mathcal{D}$ define

$$X = v(u/v)', \qquad Y = Av'/v.$$

The following identity will now be established, valid at every point in (α, β):

$$AX^2 - 2BuX + Gu^2 + (u^2Y)' = F[u] + \frac{u^2}{v} Lv. \tag{1.26}$$

In fact, the left member of (1.26) is equal to

$$\frac{A}{v^2}(vu' - uv')^2 - \frac{2Bu}{v}(vu' - uv') + Gu^2$$

$$+ \frac{2Auu'v'}{v} + \frac{u^2}{v^2}[v(Av')' - Av'^2]$$

$$= Au'^2 - 2Buu' + (G - C)u^2 + \frac{u^2}{v}Lv$$

by (1.20), as required.

Since $Lv = 0$ in (α, β), integration of (1.26) over (α, β) yields

$$J[u] = \int_\alpha^\beta [AX^2 - 2BuX + Gu^2]\, dx + \lim_{y,\, z \to \alpha,\, \beta} \left[\frac{Au^2v'}{v}\right]_y^z. \qquad (1.27)$$

As in the proof of Lemma 1.3, the second term of the right member vanishes. The integrand in the first term of the right member is a positive semidefinite form by the hypothesis (1.23). The contradiction $J[u] \geq 0$ then establishes Lemma 1.11.

The proof just completed suggests the following stronger result.

Lemma 1.12   *Suppose $G \geq B^2/A$ in (α, β). If there exists $u \in \mathfrak{D}$, not identically zero in any open subinterval of (α, β), such that $J[u] \leq 0$, then every solution v of $Lv = 0$ has one of the following properties: (1) v has at least one zero in (α, β), or (2) $G \equiv B^2/A$ in (α, β) and $v(x)$ is a constant multiple of*

$$u(x) \exp\left\{\int_{x_0}^x [-B(x)/A(x)]\, dx\right\}$$

for some constant x_0 in the interval $[\alpha, \beta]$.

Proof   Upon reduction of the integrand in (1.27) to a sum of squares, we obtain

$$J[u] = \int_\alpha^\beta \left[A\left(X - \frac{Bu}{A}\right)^2 + \left(G - \frac{B^2}{A}\right)u^2\right] dx.$$

Since $A > 0$ and $G \geq B^2/A$ in (α, β), $J[u] \geq 0$, equality if and only if $G \equiv B^2/A$ and $X \equiv Bu/A$ in (α, β). The latter condition is equivalent to

$$\frac{d}{dx}\left(\frac{u}{v}\right) = \frac{Bu}{Av},$$

or

$$\frac{u}{v} = K \exp\left(\int_{x_0}^x [B(x)/A(x)]\, dx\right)$$

where K and x_0 are constants, $K \neq 0$. Hence $J[u] > 0$ unless $G \equiv B^2/A$ and v is a constant multiple of

$$\exp\left(\int_{x_0}^{x} [-B(x)/A(x)] \, dx\right).$$

In the self-adjoint case, $B \equiv 0$, and the choice $G \equiv 0$ in (1.25) guarantees the hypothesis $G > B^2/A$ of Lemma 1.12. Thus every solution of $Lv = 0$ has a zero in (α, β) unless v is a constant multiple of u, which is the content of the previous lemma 1.3.

In addition to (1.24), consider the quadratic functional j defined by

$$j[u] = \int_{\alpha}^{\beta} (au'^2 - 2buu' - cu^2) \, dx, \qquad u \in \mathfrak{D} \tag{1.28}$$

and the variation

$$V[u] = j[u] - J[u] \qquad (u \in \mathfrak{D})$$

$$= \int_{\alpha}^{\beta} [(a - A)u'^2 - 2(b - B)uu' + (C - c - G)u^2] \, dx. \tag{1.29}$$

In the case that b and B are of class $\mathscr{C}^1(\alpha, \beta)$ (actually less stringent conditions will suffice), an integration by parts yields the alternative form

$$V[u] = \int_{\alpha}^{\beta} [(a - A)u'^2 + (b' - B' + C - c - G)u^2] \, dx. \tag{1.30}$$

Theorem 1.13 *Suppose $G \geq B^2/A$ in (α, β). If there exists a nontrivial real solution u of $lu = 0$ in (α, β) such that $u(\alpha) = u(\beta) = 0$ and $V[u] > 0$, then every real solution of $Lv = 0$ has at least one zero in (α, β).*

Proof The hypothesis $V[u] > 0$ is equivalent to $J[u] < j[u]$. Since $u(\alpha) = u(\beta) = 0$ and $lu = 0$ in (α, β), it follows from Green's formula

$$\int_{\alpha}^{\beta} ulu \, dx + j[u] = \left[auu' \right]_{\alpha}^{\beta}$$

(which has the same form as (1.11) in the nonself-adjoint case) that $j[u] = 0$. Thus $J[u] < 0$ and the conclusion follows from Lemma 1.11.

Theorem 1.14 *Suppose $G \geq B^2/A$ in (α, β). If there exists a nontrivial real solution u of $lu = 0$ in (α, β) such that $u(\alpha) = u(\beta) = 0$ and $V[u] \geq 0$, then every real solution of $Lv = 0$ has one of the following properties: (1) v has at least one zero in (α, β), or (2) $G \equiv B^2/A$ in (α, β) and $v(x)$ is a constant multiple of*

$$u(x) \exp\left\{\int_{x_0}^{x} [-B(x)/A(x)] \, dx\right\}$$

for some constant x_0 in the interval $[\alpha, \beta]$.

Proof As in the proof of Theorem 1.13, $J[u] \le 0$. Since a nontrivial solution of $lu = 0$ cannot vanish in any open interval, the conclusion follows from Lemma 1.12.

In the case that equality holds in (1.23), that is $G \equiv B^2/A$ *in* (α, β), we define

$$\delta = b' - B' + C - c - B^2/A, \tag{1.31}$$

and (1.30) becomes

$$V[u] = \int_\alpha^\beta [(a - A)u'^2 + \delta u^2]\, dx. \tag{1.32}$$

As in (1.30), it is now assumed that $b \in \mathscr{C}^1(\alpha, \beta)$ and $B \in \mathscr{C}^1(\alpha, \beta)$.

The differential operator L is called a strict Sturmian majorant of l when the following conditions hold: (1) $a(x) \ge A(x)$ and $\delta(x) \ge 0$ in (α, β), and (2) either $\delta(x) \ne 0$ for some x in (α, β) or $a(x) > A(x)$ and $c(x) \ne 0$ for some x. The following result extends Theorem 1.7 to the nonself-adjoint case.

Theorem 1.15 *Suppose in addition to the assumptions on a, b, c, A, B, and C stated below (1.20) that a, b, and B are of class $\mathscr{C}^1(\alpha, \beta)$, and that L is a strict Sturmian majorant of l. If there exists a nontrivial real solution of $lu = 0$ such that $u(\alpha) = u(\beta) = 0$, then every real solution of $Lv = 0$ has a zero in (α, β).*

Proof Since $a \in \mathscr{C}^1(\alpha, \beta)$, a nontrivial solution of $lu = 0$ cannot vanish identically in any open subinterval of (α, β). In the case that $\delta > 0$ at some point in (α, β), it then follows from (1.32) that $V[u] > 0$. In the case that $\delta \equiv 0$ in (α, β), it follows from (1.32) and the hypothesis $a(x) > A(x)$ that $V[u] > 0$ unless $u'(x) \equiv 0$ in some open subinterval I of (α, β), that is $u(x)$ is constant in I. Since $c(x_0) \ne 0$ for some $x_0 \in I$ by hypothesis, the differential equation (1.19) would not be satisfied at x_0. Hence $V[u] > 0$ also in the case that $\delta \equiv 0$. The conclusion of Theorem 1.15 then follows from Theorem 1.13.

Theorem 1.16 *If $a = A$, $b = B$, and $c = C - b^2/a$, then every real solution u of (1.20) has a zero between consecutive zeros of every nontrivial real solution v of (1.19) unless $v(x)$ is a constant multiple of*

$$u(x) \exp\left\{\int_{x_0}^x [-B(x)/A(x)]\, dx\right\}.$$

Analogs of the comparison theorems of this section can easily be obtained when the differential equation $Lv = 0$ is replaced by the differential inequality $Lv \le 0$. (See Exercise 4 below.) A detailed study of the theory of differential inequalities is not within the theme of this book; detailed references to this topic were given at the end of Section 1. However, we mention in passing the following typical and fundamental theorem of Čaplygin [27]:

Let b and c be continuous functions with c nonnegative on $0 \le x < \infty$. If u and v are functions of class $\mathscr{C}^2[0, \infty)$ such that

$$u'' + b(x)u' - c(x)u > 0$$

and

$$v'' + b(x)v' - c(x)v = 0$$

on $0 \le x < \infty$, and $u(0) = v(0) = u'(0) = v'(0)$, then $u(x) > v(x)$ in $0 < x < \infty$.

The proof is very simple. It follows from the hypotheses that $w = u - v$ satisfies

$$w'' + b(x)w' - c(x)w > 0, \qquad w(0) = w'(0) = 0, \qquad (*)$$

and hence $w(x) > 0$ in some interval $0 < x \le x_0$. Suppose to the contrary that $w(x) \le 0$ for some $x > x_0$. Then $w(x)$ would have a local maximum at some point $x_1 > 0$, and hence $w'(x_1) = 0$ and $w(x_1) > 0$. Consequently $w''(x_1) > 0$ by $(*)$, which contradicts the assumption that x_1 is a local maximum point.

Čaplygin's method has been used to obtain oscillation criteria for linear and nonlinear differential equations. The reader is referred to the book by Beckenbach and Bellman [13] for a discussion of related topics and an extensive bibliography.

Exercises

1. Give the details of the proof of Theorem 1.16.
2. Show that Theorem 1.8 follows as a special case of Theorem 1.16 when $B(x) \equiv 0$.
3. Obtain Theorems 1.4–1.7 as consequences of the theorems of this section.
4. State and prove analogs of Theorems 1.13–1.15 for subsolutions and super-solutions. (Compare Exercise 8 of Section 1.1.)
5. Prove that every solution of

$$v'' + B(x)v' + C(x)v = 0 \qquad (1.33)$$

has a zero in the interval $(0, \pi)$ if

$$\int_0^\pi [C(x) - B'(x) - B^2(x) - 1] \sin^2 x \, dx > 0. \qquad (1.34)$$

6. Prove that every solution of (1.33) has a zero in $(n\pi, (n + 1)\pi)$ $(n = 1,$
   $2, \ldots)$ if

$$C(x) - B'(x) - B^2(x) > 1 \qquad (1.35)$$

in this interval, and hence if (1.35) holds, every solution of (1.33) has an
infinite sequence of zeros x_n on the positive x-axis such that $x_n \to \infty$ as
$n \to \infty$.

7. Prove from Exercise 6 or otherwise that every solution of the differential
   equation

$$y'' + x^{-1}y' + xy = 0$$

has an infinite sequence of zeros $x_n \uparrow \infty$.

8. If $0 < k < \pi/2 - 1$, show that every solution of the differential equations

$$v'' \pm v' + (x + 1 - k)v = 0$$

has a zero in $(0, \pi)$. (*Hint:* Use (1.34) and compare Example 1 of Section 1.)

9. If a solution $v(x)$ of (1.33) is not a constant multiple of

$$\exp\left(-\int_0^x B(x)\, dx\right) \sin x,$$

prove that it must have a zero in $(0, \pi)$ whenever the left side of (1.34) is
nonnegative.

4. Comparison Theorems for Singular Equations

Analogs of the results in Section 3 will be obtained for the differential
equations (1.19) and (1.20) in an open interval $\alpha < x < \beta$, where now the
continuity of a, b, c, A, B, and C and the positivity of a and A are assumed only
in (α, β). The possibility that the interval is unbounded is not excluded. Under
these assumptions the differential equations are said to be *singular*. (This
terminology is used without regard to the possibility of extending the coefficients to the closed interval $[\alpha, \beta]$ in a continuous way.) Theorems 1.18 and
1.19 are the main results of this section and Theorem 1.20 deals with the
special case that L is a strict Sturmian majorant of l. Theorem 1.21 is a slight
modification of Theorem 1.19 in the case that the coefficients are defined and
continuous in the half-open interval $[\alpha, \beta)$.

The domain $\mathfrak{D}_l$ of l (defined by (1.19)) is defined to be the set of all real-
valued functions in (α, β) such that $au' \in \mathscr{C}^1(\alpha, \beta)$, and $\mathfrak{D}_L$ is the analog with A
replacing a. A "solution" of $lu = 0$ is a function $u \in \mathfrak{D}_l$ satisfying $lu = 0$ at
every point in (α, β).

For $\alpha < \zeta < \sigma < \beta$, let $J_{\zeta\sigma}$ be the quadratic functional defined by

$$J_{\zeta\sigma}[u] = \int_{\zeta}^{\sigma} F[u] \, dx, \tag{1.36}$$

where $F[u]$ is given by (1.25), and define

$$J[u] = \lim_{\substack{\zeta \to \alpha+ \\ \sigma \to \beta-}} J_{\zeta\sigma}[u]$$

whenever the limit exists. The domain $\mathfrak{D}_J$ of J is defined to be the set of all real-valued continuous functions $u \in \mathscr{C}^1(\alpha, \beta)$ such that $J[u]$ exists. We shall use the notation

$$Q_{\alpha\beta}[u, v] = \lim_{x \to \beta-} \frac{A(x)u^2(x)v'(x)}{v(x)} - \lim_{x \to \alpha+} \frac{A(x)u^2(x)v'(x)}{v(x)} \tag{1.37}$$

whenever the limits on the right side exist.

Lemma 1.17 *Suppose the function G in (1.25) satisfies $G \geq B^2/A$ in (α, β). If there exists a function $u \in \mathfrak{D}_J$, not identically zero in any open subinterval of (α, β), such that $J[u] \leq 0$, then every solution v of $Lv = 0$ satisfying $Q_{\alpha\beta}[u, v] \geq 0$ has one of the following properties: (1) v has at least one zero in (α, β), or (2) $G \equiv B^2/A$ in (α, β) and $v(x)$ is a constant multiple of*

$$u(x) \exp\left\{ \int_{x_0}^{x} [-B(x)/A(x)] \, dx \right\} \tag{1.38}$$

for some x_0 in (α, β). If the stronger condition $J[u] < 0$ holds, then every solution of $Lv = 0$ satisfying $Q_{\alpha\beta}[u, v] \geq 0$ has a zero in (α, β).

Proof To prove the last statement, assume to the contrary that there exists a solution $v \neq 0$ in (α, β). Integration of (1.26) over (ζ, σ) yields

$$J_{\zeta\sigma}[u] = \int_{\zeta}^{\sigma} \left[A\left(X - \frac{Bu}{A}\right)^2 + \left(G - \frac{B^2}{A}\right)u^2 \right] dx + \left[\frac{A(x)u^2(x)v'(x)}{v(x)} \right]_{\zeta}^{\sigma}. \tag{1.39}$$

Since the integrand is nonnegative it follows from (1.37) that

$$J[u] \geq \lim_{\substack{\zeta \to \alpha+ \\ \sigma \to \beta-}} \left[\frac{A(x)u^2(x)v'(x)}{v(x)} \right]_{\zeta}^{\sigma} = Q_{\alpha\beta}[u, v] \geq 0$$

by hypothesis, which contradicts $J[u] < 0$.

   Furthermore, $J[u] = 0$ if and only if $G \equiv B^2/A$ and $X = Bu/A$ in (α, β). As in the proof of Lemma 1.12, the latter implies that $v(x)$ is a constant multiple of (1.38). Thus, if v does not have a zero in (α, β), the hypothesis is contradicted unless $v(x)$ is a constant times (1.38).

In addition to (1.36), consider the quadratic functional defined by

$$j_{\zeta\sigma}[u] = \int_\zeta^\sigma (au'^2 - 2buu' - cu^2)\, dx \qquad (1.40)$$

and

$$j[u] = \lim_{\substack{\zeta \to \alpha+ \\ \sigma \to \beta-}} j_{\zeta\sigma}[u], \qquad (1.41)$$

whose domain $\mathfrak{D}_j$ is the set of all real $u \in \mathscr{C}^1(\alpha, \beta)$ such that $j[u]$ exists. The variation $V[u] = j[u] - J[u]$ is given by (1.29), with domain $\mathfrak{D} = \mathfrak{D}_j \cap \mathfrak{D}_J$.

Theorem 1.18 *Suppose the function G in (1.25) satisfies $G \geq B^2/A$ in (α, β). If there exists a nontrivial real solution $u \in \mathfrak{D}$ of $lu = 0$ in (α, β) such that*

$$\lim_{x \to \alpha+} a(x)u(x)u'(x) \geq 0, \qquad \lim_{x \to \beta-} a(x)u(x)u'(x) \leq 0, \qquad (1.42)$$

and $V[u] > 0$, then every real solution v of $Lv = 0$ satisfying $Q_{\alpha\beta}[u, v] \geq 0$ has a zero in (α, β). If the condition $V[u] > 0$ is weakened to $V[u] \geq 0$, the same conclusion holds unless $v(x)$ is a constant multiple of (1.38).

Proof It follows from Green's formula (1.11) that

$$\int_\zeta^\sigma ulu\, dx + j_{\zeta\sigma}[u] = \left[auu'\right]_\zeta^\sigma. \qquad (1.43)$$

From (1.42) and the differential equation $lu = 0$, we obtain in the limit $\zeta, \sigma \to \alpha, \beta$ that $j[u] \leq 0$. Since the hypothesis $V[u] > 0$ is equivalent to $J[u] < j[u]$, the condition $J[u] < 0$ of Lemma 1.17 is fulfilled and v must have a zero in (α, β). If $V[u] \geq 0$, then $J[u] \leq 0$ and the conclusion again follows from Lemma 1.17.

In the self-adjoint case the last result specializes as follows [192].

Theorem 1.19 (Self-Adjoint Case) *Suppose that $b(x) = B(x) = 0$ in (1.19 and (1.20), $\alpha < x < \beta$. If there exists a nontrivial real solution $u \in \mathfrak{D}$ of $lu = 0$ in (α, β) such that the inequalities (1.42) hold and*

$$\int_\alpha^\beta [(a - A)u'^2 + (C - c)u^2]\, dx > 0, \qquad (1.44)$$

then every real solution v of $Lv = 0$ satisfying $Q_{\alpha\beta}[u, v] \geq 0$ has a zero in (α, β). If the left member of (1.44) is only nonnegative, the same conclusion holds unless $v(x)$ is a constant multiple of $u(x)$.

The proof is left as an exercise.

In the case that equality holds in (1.23), that is $G \equiv B^2/A$, and b, $B \in \mathcal{C}^1(\alpha, \beta)$, define

$$\delta = b' - B' + C - c - B^2/A.$$

It follows from (1.29) by partial integration that

$$V[u] = \int_\alpha^\beta [(a - A)u'^2 + \delta u^2] \, dx + \Omega,$$

where

$$\Omega = \lim_{x \to \beta-} [B(x) - b(x)]u^2(x) - \lim_{x \to \alpha+} [B(x) - b(x)]u^2(x)$$

(whenever the limit exists). L is called a *strict Sturmian majorant of l* in the singular case whenever the following conditions hold:

1. $a(x) \geq A(x)$ and $\delta(x) \geq 0$ in (α, β);
2. Either $\delta(x) \neq 0$ for some x in (α, β) or (if $\delta(x) \equiv 0$) $a(x) > A(x)$ and $c(x) \neq 0$ for some x; and
3. $\Omega \geq 0$.

Theorem 1.20 *Suppose in addition to the assumptions stated at the beginning of this section that a, b, and B are of class $\mathcal{C}^1(\alpha, \beta)$ and that L is a strict Sturmian majorant of l. If there exists a nontrivial real solution of $lu = 0$ such that (1.42) holds, then every real solution of $Lv = 0$ satisfying $Q_{\alpha\beta}[u, v] \geq 0$ has a zero in (α, β).*

The proof is virtually the same as that of Theorem 1.15.

The following is a modification of Theorem 1.19 to the case that the coefficients a, c, A, and C are continuous and a, A are positive in the half-open interval $[\alpha, \beta)$.

Theorem 1.21   (Self-Adjoint Case) *Suppose that $b = B = 0$, a, c, A, and C are continuous, and a, A are positive in $[\alpha, \beta)$. If there exists a nontrivial real solution $u \in \mathfrak{D}$ of $lu = 0$ such that $u(\alpha) = 0$, $\lim[a(x)u(x)u'(x)] \leq 0$ $(x \to \beta-)$, and (1.44) holds, then every real solution v of $Lv = 0$ for which $A(x)u^2(x)v'(x)/v(x)$ has a nonnegative limit as $x \to \beta-$ has a zero in (α, β). If the left member of (1.44) is only nonnegative, the same conclusion holds unless $v(x)$ is a constant multiple of $u(x)$.*

Proof Since the differential equation $lu = 0$ is regular at α by hypothesis, $\lim u'(x)$ $(x \to \alpha)$ exists and is finite. Hence we again obtain from (1.43) that $j[u] \leq 0$, and since $V[u] = j[u] - J[u] > 0$ by (1.44), the condition $J[u] < 0$ of

Lemma 1.17 is fulfilled. If the left member of (1.44) is only nonnegative, i.e., $V[u] \geq 0$, then $J[u] \leq 0$ and the conclusion again follows from Lemma 1.17.

As an example of Theorem 1.21, consider the differential equations

$$u'' + (2n + 1 - x^2)u = 0, \tag{1.45}$$

$$v'' + [2n + 1 - x^2 + p(x)]v = 0, \tag{1.46}$$

on a half-open interval $[\alpha, \infty)$, where n is a nonnegative integer and $p(x)$ is a polynomial in x. Equation (1.45) has the well-known [44] solution $u(x) = \exp(-x^2/2)H_n(x)$, where $H_n(x)$ denotes the Hermite polynomial of degree n. In this case the inequality (1.44) reduces to

$$\int_\alpha^\infty p(x)u^2(x)\, dx > 0. \tag{1.47}$$

Clearly the integral exists and hence $u \in \mathfrak{D}$. Since every solution v of (1.46) is known to have the property that $v'(x)/v(x)q(x)$ is bounded as $x \to \infty$ for some polynomial $q(x)$ [43], it follows that the hypothesis

$$\lim_{x \to \infty} \frac{u^2(x)v'(x)}{v(x)} = 0$$

of Theorem 1.21 is fulfilled. Hence if α is a zero of $H_n(x)$ and (1.47) holds, then every solution of (1.46) has at least one zero in (α, ∞).

We remark that (1.45) is the differential equation governing the linear harmonic oscillator in quantum mechanics [176], and (1.46) can be regarded as a perturbation of (1.45).

Exercises
1. Prove Theorem 1.19.
2. Prove Theorem 1.20.
3. State and prove an analog of Theorem 1.21 for the half-open interval $(\alpha, \beta]$.
4. Extend Theorem 1.21 to the general second order linear equations (1.19) and (1.20).
5. State and prove analogs of the theorems of this section for subsolutions and supersolutions. (Compare Exercise 8, Section 1.)

5. Comparison Theorems for Eigenfunctions

Comparison theorems of Sturm's type will now be obtained for eigenfunctions, i.e., solutions of differential equations of the form (1.1) which satisfy the homogeneous boundary conditions

$$p_\alpha[u] \equiv ru(\alpha) - a(\alpha)u'(\alpha) = 0$$
$$p_\beta[u] \equiv su(\beta) + a(\beta)u'(\beta) = 0, \tag{1.48}$$

for some numbers r and s. The possibility that r (or s) is ∞ is not excluded; and in this case it is understood that the first (or second) boundary condition is to be replaced by $u(\alpha) = 0$ (or $u(\beta) = 0$). Equations (1.48) define the *boundary operators* p_α and p_β.

The theorems of this section can be proved by methods similar to those of Section 1, but instead the proofs will be carried out by a different method involving Courant's minimum principle [39, 130]. The latter has the advantage that it generalizes easily to differential equations of order exceeding 2 as well as to partial differential equations.

In order to obtain greater generality than in Section 1, we shall consider differential operators l defined by

$$lu = \frac{1}{k(x)} \left\{ -\frac{d}{dx} \left[a(x) \frac{du}{dx} \right] + c(x)u \right\}, \tag{1.49}$$

where a, c, and k are real-valued continuous functions on $[\alpha, \beta]$, a and k are positive on $[\alpha, \beta]$, and $a \in \mathscr{C}^1(\alpha, \beta)$. The domain $\mathfrak{D}_l$ is the same as that defined in Section 1, i.e. $\mathfrak{D}_l = \mathscr{C}^1[\alpha, \beta] \cap \mathscr{C}^2(\alpha, \beta)$ under the above assumptions on the coefficients in (1.49).

An *eigenvalue* λ is defined to be a number with the property that there exists a nontrivial solution $u \in \mathfrak{D}_l$ of the differential equation $lu = \lambda u$ satisfying the boundary conditions (1.48). The solution u is called an *eigenfunction* corresponding to the eigenvalue λ. The differential equation $lu = \lambda u$ is clearly equivalent to

$$\frac{d}{dx} \left[a(x) \frac{du}{dx} \right] + [\lambda k(x) - c(x)]u = 0,$$

which has the form (1.1). If $\lambda = 0$, $r = \infty$, and $s = \infty$, an eigenfunction is a nontrivial solution of (1.1) (with $-c(x)$ replacing $c(x)$) satisfying $u(\alpha) = u(\beta)$, and accordingly it is (if real-valued) a function of the type considered in the comparison theorems of Section 1.

Let $j[u]$ be the quadratic functional defined by (for finite r and s)

$$j[u] = \int_\alpha^\beta (a\,|u'|^2 + c\,|u|^2)\,dx + s\,|u(\beta)|^2 + r\,|u(\alpha)|^2 \tag{1.50}$$

with domain $\mathfrak{D} = \mathscr{C}^1[\alpha, \beta]$. The analog of (1.50) in the case $r = \infty$ and s finite is

$$j_\alpha[u] = \int_\alpha^\beta (a\,|u'|^2 + c\,|u|^2)\,dx + s\,|u(\beta)|^2, \tag{1.51}$$

whose domain $\mathfrak{D}_\alpha$ is defined to be the set of all $u \in \mathfrak{D}$ such that $u(\alpha) = 0$. Likewise the functionals $j_\beta[u]$ and $j_{\alpha\beta}[u]$ are defined by

$$j_\beta[u] = \int_\alpha^\beta (a\,|u'|^2 + c\,|u|^2)\,dx + r\,|u(\alpha)|^2, \qquad (1.52)$$

$$j_{\alpha\beta}[u] = \int_\alpha^\beta (a\,|u'|^2 + c\,|u|^2)\,dx, \qquad (1.53)$$

with domains $\mathfrak{D}_\beta = \{u \in \mathfrak{D}: u(\beta) = 0\}$, $\mathfrak{D}_{\alpha\beta} = \{u \in \mathfrak{D}: u(\alpha) = u(\beta) = 0\}$, respectively.

The *inner product* of two functions $u, v \in \mathfrak{D}$ is defined as†

$$\langle u, v \rangle = \int_\alpha^\beta u(x)\bar{v}(x)k(x)\,dx,$$

and the *norm* of $u \in \mathfrak{D}$ as

$$\|u\| = \langle u, u \rangle^{1/2} = \left[\int_\alpha^\beta |u(x)|^2 k(x)\,dx \right]^{1/2}.$$

The eigenvalue problem

$$lu = \lambda u, \qquad p_\alpha[u] = p_\beta[u] = 0 \qquad (1.54)$$

under consideration has the following properties:

1. Every eigenvalue λ is real, and in fact positive if $r \geq 0$, $s \geq 0$, and $c(x) \geq 0$ with strict inequality at some x in (α, β).
2. The eigenfunctions are nondegenerate, i.e., any two eigenfunctions corresponding to the same eigenvalue are linearly dependent; and
3. Eigenfunctions corresponding to distinct eigenvalues are orthogonal, i.e., if u satisfies (1.54) and v satisfies

$$lv = \mu v, \qquad p_\alpha[v] = p_\beta[v] = 0$$

with $\mu \neq \lambda$, then $\langle u, v \rangle = 0$.

Proof For finite r and s, a routine integration by parts yields the formula

$$j[u] = \langle lu, u \rangle + \bar{u}(\beta)p_\beta[u] + \bar{u}(\alpha)p_\alpha[u] \qquad (1.55)$$

upon use of (1.48), (1.49), and (1.50). If u is an eigenfunction of (1.54) corresponding to the eigenvalue λ, (1.55) shows that

$$j[u] = \langle \lambda u, u \rangle = \lambda \|u\|^2. \qquad (1.56)$$

† $\bar{v}$ denotes the complex conjugate of v.

It follows from (1.50) that λ is positive if $r \geq 0$, $s \geq 0$, and $c(x) \geq 0$ $(c(x) \not\equiv 0)$ and real in any event.

In the case $r = \infty$ and s finite, (1.55) is replaced by

$$j_\alpha[u] = \langle lu, u \rangle + \bar{u}(\beta)p_\beta[u] - a(\alpha)\bar{u}(\alpha)u'(\alpha)$$

and (1.56) is again obtained since the boundary conditions are $u(\alpha) = p_\beta[u] = 0$. The arguments in the other cases are similar and will be omitted.

To prove (2), we notice from (1.49) that

$$k(ulv - vlu) = [a(vu' - uv')]', \qquad u, v \in \mathfrak{D}_1. \qquad (1.57)$$

If $lu = \lambda u$ and $lv = \lambda v$, then $a(vu' - uv')$ is constant on $[\alpha, \beta]$. However, from (1.48) and (1.54),

$$0 = p_\alpha[u] = ru(\alpha) - a(\alpha)u'(\alpha)$$
$$0 = p_\alpha[v] = rv(\alpha) - a(\alpha)v'(\alpha)$$

and hence $a(\alpha)[v(\alpha)u'(\alpha) - u(\alpha)v'(\alpha)] = 0$. Thus $a(x)[v(x)u'(x) - u(x)v'(x)]$ is identically zero. Since $a(x) > 0$ on $[\alpha, \beta]$, the Wronskian $v(x)u'(x) - u(x)v'(x)$ is identically zero, which implies that u and v are linearly dependent. This result could also have been obtained from Abel's formula [90, p. 75].

To prove (3), we use Green's symmetric formula

$$\langle u, lv \rangle - \langle lu, v \rangle = \left[a(\bar{v}u' - u\bar{v}') \right]_\alpha^\beta, \qquad (1.58)$$

which is a consequence of (1.57). If u and v are eigenfunctions of (1.54), then in particular

$$0 = p_\alpha[u] = ru(\alpha) - a(\alpha)u'(\alpha)$$
$$0 = p_\alpha[\bar{v}] = r\bar{v}(\alpha) - a(\alpha)\bar{v}'(\alpha)$$

and hence

$$a(\alpha)[\bar{v}(\alpha)u'(\alpha) - u(\alpha)\bar{v}'(\alpha)] = 0.$$

Likewise

$$a(\beta)[\bar{v}(\beta)u'(\beta) - u(\beta)\bar{v}'(\beta)] = 0.$$

Since $lu = \lambda u$ and $l\bar{v} = \mu\bar{v}$, (1.58) implies that $(\mu - \lambda)\langle u, v \rangle = 0$. Hence $\langle u, v \rangle = 0$ provided $\mu \neq \lambda$.

If u is an eigenfunction of (1.54) corresponding to the eigenvalue λ, then so is γu for any constant γ, and by property (2) every eigenfunction corresponding to λ has this form. Every eigenfunction u is *essentially real*, i.e., $u = \gamma$ Re u or $u = \gamma$ Im u for some constant γ; in fact, Re u and Im u are eigenfunctions of (1.54) corresponding to the same eigenvalue as u, and hence Re u and Im u must be linearly dependent by property (2).

If $\|u\| = 1$, u is said to be *normalized*. A normalized eigenfunction u corresponding to an eigenvalue λ of (1.54) is uniquely determined except for a constant factor of modulus one, i.e., $\|\gamma u\| = |\gamma| \, \|u\| = 1$ if and only if $|\gamma| = 1$.

If u is an eigenfunction of (1.54) with $\|u\| = 1$ (1.56) shows that $j[u] = \lambda$. Courant's minimum principle states that the minimum of $j[u]$ among all $u \in \mathfrak{D}$ with $\|u\| = 1$ actually is attained by an eigenfunction corresponding to the smallest eigenvalue λ of (1.54), and therefore by (1.56) this minimum is equal to λ. Since evidently it is enough to consider real u, we shall let $\mathfrak{D}^*$, $\mathfrak{D}_\alpha^*$, $\mathfrak{D}_\beta^*$, $\mathfrak{D}_{\alpha\beta}^*$ denote the set of all real-valued functions in $\mathfrak{D}$, $\mathfrak{D}_\alpha$, $\mathfrak{D}_\beta$, $\mathfrak{D}_{\alpha\beta}$, respectively, and state Courant's minimum principle as follows:

Theorem 1.22   (Courant)   *A function $u_0 \in \mathfrak{D}^*$ which minimizes $j[u]$ under the condition $\|u\| = 1$ is an eigenfunction (unique except for a constant factor of modulus 1) corresponding to the smallest eigenvalue $\lambda_0 = j[u_0]$ of (1.54). The same conclusion holds if $\mathfrak{D}^*$ is replaced by $\mathfrak{D}_\alpha^*$, $\mathfrak{D}_\beta^*$, or $\mathfrak{D}_{\alpha\beta}^*$, $j[u]$ is replaced by $j_\alpha[u]$, $j_\beta[u]$, or $j_{\alpha\beta}[u]$, and the boundary conditions in (1.54) are replaced by $u(\alpha) = p_\beta[u] = 0$, $p_\alpha[u] = u(\beta) = 0$, or $u(\alpha) = u(\beta) = 0$, respectively.*

Proof   The proof of the existence of a minimizing function of class $\mathscr{C}^2(\alpha, \beta)$ has been given, for example, by Mikhlin [130, 131] and will not be included here. If u_0 denotes the minimizing function and $\lambda_0 = j[u_0]$, we assert that

$$j[u_0 + \varepsilon w] \geq \lambda_0 \|u_0 + \varepsilon w\|^2 \tag{1.59}$$

for arbitrary $w \in \mathfrak{D}^*$ and arbitrary real ε. In fact, this is obvious if $\|u_0 + \varepsilon w\| = 0$, and since u_0 is a minimizing function,

$$j\left[\frac{u_0 + \varepsilon w}{\|u_0 + \varepsilon w\|}\right] \geq j[u_0] = \lambda_0$$

if $\|u_0 + \varepsilon w\| \neq 0$, which is equivalent to (1.59).

In addition to (1.50), we define the bilinear functional

$$j[u, v] = \int_\alpha^\beta (au'v' + cuv) \, dx + su(\beta)v(\beta) + ru(\alpha)v(\alpha), \qquad u, v \in \mathfrak{D}^*.$$

It is easily verified that

$$j[u_0 + \varepsilon w] = j[u_0] + 2\varepsilon j[u_0, w] + \varepsilon^2 j[w],$$

and

$$\|u_0 + \varepsilon w\|^2 = \|u_0\|^2 + 2\varepsilon \langle u_0, w \rangle + \varepsilon^2 \|w\|^2.$$

Hence (1.59) yields, since $j[u_0] = \lambda_0 = \lambda_0 \|u_0\|$,

$$2\varepsilon j[u_0, w] + \varepsilon^2 j[w] \geq 2\lambda_0 \varepsilon \langle u_0, w \rangle + \lambda_0 \varepsilon^2 \|w\|^2.$$

Since ε is an arbitrary (positive or negative) number, it follows that $j[u_0, w] = \lambda_0 \langle u_0, w \rangle$ for all $w \in \mathfrak{D}^*$. The analog of (1.55) for $j[u_0, w]$ is

$$j[u_0, w] = \langle lu_0, w \rangle + w(\beta)p_\beta[u_0] + w(\alpha)p_\alpha[u_0]. \tag{1.60}$$

Since w is arbitrary, $\langle \lambda_0 u_0, w \rangle = j[u_0, w] = \langle l u_0, w \rangle$ or $\langle l u_0 - \lambda_0 u_0, w \rangle = 0$. Since $l u_0 - \lambda_0 u_0 \in \mathscr{C}(\alpha, \beta)$, it follows from a standard theorem of analysis [130, p. 76] that $l u_0 - \lambda_0 u_0 = 0$ in (α, β). Then (1.60) shows that

$$0 = \langle \lambda_0 u_0 - l u_0, w \rangle = w(\beta) p_\beta[u_0] + w(\alpha) p_\alpha[u_0]$$

for arbitrary $w \in \mathfrak{D}^*$. Hence $p_\alpha[u_0] = p_\beta[u_0] = 0$ and u_0 is an eigenfunction of (1.54) corresponding to the eigenvalue λ_0 (necessarily the smallest one).

In the case that $u_0 \in \mathfrak{D}_\alpha^*$ minimizes $j_\alpha[u]$, (1.60) is replaced by

$$j_\alpha[u_0, w] = \langle l u_0, w \rangle + w(\beta) p_\beta[u_0] - a(\alpha) w(\alpha) u_0'(\alpha),$$

for arbitrary $w \in \mathfrak{D}^*$, and hence $l u_0 - \lambda_0 u_0 = 0$ and $p_\beta[u_0] = 0$ as before. Since the domain $\mathfrak{D}_\alpha$ is by definition restricted by the condition $u(\alpha) = 0$, u_0 is an eigenfunction of the problem

$$l u = \lambda_0 u, \qquad u(\alpha) = p_\beta[u] = 0.$$

The proofs in the cases $u_0 \in \mathfrak{D}_\beta^*$ and $u_0 \in \mathfrak{D}_{\alpha\beta}^*$ are left as exercises.

In addition to (1.48) and (1.49), consider a second differential operator L of the same type and additional boundary operators P_α, P_β defined by

$$Lu = \frac{1}{k(x)} \left\{ -\frac{d}{dx} \left[A(x) \frac{du}{dx} \right] + C(x)u \right\}, \qquad (1.61)$$

$$\begin{aligned} P_\alpha[u] &= Ru(\alpha) - A(\alpha)u'(\alpha) \\ P_\beta[u] &= Su(\beta) + A(\beta)u'(\beta), \end{aligned} \qquad (1.62)$$

under the same hypotheses as those stated relative to (1.48) and (1.49). The eigenvalue problem for these operators (the analog of (1.54)) is

$$Lv = \lambda v, \qquad P_\alpha[v] = P_\beta[v] = 0. \qquad (1.63)$$

The associated quadratic functionals are

$$J[u] = \int_\alpha^\beta (A|u'|^2 + C|u|^2)\, dx + S|u(\beta)|^2 + R|u(\alpha)|^2$$
$$|R| < \infty, \qquad |S| < \infty, \qquad u \in \mathfrak{D};$$

$$J_\alpha[u] = \int_\alpha^\beta (A|u'|^2 + C|u|^2)\, dx + S|u(\beta)|^2$$
$$|S| < \infty, \qquad u \in \mathfrak{D}_\alpha; \qquad (1.64)$$

$$J_\beta[u] = \int_\alpha^\beta (A|u'|^2 + C|u|^2)\, dx + R|u(\alpha)|^2$$
$$|R| < \infty, \qquad u \in \mathfrak{D}_\beta;$$

$$J_{\alpha\beta}[u] = \int_\alpha^\beta (A|u'|^2 + C|u|^2)\, dx, \qquad u \in \mathfrak{D}_{\alpha\beta}.$$

The *variation* of $j[u]$ is defined as $V[u] = j[u] - J[u]$, i.e.,

$$V[u] = \int_\alpha^\beta [(a - A)|u'|^2 + (c - C)|u|^2] \, dx + (s - S)|u(\beta)|^2$$
$$+ (r - R)|u(\alpha)|^2, \qquad u \in \mathfrak{D}, \tag{1.65}$$

in the case that r, R, s, and S are all finite.

Theorem 1.23 *Suppose that r, R, s, and S are all finite. If the eigenvalue problem (1.54) for l has an eigenvalue λ with an associated eigenfunction u satisfying $V[u] > 0$, then the problem (1.63) has at least one eigenvalue less than λ.*

Proof It is sufficient to consider the case that u is a real-valued eigenfunction since in any event $u = \gamma v$, where γ is a nonzero constant and v is a real-valued eigenfunction satisfying the hypothesis $V[v] = |\gamma|^{-1} V[u] > 0$.

Since u is an eigenfunction of (1.54) it follows from (1.56) that $j[u] = \lambda \|u\|^2$. The hypothesis $V[u] > 0$ is equivalent to $J[u] < j[u]$. Hence the minimum of $J[u]$ among $u \in \mathfrak{D}^*$ with $\|u\| = 1$ is less than λ. By Courant's minimum principle (Theorem 1.22) applied to $J[u]$, the lowest eigenvalue of (1.63) is less than λ.

The next theorem contains six analogs of Theorem 1.23 in the cases that various of the boundary parameters r, R, s, and S are replaced (formally) by ∞. We shall use the following modified variations relative to these cases:

$$\begin{array}{lll} (1) & V_{\alpha, 0}[u] = j_\alpha[u] - J[u], & u \in \mathfrak{D}_\alpha \\ (2) & V_{\beta, 0}[u] = j_\beta[u] - J[u], & u \in \mathfrak{D}_\beta \\ (3) & V_{\alpha\beta, 0}[u] = j_{\alpha\beta}[u] - J[u], & u \in \mathfrak{D}_{\alpha\beta} \\ (4) & V_{\alpha, \alpha}[u] = j_\alpha[u] - J_\alpha[u], & u \in \mathfrak{D}_\alpha \\ (5) & V_{\beta, \beta}[u] = j_\beta[u] - J_\beta[u], & u \in \mathfrak{D}_\beta \\ (6) & V_{\alpha\beta, \alpha\beta}[u] = j_{\alpha\beta}[u] - J_{\alpha\beta}[u], & u \in \mathfrak{D}_{\alpha\beta}. \end{array}$$

These can be written out similarly to (1.65) by using the definitions of $j_\alpha[u]$, $J_\alpha[u]$, etc. For example,

$$V_{\alpha, \alpha}[u] = \int_\alpha^\beta [(a - A)|u'|^2 + (c - C)|u|^2] \, dx + (s - S)|u(\beta)|^2,$$
$$u \in \mathfrak{D}_\alpha.$$

Theorem 1.24 *If the eigenvalue problem (1.54) for l, with finite boundary parameters as listed in Table I, has an eigenvalue λ with an associated eigenfunction satisfying the corresponding condition, then (1.63), with the finite parameters listed in Table I, has at least one eigenvalue less than λ.*

TABLE I

Case	Finite boundary parameters	Condition
1	s, R, S	$V_{\alpha, 0}[u] > 0$
2	r, R, S	$V_{\beta, 0}[u] > 0$
3	R, S	$V_{\alpha\beta, 0}[u] > 0$
4	s, S	$V_{\alpha, \alpha}[u] > 0$
5	r, R	$V_{\beta, \beta}[u] > 0$
6	None	$V_{\alpha\beta, \alpha\beta}[u] > 0$

Proof In case (1) it follows as in the proof of the preceding theorem that $j_\alpha[u] = \lambda \|u\|^2$, $u \in \mathfrak{D}_\alpha^*$, and hence

$$J[u] = j_\alpha[u] - V_{\alpha, 0}[u] < j_\alpha[u] = \lambda \|u\|^2$$

by hypothesis. Since $\mathfrak{D}_\alpha^* \subset \mathfrak{D}^*$, the minimum of $J[u]$ among $u \in \mathfrak{D}^*$ with $\|u\| = 1$ is less than λ. By Courant's minimum principle, the lowest eigenvalue of (1.63) in case (1) has at least one eigenvalue less than λ. The proofs in the other cases are virtually the same and will be left as exercises.

We shall use the notation $\lambda_0(R, S)$ for the smallest eigenvalue of (1.63) to indicate the dependence on the boundary parameters R, S.

Lemma 1.25 If $R < R' \leq \infty$ and $S < \infty$, then $\lambda_0(R, S) < \lambda_0(R', S)$. If $S < S' \leq \infty$ and $R < \infty$, then $\lambda_0(R, S) < \lambda_0(R, S')$.

Proof By Theorem 1.22, $\lambda_0(R, S)$ is the minimum of $J[u]$ among $u \in \mathfrak{D}^*$ satisfying $\|u\| = 1$, where $J[u]$ is given by (1.64). Likewise $\lambda(R', S)$ is the minimum of $J[u] + (R' - R)u^2(\alpha)$ among $u \in \mathfrak{D}^*$ with $\|u\| = 1$ (if $R' < \infty$). Hence $\lambda_0(R, S) < \lambda_0(R', S)$ (if $R < R' < \infty$).

In the case $R' = \infty$, Theorem 1.22 shows there is an eigenfunction $u_0 \in \mathfrak{D}_\alpha^*$, $\|u_0\| = 1$, such that

$$\lambda_0(\infty, S) = J_\alpha[u_0] = J[u_0]$$

since $u_0(\alpha) = 0$. It follows from the inclusion $\mathfrak{D}_\alpha^* \subset \mathfrak{D}^*$ that

$$\lambda_0(R, S) = \min_{\substack{u \in \mathfrak{D}^* \\ \|u\| = 1}} J[u] \leq J[u_0] = \lambda_0(\infty, S).$$

Hence, if $R < R'' < \infty$, $\lambda_0(R, S) < \lambda_0(R'', S) \leq \lambda_0(\infty, S)$. This proves the first statement of Lemma 1.25, and an interchange of R and S establishes the second statement.

Theorem 1.26   *Suppose that r, s, R, and S are all finite. If* (1.54) *has an eigenfunction u such that V* [u] > 0, *then every solution v of* (1.63) (*with the same* λ) *has a zero in* (α, β).

Proof   According to Theorem 1.23, the smallest eigenvalue λ_0 of (1.63) is less than λ. We assert that there is an eigenfunction v_0 of (1.63) corresponding to λ_0 which has positive values everywhere in (α, β). To establish this, it is sufficient to show that v_0 does not have any zeros in (α, β). Suppose to the contrary that $v_0(\alpha') = 0$ ($\alpha < \alpha' < \beta$). Then v_0 is an eigenfunction of the problem

$$Lv_0 = \lambda_0 v_0, \qquad v_0(\alpha') = P_\beta[v_0] = 0.$$

Since $\alpha < \alpha'$, the smallest eigenvalue $\lambda_0(\infty, S)$ of the problem

$$Lw = \lambda w, \qquad w(\alpha) = P_\beta[w] = 0,$$

satisfies $\lambda_0(\infty, S) \leq \lambda_0$ [39, p. 409], which contradicts Lemma 1.25. Hence there is an eigenfunction v_0 with only positive values in (α, β). Since v_0 and v are eigenfunctions of (1.63) corresponding to distinct eigenvalues λ_0 and λ, it follows that v is orthogonal to v_0. Hence v must vanish at some point in (α, β).

Theorem 1.27   *Suppose the eigenvalue problem* (1.54) *has finite boundary parameters as listed in one of the six cases of Table I. If* (1.54) *has an eigenfunction u satisfying the corresponding condition of the table, then every solution of* (1.63) (*with the same* λ) *has a zero in* (α, β).

Proof   Theorem 1.24 shows that the smallest eigenvalue of (1.63) is less than λ in each of the six cases. The proof is then completed in the same way as that of the preceding theorem.

Theorem 1.28   *Suppose that s* $\geq$ *S, r* $\geq$ *R, and a* $\geq$ *A, c* $\geq$ *C in* (α, β). *Suppose in addition that either c* > *C at some point or that a* > *A and c* $\neq$ 0 *at some point. If* (1.54) *has an eigenfunction, then every solution of* (1.63) (*with the same* λ) *has a zero in* (α, β).

Proof   In the case $r < \infty$, $s < \infty$, it follows from the hypotheses that $V[u] > 0$ by the same argument used in the proof of Theorem 1.15. The conclusion then follows from Theorem 1.26 in this case, and similarly from Theorem 1.27 in the other cases.

   Some physical interpretations of the ideas of Section 5 can be found, for example, in the books by Courant and Hilbert [39], Mikhlin [130], and Schiff [176].

Exercises

1. Prove that the eigenvalues of (1.54) are all positive in the case $r = s = \infty$,
   $c \geq 0$ ($c \not\equiv 0$).

2. Prove Theorem 1.22 in the cases $u_0 \in \mathfrak{D}_\beta{}^*$ and $u_0 \in \mathfrak{D}_{\alpha\beta}^*$.
3. Write out the variations $V_{\beta,0}[u]$, $V_{\alpha,\alpha}[u]$, $V_{\alpha\beta,0}[u]$, $V_{\alpha\beta,\alpha\beta}[u]$ after the fashion of (1.65).
4. Prove Theorem 1.24 in cases (2)–(6).
5. Give the detailed proof of Theorem 1.28 in all the cases.

6. Reid's Comparison Theorems on Focal Points [170].

The differential equations under consideration are (1.1) and (1.2), reproduced here for convenience:

$$lu \equiv \frac{d}{dx}\left[a(x)\frac{du}{dx}\right] + c(x)u = 0, \qquad \alpha \le x \le \beta \tag{1.1}$$

$$Lv \equiv \frac{d}{dy}\left[A(y)\frac{dv}{dy}\right] + C(y)v = 0, \qquad \gamma \le y \le \delta, \tag{1.2}$$

where c, C are real-valued continuous functions on $[\alpha, \beta]$, $[\gamma, \delta]$, respectively, and a, A are positive-valued functions of class $\mathscr{C}^1[\alpha, \beta]$, $\mathscr{C}^1[\gamma, \delta]$, respectively.

If there exists a nontrivial solution u of (1.1) such that $u'(x_0) = 0$ and $u(x_1) = 0$, then x_1 is said to be a focal point of x_0 relative to the differential equation (1.1). The least (greatest) focal point to the right of (left of) x_0 will be denoted by $f^+(x_0)(f^-(x_0))$. The set of all x_0 in (α, β) such that $f^+(x_0)$ exists and lies in (α, β) will be denoted by s^+; and the set of all x_0 in (α, β) such that $f^-(x_0)$ exists and lies in (α, β) by s^-. Let i^+, j^+ denote, respectively, the inf, sup of $f^+(x) - x$ over s^+, and let i^-, j^- denote, respectively, the inf, sup of $x - f^-(x)$ over s^-. For the differential equation (1.2), the quantities corresponding to $f^\pm(x)$, $s^\pm$, $i^\pm$, and $j^\pm$ are denoted by $F^\pm(y)$, $S^\pm$, $I^\pm$, $J^\pm$, respectively.

Theorem 1.29 *Suppose that the intervals in (1.1) and (1.2) are identical and that $(A/a)' \ge 0$, $c > 0$, and $C/A \le c/a$ on the common interval. Then the existence of $F^+(x_0)$ implies $f^+(x_0)$ exists and satisfies $f^+(x_0) \le F^+(x_0)$. Correspondingly, if $(A/a)' \ge 0$, $C > 0$, and $c/a \le C/A$ on the common interval, then the existence of $f^-(x_0)$ implies that $F^-(x_0)$ exists and satisfies $f^-(x_0) \le F^-(x_0)$.*

Proof To prove the first statement, suppose to the contrary that $F^+(x_0)$ exists but $f^+(x_0)$ does not exist and satisfy $f^+(x_0) \le F^+(x_0)$. Then the uniquely determined solution u of the initial value problem

$$lu = 0, \qquad u(x_0) = 1, \qquad u'(x_0) = 0$$

is positive on the interval $[x_0, F^+(x_0)]$. Since $a > 0$ and $c > 0$ in the differential equation $lu = au'' + a'u' + cu = 0$, it follows that $u''(x_0) < 0$, and hence

$u'(x_0)$ is negative immediately to the right of x_0. But then $u'(x) < 0$ on the whole interval $[x_0, F^+(x_0)]$, for if $u'(x)$ had a zero on this interval, say $u'(x_1) = 0$, then $u''(x_1) < 0$ would be a consequence of the differential equation $lu = 0$, which is impossible for consecutive zeros x_0, x_1 of u'. Since $lu = 0$, $u'' = -(a'u' + cu)/a$, and hence

$$uLu = u(Au')' + Cu^2$$
$$= u[-(A/a)a'u' - (c/a)Au + A'u'] + Cu^2$$
$$= auu'[(A'/a) - (Aa'/a^2)] + Au^2[(C/A) - (c/a)]$$
$$= auu'(A/a)' + Au^2[(C/A) - (c/a)].$$

The hypotheses of the first part of the theorem then imply that $uLu \leq 0$ on $[x_0, F^+(x_0)]$.

For arbitrary $h \in \mathscr{C}^1$, an elementary calculation yields the identity

$$A(uh)'^2 - C(uh)^2 = [u(Au')h^2]' - h^2uLu + A(uh')^2. \tag{1.66}$$

By hypothesis there is a solution of $Lv = 0$ satisfying $v'(x_0) = v(x_1) = 0$ $(x_1 > x_0)$. Choose $h = v/u$ in (1.66) to obtain

$$\int_{x_0}^{x_1} (Av'^2 - Cv^2) \, dx \geq \int_{x_0}^{x_1} A(uh')^2 \, dx > 0.$$

However, integration by parts shows that

$$\int_{x_0}^{x_1} (Av'^2 - Cv^2) \, dx = \left[Avv' \right]_{x_0}^{x_1} - \int_{x_0}^{x_1} vLv \, dx = 0.$$

The contradiction shows that $[x_0, F^+(x_0)]$ has a focal point of x_0 relative to l, i.e., $f^+(x_0) \leq F^+(x_0)$. The second statement is proved by a similar argument on the interval $[F^-(x_0), x_0]$.

The following corollary is obtained in the case that the hypothesis of both statements of Theorem 1.29 are fulfilled.

Corollary 1.30 If $(A/a)' \geq 0$, $c > 0$, $C > 0$, and $C/A = c/a$ on $[\alpha, \beta]$, then (1) if $F^+(x_0)$ exists then also $f^+(x_0)$ exists and satisfies $f^+(x_0) \leq F^+(x_0)$, and (2) if $f^-(x_0)$ exists then also $F^-(x_0)$ exists and satisfies $f^-(x_0) \leq F^-(x_0)$.

In the case that $a(t) \equiv c(t)$ and $A(t) \equiv C(t)$ in (1.1) and (1.2), $\alpha \leq t \leq \beta$, Corollary 1.30 is simplified as follows:

Corollary 1.31 If $a = c > 0$, $A = C > 0$, and $A'/A \geq a'/a$ on $[0, \beta]$, then (1) if $F^+(0)$ exists then also $f^+(0)$ exists and satisfies $f^+(0) \leq F^+(0)$, and (2) if $f^-(0)$ exists then $F^-(0)$ exists and satisfies $f^-(0) \leq F^-(0)$.

Reid [170] used Corollary 1.31 to obtain the following comparison theorem on focal points, relative to the differential equations

$$[a(x)u']' + a(x)u = 0, \qquad \alpha \le x \le \beta \tag{1.67}$$

$$[A(y)v']' + A(y)v = 0, \qquad \gamma \le y \le \delta \tag{1.68}$$

(special cases of (1.1), (1.2), respectively).

Theorem 1.32 *If $A'(y)/A(y) \ge a'(x)/a(x)$ on $\alpha \le x \le \beta$, $\gamma \le y \le \delta$, then:* (1) *If S^+ is nonempty and $I^+ < \beta - \alpha$, then s^+ is nonempty, contains all x such that $[x, \ x + I^+] \subset [\alpha, \beta]$, and $j^+ \le I^+$; and* (2) *If s^- is nonempty and $i^- < \delta - \gamma$, then S^- is nonempty, contains all y such that $[y - i^-, \ y] \subset [\gamma, \delta]$, and $J^- \le i^-$.*

Proof Let $\varepsilon_0 = \beta - \alpha - I^+$. Then $I^+ + \varepsilon < \beta - \alpha$ for all ε satisfying $0 < \varepsilon \le \varepsilon_0$. Let y_0 be a point in S^+ such that $F^+(y_0) - y_0 < I^+ + \varepsilon$ and let x_0 be a point in (α, β) such that $[x_0, x_0 + I^+ + \varepsilon] \subset [\alpha, \beta]$.

Let $u(x)$ be the solution of (1.67) satisfying the initial conditions $u(x_0) = 1$, $u'(x_0) = 0$, and let $v(y)$ be the solution of (1.68) satisfying $v(y_0) = 1$, $v'(y_0) = 0$. We now apply Corollary 1.31 to the case that $a(t)$, $A(t)$ in that corollary are replaced by $a(x_0 + t)$, $A(y_0 + t)$, respectively, on the t-interval $[0, F^+(y_0) - y_0]$ (which is included in the interval $[0, I^+ + \varepsilon]$ by the foregoing). Under the substitutions $x = x_0 + t$, $y = y_0 + t$, Eqs. (1.67), (1.68), respectively, transform into the equations considered in Corollary 1.31 on the t-interval $[0, \beta]$, $\beta = F^+(y_0) - y_0$. Thus Corollary 1.31 yields

$$0 < f^+(x_0) - x_0 \le F^+(y_0) - y_0 < I^+ + \varepsilon.$$

By continuity it follows that s^+ contains all x for which $[x, x + I^+] \subset [\alpha, \beta]$ and $f^+(x) - x \le I^+$ for all such x. Therefore $f^+(x) - x \le I^+$ for all $x \in s^+$ and consequently $j^+ \le I^+$. This completes the proof of the first statement of Theorem 1.32. The proof of the second statement is similar and will be omitted.

The following result is obtained upon reflection of the x-axis through the origin and application of Theorem 1.32.

Theorem 1.32' *If $A'(y)/A(y) \ge -a'(x)/a(x)$ on $\alpha \le x \le \beta, \gamma \le y \le \delta$ then:* (1) *If S^+ is nonempty and $I^+ < \beta - \alpha$, then s^- is nonempty, contains all x such that $[x - I^+, x] \subset [\alpha, \beta]$, and $j^- \le I^+$; and* (2) *If s^+ is nonempty and $i^+ < \delta - \gamma$, then S^- is nonempty, contains all y such that $[y - i^+, y] \subset [\gamma, \delta]$, and $J^- \le i^+$.*

Theorems 1.32 and 1.32' together imply the following result:

Theorem 1.33   (Reid)   *Suppose that*

$$A'(y)/A(y) \geq |a'(x)/a(x)|, \qquad \alpha \leq x \leq \beta, \quad \gamma \leq y \leq \delta. \qquad (1.69)$$

(1) If S^+ is nonempty and $2I^+ < \beta - \alpha$, then $s^+ \cap s^-$ is nonempty, contains all x such that $[x - I^+, \; x + I^+] \subset [\alpha, \beta]$, and $f^+(x) - f^-(x) \leq 2I^+$ for all $x \in s^+ \cap s^-$. (2) If $s^+ \cap s^-$ is nonempty and there exists a number $x \in s^+ \cap s^-$ such that $f^+(x) - f^-(x) < \delta - \gamma$, then S^- is nonempty and $2J^- \leq f^+(x) - f^-(x)$ for all $x \in s^+ \cap s^-$.

Let $u(x)$ be a solution of (1.67) with two or more zeros $x_1, x_2, \ldots$ on $[\alpha, \beta]$, and let M denote the maximum distance between consecutive zeros, say $M = u(x_2) - u(x_1)$. Then there exists a number x_0 in the interval (x_1, x_2) such that $u'(x_0) = 0$, and x_1, x_2 are the first focal points to the left, right of x_0, respectively. Thus $M = f^+(x_0) - f^-(x_0)$. Let $v(y)$ be a solution of (1.68) and let m denote the minimum distance between its zeros on $[\gamma, \delta]$. Then

$$I^+ = \inf_{x \in S^+} F^+(x) - x \leq m.$$

It then follows from the first statement of Theorem 1.33 that

$$M = f^+(x_0) - f^-(x_0) \leq 2I^+ \leq 2m.$$

This result was first obtained by Weinberger [206] in connection with Cauchy's problem for hyperbolic partial differential equations. It can be formulated as follows:

Theorem 1.34   (Weinberger)   *Let u, v be nontrivial solutions of (1.67), (1.68), respectively. Let m be the minimum distance between the zeros of $v(y)$ on $[\gamma, \delta]$, and let M be the maximum length of any subinterval of $[\alpha, \beta]$ that contains no zeros of $u(x)$. If the inequality (1.69) holds, then $m/M \geq \frac{1}{2}$.*

In the special case that $a(x) \equiv 1$ in (1.67), the inequality (1.69) reduces to $A'(y) \geq 0$, $M = \pi$, and the conclusion of Weinberger's theorem becomes $m \geq \pi/2$. This inequality can be used to find lower bounds for eigenvalues. Consider, for example, the eigenvalue problem

$$\frac{d}{dz}\left[p(z)\frac{dw}{dz}\right] + \lambda q(z)w = 0, \qquad w(\alpha) = w(\beta) = 0, \qquad (1.70)$$

where p and q are positive-valued continuous functions on $[\alpha, \beta]$ and $p \in \mathscr{C}^1[\alpha, \beta]$. This can be put into the canonical form (1.68) by the change of variable

$$y(z) = \int_\alpha^z [\lambda q(t)/p(t)]^{1/2} dt, \qquad v(y) = w(z),$$

$$A(y) = [\lambda p(z)q(z)]^{1/2},$$

as shown by an easy calculation. Thus if $d(pq)^{1/2}/dz \geq 0$, the minimum distance between the zeros of $v(y)$ on $[0, y(\beta)]$ is not less than $\pi/2$. Consequently, if $N + 1$ denotes the number of zeros of $v(y)$ on this interval (which includes the two known zeros at the endpoints), then $y(\beta) \geq N\pi/2$, or

$$N + 1 \leq 1 + 2y(\beta)/\pi.$$

It follows that $w(z)$ has at most $1 + 2y(\beta)/\pi$ zeros on $[\alpha, \beta]$.

If $\lambda = \lambda_N$ is the Nth eigenvalue of (1.70), it is well known [35] that the corresponding eigenfunction $w_N(z)$ has exactly $N + 1$ zeros on $[\alpha, \beta]$. Hence

$$N \leq 2y(\beta)/\pi = (2/\pi)\lambda_N^{1/2} \int_\alpha^\beta [q(t)/p(t)]^{1/2} \, dt,$$

or

$$\lambda_N \geq (N^2\pi^2/4)\left[\int_\alpha^\beta [q(t)/p(t)]^{1/2} \, dt\right]^{-2}.$$

7. Levin's Comparison Theorems

In 1960 Levin [118] extended Sturm's theorem 1.1 in a direction somewhat different from that considered in the previous sections. The method used by Levin involves the transformation of the differential equations

$$u'' + c(x)u = 0 \tag{1.71}$$

$$v'' + C(x)v = 0, \qquad \alpha \leq x \leq \beta \tag{1.72}$$

into the Riccati equations

$$w' = w^2 + c(x) \tag{1.73}$$

$$z' = z^2 + C(x) \tag{1.74}$$

by the substitutions $w = -u'/u$, $z = -v'/v$, respectively. This technique had been used earlier by Hille [81], Hartman [69–74], and Wintner [211–215] among others in connection with oscillation criteria for differential equations. This topic will be treated in detail in Chapter 2.

Equations (1.71) and (1.72) are special cases of (1.1), (1.2), respectively, when $a(x) \equiv 1$ and $A(x) \equiv 1$. It will be assumed as before that $c(x)$ and $C(x)$ are continuous on $[\alpha, \beta]$. (Actually integrability of these functions will suffice, but then solutions of (1.71) or (1.72) are understood only to satisfy these equations almost everywhere.)

Theorem 1.35   (Levin)   *Let u and v be nontrivial solutions of* (1.71), (1.72), *respectively, such that u(x) does not vanish on* [α, β], $v(\alpha) \neq 0$, *and the inequality*

$$-\frac{u'(\alpha)}{u(\alpha)} + \int_\alpha^x c(t)\, dt > \left| -\frac{v'(\alpha)}{v(\alpha)} + \int_\alpha^x C(t)\, dt \right| \qquad (1.75)$$

holds for all x on [α, β]. *Then v(x) does not vanish on* [α, β] *and*

$$-\frac{u'(x)}{u(x)} > \left| \frac{v'(x)}{v(x)} \right|, \qquad \alpha \le x \le \beta. \qquad (1.76)$$

The same theorem holds *verbatim et literatim* if the inequality signs in (1.75) and (1.76) are replaced by $\ge$.

Proof   Since $u(x)$ does not vanish, $w = -u'/u$ is continuous on [α, β] and satisfies the Riccati equation (1.73), which is equivalent to the integral equation

$$w(x) = w(\alpha) + \int_\alpha^x w^2(t)\, dt + \int_\alpha^x c(t)\, dt. \qquad (1.77)$$

By the hypothesis (1.75),

$$w(x) \ge -\frac{u'(\alpha)}{u(\alpha)} + \int_\alpha^x c(t)\, dt > 0. \qquad (1.78)$$

Since $v(\alpha) \neq 0$, $z = -v'/v$ is continuous on some interval [α, γ], $\alpha < \gamma \le \beta$. On this interval (1.74) is well defined and implies the integral equation

$$z(x) = z(\alpha) + \int_\alpha^x z^2(t)\, dt + \int_\alpha^x C(t)\, dt. \qquad (1.79)$$

Thus by (1.75) and (1.78) in turn,

$$z(x) \ge z(\alpha) + \int_\alpha^x C(t)\, dt$$

$$> -w(\alpha) - \int_\alpha^x c(t)\, dt$$

$$\ge -w(x), \qquad \alpha \le x \le \gamma,$$

and consequently $w(x) > -z(x)$. In order to show that

$$|z(x)| < w(x) \qquad \text{on} \quad \alpha \le x \le \gamma, \qquad (1.80)$$

it is then sufficient to show that $w(x) > z(x)$ on this interval. Suppose to the contrary that there exists a point x_0 on [α, γ] such that $z(x_0) \ge w(x_0)$. Then, since $|z(\alpha)| < w(\alpha)$ from (1.75) (with $x = \alpha$) and since w and z are continuous on [α, γ], there exists x_1 in $\alpha < x_1 \le x_0$ such that $z(x_1) = w(x_1)$ and $z(x) < w(x)$ for $a \le x < x_1$. Since $w(x) > -z(x)$ was established previously, it follows that $|z(x)| < w(x)$ for $\alpha \leq x < x_1$, and consequently

$$\int_\alpha^{x_1} z^2(t)\, dt < \int_\alpha^{x_1} w^2(t)\, dt.$$

Use of (1.79), (1.75), and (1.77) in turn yields

$$z(x_1) = z(\alpha) + \int_\alpha^{x_1} C(t)\, dt + \int_\alpha^{x_1} z^2(t)\, dt$$

$$< w(\alpha) + \int_\alpha^{x_1} c(t)\, dt + \int_\alpha^{x_1} w^2(t)\, dt$$

$$= w(x_1),$$

contradicting $z(x_1) = w(x_1)$.

Thus (1.80) holds on any interval of continuity $[\alpha, \gamma]$ of z, $\alpha < \gamma \leq \beta$, but this implies that z is continuous on the entire interval $[\alpha, \beta]$ since $w(x)$ is bounded and $z(x)$ has only poles at its points of discontinuity (if any). Thus (1.80) holds on all of the interval $[\alpha, \beta]$. This proves (1.76), and since the left member is bounded on $[\alpha, \beta]$, $v(x)$ cannot have a zero on this interval.

A slight modification of the proof shows that if $>$ is replaced by $\geq$ in the hypothesis (1.75), then the conclusion is still valid provided $>$ is replaced by $\geq$ in (1.76). This completes the proof of Theorem 1.35.

Theorem 1.36   (Levin)   *Let u and v be nontrivial solutions of (1.71), (1.72), respectively, such that $u(x)$ does not vanish on $[\alpha, \beta]$, $v(\beta) \neq 0$, and the inequality*

$$\frac{u'(\beta)}{u(\beta)} + \int_x^\beta c(t)\, dt > \left| \frac{v'(\beta)}{v(\beta)} + \int_x^\beta C(t)\, dt \right| \qquad (1.81)$$

holds for all x on $[\alpha, \beta]$. Then $v(x)$ does not vanish on $[\alpha, \beta]$ and

$$\frac{u'(x)}{u(x)} > \left| \frac{v'(x)}{v(x)} \right|, \qquad \alpha \leq x \leq \beta. \qquad (1.82)$$

The same holds if $>$ in (1.81) and (1.82) is replaced by $\geq$.

Proof   Let new functions u_1, v_1, c_1 and C_1 be defined on $\alpha \leq x \leq \beta$ by the equations

$$u_1(x) = u(\alpha + \beta - x), \qquad v_1(x) = v(\alpha + \beta - x)$$

$$c_1(x) = c(\alpha + \beta - x), \qquad C_1(x) = C(\alpha + \beta - x).$$

Then $u_1(x)$ does not vanish on $[\alpha, \beta]$, $v_1(\alpha) = v(\beta) \neq 0$, and

$$-\frac{u_1'(\alpha)}{u_1(\alpha)} + \int_\alpha^{\alpha+\beta-x} c_1(t)\, dt = \frac{u'(\beta)}{u(\beta)} + \int_x^\beta c(s)\, ds;$$

$$-\frac{v_1'(\alpha)}{v_1(\alpha)} + \int_\alpha^{\alpha+\beta-x} C_1(t)\, dt = \frac{v'(\beta)}{v(\beta)} + \int_x^\beta C(s)\, ds.$$

Thus the hypothesis (1.81) is equivalent to the hypothesis (1.75) of Theorem 1.35 since $x \in [\alpha, \beta]$ iff $\alpha + \beta - x \in [\alpha, \beta]$, and the conclusion (1.82) follows from Theorem 1.35.

    It can also be shown by a slight modification of the proof that Theorems 1.35 and 1.36 can be refined as follows: If (1.75) (or (1.81)) is satisfied on $[\alpha, \beta]$ with the weak inequality $\geq$ throughout and the strict inequality at some point $x_0 \in [\alpha, \beta]$, then (1.76) (or 1.82)) holds with the weak inequality throughout and the strict inequality on $[x_0, \beta]$ (or $[\alpha, x_0]$).

    Under the hypotheses of Theorems 1.35, 1.36, respectively, the following inequalities are valid:

$$\frac{v'(x)}{v(x)} - \frac{u'(x)}{u(x)} > \frac{v'(\alpha)}{v(\alpha)} - \frac{u'(\alpha)}{u(\alpha)} + \int_\alpha^x [c(t) - C(t)]\, dt, \tag{1.83}$$

$$\frac{u'(x)}{u(x)} - \frac{v'(x)}{v(x)} > \frac{u'(\beta)}{u(\beta)} - \frac{v'(\beta)}{v(\beta)} + \int_x^\beta [c(t) - C(t)]\, dt. \tag{1.84}$$

In fact, the integral equations (1.77) and (1.79) together with the inequality (1.80) yield the inequality

$$z(x) - z(\alpha) - \int_\alpha^x C(t)\, dt < w(x) - w(\alpha) - \int_\alpha^x c(t)\, dt,$$

and since $z' = -v'/v$ and $w' = -u'/u$, this is equivalent to (1.83). The inequality (1.84) is obtained from (1.83) by the substitutions used in the proof of Theorem 1.36.

Theorem 1.37   (Levin) *Suppose there exists a nontrivial solution v of (1.72) which satisfies the conditions $v(\alpha) = v(\beta) = v'(\gamma) = 0$, $\alpha < \gamma < \beta$. If the inequalities*

$$\int_x^\gamma c(t)\, dt \geq \left|\int_x^\gamma C(t)\, dt\right|, \qquad \int_\gamma^x c(t)\, dt \geq \left|\int_\gamma^x C(t)\, dt\right| \tag{1.85}$$

hold for all x on $[\alpha, \gamma]$, $[\gamma, \beta]$, respectively, then every solution of Eq. (1.71) has at least one zero on $[\alpha, \beta]$.

Proof   Let u be a nontrivial solution of (1.71) satisfying $u'(\gamma) = 0$. We assert that u has at least one zero in each of the intervals $[\alpha, \gamma)$ and $(\gamma, \beta]$. Observe first that $u(\gamma) \neq 0$, for otherwise u would be a solution of the initial value problem $u'' + c(x)u = 0$, $u(\gamma) = u'(\gamma) = 0$, and since the solution is well known to be unique [35], u would be identically zero. Thus $u(\gamma) \neq 0$ and likewise $v(\gamma) \neq 0$. If u had no zero in $(\gamma, \beta]$, and hence no zero on $[\gamma, \beta]$, all the hypotheses of Theorem 1.35 would be fulfilled on account of (1.85), and thus v would have no zero on $[\gamma, \beta]$. This contradicts the hypothesis $v(\beta) = 0$. Likewise, if u had no zero in $[\alpha, \gamma)$ an application of Theorem 1.36 would yield the contradiction that v has no zero on $[\alpha, \gamma]$.

It follows that u has at least two zeros on $[\alpha, \beta]$, and hence every solution of Eq. (1.71) has at least one zero on $[\alpha, \beta]$ by the Sturm separation theorem 1.8.

In the special case that $c(x) > C(x)$ throughout the interval $[\alpha, \beta]$, the inequalities (1.85) are satisfied trivially, and Theorem 1.37 shows that if there exists a nontrivial solution v of (1.72) satisfying $v(\alpha) = v(\beta) = 0$, then every solution of (1.71) has at least one zero on $[\alpha, \beta]$. However, it cannot be concluded that every solution of (1.71) has a zero in the *open* interval (α, β), nor can any of the strong forms of Sturm's comparison theorem (Theorems 1.4–1.7) be deduced.

Exercises

1. Show that Theorem 1.35 is valid if the inequality signs in (1.75) and (1.76) are replaced by $\geq$.
2. Show qualitatively that there are functions c and C for which the inequalities (1.85) hold but the pointwise inequality $c(t) \geq C(t)$ throughout $[\alpha, \beta]$ does not hold.
3. If $a(t) > 0$ and $A(t) > 0$ on $[\alpha, \beta]$, show that the substitutions

$$y = f(x) = \int_\alpha^x \frac{dt}{a(t)}, \qquad z = F(x) = \int_\alpha^x \frac{dt}{A(t)}$$

transform Eqs. (1.1), (1.2), respectively, into

$$\frac{d^2u}{dy^2} + a[f^{-1}(y)]c[f^{-1}(y)]u = 0,$$

$$\frac{d^2v}{dz^2} + A[F^{-1}(z)]C[F^{-1}(z)]v = 0,$$

where f^{-1}, F^{-1} denote the inverses of the (monotone) functions f, F.
4. Obtain comparison theorems for Eqs. (1.1) and (1.2) by using the previous exercise and Theorem 1.37.
5. One difficulty which arises in the application of Theorem 1.37 is that the number γ must be known as well as the zeros α and β of v. Show that this difficulty disappears in the case of the equations

$$v'' + v = 0, \qquad u'' + (x + 1 - k)u = 0 \qquad\qquad (1.86)$$

on the interval $[0, \pi]$, where k is a number in the interval $0 < k \leq \pi/4$. For $\gamma = \pi/2$, show that the inequalities (1.85) reduces to

$$|x - k| \leq \pi/2 - k \qquad \text{on} \quad 0 \leq x \leq \pi/2,$$

$$|x - k| \geq \pi/2 - k \qquad \text{on} \quad \pi/2 \leq x \leq \pi,$$

which are satisfied if $0 < k \leq \pi/4$, and therefore that every solution of the second equation (1.86) has at least one zero on $[0, \pi]$. Compare this result with the example (1.13), (1.14) of Section 1.

8. The Order of Zeros

The differential equation (1.19) will be considered in the form

$$a(x)u'' + b(x)u' + c(x)u = 0, \tag{1.87}$$

where a, b, and c are continuous and a is positive in an open interval $\alpha < x < \beta$. The possibility that α, β are $-\infty$, ∞ is not excluded. We assume in this section that there exists a solution u_1 which has a *first zero* x_0 in (α, β), i.e., $u_1(x_0) = 0$ but $u_1(x) \neq 0$ in (α, x_0). Then every nontrivial solution of (1.87) with zeros has a first zero in (α, β) by the Sturm separation theorem (Exercise 11 of Section 1). The following problems will be solved: (1) Given two nontrivial solutions of (1.87) in (γ, β), $\gamma \geq \alpha$, which one has the largest first zero (and hence the largest kth zero ($k = 2, 3, \ldots$) since the zeros of linearly independent solutions are interlaced)? (2) Among all solutions of (1.87), does there exist one with the largest first zero (and hence the largest kth zero)? These questions were considered by Morse and Leighton in 1936 [138] and again by Lorch and Newman in 1965 [126] by a different approach.

Theorem 1.38   (Lorch and Newman)   *Let u_1 and u_2 be linearly independent solutions of* (1.87) *under the above hypotheses and let*

$$\omega = \lim_{x \to \gamma+} \left| \frac{u_1(x)}{u_2(x)} \right|, \qquad \alpha \leq \gamma < \beta. \tag{1.88}$$

Suppose there exists a number $\delta > \gamma$ such that $|u_1(x)/u_2(x)| > \omega$ in $\gamma < x \leq \delta$. If $x_0 = \gamma$ and x_k, ξ_k denote the kth zero of u_1, u_2, respectively, in (γ, β), then $x_{k-1} < \xi_k < x_k$ ($k = 1, 2, \ldots$).

Proof   We observe first that the limit in (1.88) exists because of the hypothesis that the solutions of (1.87) have a smallest zero in (α, β), and hence *a fortiori* in (γ, β), i.e., γ is not a limit point of zeros of $u_2(x)$.

Let $W(u_1, u_2; x)$ denote the Wronskian determinant of the two solutions u_1, u_2 at the point x:

$$W(u_1, u_2; x) = u_1(x)u_2'(x) - u_2(x)u_1'(x).$$

Since $W(u_1, u_2; x)$ satisfies the differential equation $a(x)W' + b(x)W = 0$ by direct calculation from (1.87), it is given by Abel's formula

$$W(u_1, u_2; x) = W(u_1, u_2; x_0) \exp\left\{-\int_{x_0}^x \frac{b(t)}{a(t)} dt\right\},$$

and hence it cannot change sign in (α, β).

We may assume without loss of generality that $u_1(x)$ and $u_2(x)$ are positive in (γ, δ); for $-u_1, -u_2$ are solutions along with u_1, u_2 and have the same zeros, and the δ chosen in connection with (1.88) can be decreased if necessary. We assert that $W(u_1, u_2; x) < 0$ in $\alpha < x < \beta$, for otherwise $u_2'(x)/u_2(x) \geq u_1'(x)/u_1(x)$ in $(\gamma, \delta]$, and hence

$$\int_x^\delta \frac{u_2'(t)}{u_2(t)} dt \geq \int_x^\delta \frac{u_1'(t)}{u_1(t)} dt$$

for arbitrary x satisfying $\gamma < x < \delta$. Thus

$$\log \frac{u_2(\delta)}{u_2(x)} \geq \log \frac{u_1(\delta)}{u_1(x)},$$

which implies that $u_1(x)/u_2(x) \geq u_1(\delta)/u_2(\delta)$. In the limit $x \to \gamma$, this yields the contradiction $\omega \geq u_1(\delta)/u_2(\delta)$. Thus $W(u_1, u_2; x) < 0$ in $\alpha < x < \beta$.

Now $u_1(x_1) = 0$ by hypothesis and $u_1'(x_1) < 0$ since $u_1(x)$ is positive to the left of its first zero and negative to the right (the zeros are simple). Thus

$$0 < W(u_1, u_2; x_1)/u_1'(x_1) = -u_2(x_1),$$

or $u_2(x_1) < 0$. Since $u_2(x)$ is positive in $(\gamma, \delta]$ there exists a number ξ_1 in (γ, x_1) such that $u_2(\xi_1) = 0$. If ξ denotes any zero of u_2 in (γ, x_1), then, since $u_1(x)$ is positive to the left of x_1,

$$0 > W(u_1, u_2; \xi)/u_1(\xi) = u_2'(\xi),$$

and consequently there is only one zero ξ_1 in (γ, x_1).

Repeating the argument with γ replaced by $\xi_1, x_1, \xi_2, \ldots$ in succession we find that $\xi_1 < x_1 < \xi_2 < x_2 < \cdots$.

The Sturm separation theorem 1.8 is an easy consequence of Theorem 1.38: If γ is taken to be a zero of u_1, then $\omega = 0$ and Theorem 1.38 shows that the zeros of u_1 and u_2 are interlaced.

A solution u_1 of (1.87) is said to be *zero-maximal* in (γ, β) if it has the largest first zero in (γ, β) among all solutions of (1.87). This definition is meaningful since we are assuming that γ is not a limit point of zeros of any solution. (In the language of the next chapter, this means that the differential equation is *nonoscillatory* at γ.)

Theorem 1.39 (Lorch and Newman) *Let u_1 and u_2 be linearly independent solutions of (1.87) such that $\omega = 0$, where ω is defined by (1.88). Then u_1 is zero-maximal in (γ, β). Every nonoscillatory differential equation (1.87) has a zero-maximal solution, unique except for a constant multiplicative factor.*

Proof It follows from Theorem 1.38 that $\xi_1 < x_1$, $\xi_2 < x_2$, ... If u_2 is replaced by any other solution u of (1.87) linearly independent of u_1, i.e., by $u = k_1 u_1 + k_2 u_2 \ (k_2 \neq 0)$, then

$$\tilde{\omega} = \lim_{x \to \gamma+} \left| \frac{u_1(x)}{u(x)} \right| = \lim_{x \to \gamma+} \left| \frac{u_1(x)}{u_2(x)} \left[\frac{k_1 u_1(x)}{u_2(x)} + k_2 \right]^{-1} \right|$$

and $\tilde{\omega} = 0$. Thus $\xi_1 < x_1$, $\xi_2 < x_2$, ... where ξ_1, ξ_2 denote consecutive zeros of *any* solution u of (1.87). Hence u_1 is zero-maximal in (γ, β).

 If (1.87) is nonoscillatory at γ, let u_1, u_2 be linearly independent solutions which are positive in some neighbourhood of γ. If

$$\omega = \lim_{x \to \gamma+} \frac{u_1(x)}{u_2(x)} = 0,$$

then u_1 is a zero-maximal solution by the first part of the theorem. If $\omega = \infty$, clearly u_2 is a zero-maximal solution. If $0 < \omega < \infty$, set $u = u_1 - \omega u_2$, and we obtain

$$\lim_{x \to \gamma+} \left| \frac{u(x)}{u_2(x)} \right| = \lim_{x \to \gamma+} \left| \frac{u_1(x)}{u_2(x)} - \omega \right| = 0$$

and hence u is zero-maximal. The uniqueness except for a constant multiplier is obvious from the foregoing.

Example 1 As an example of Eq. (1.87), consider Bessel's equation of order m

$$x^2 u'' + x u' + (x^2 - m^2) u = 0 \tag{1.89}$$

in the interval $0 < x < \infty$. In this case we take $\gamma = 0$. If $J_m(x)$ denotes the Bessel function of the first kind and $C_m(x)$ denotes any solution of Bessel's equation, then it is well known [44] that

$$\omega = \lim_{x \to 0+} J_m(x)/C_m(x) = 0, \qquad m \geq 0$$

if $C_m \neq J_m$, and hence the kth positive zero of $J_m(x)$ exceeds the kth positive zero of any other solution of Bessel's equation.

Theorem 1.40   (Lorch and Newman)   *Let w_1 and w_2 be linearly independent solutions of (1.87) such that w_1 is zero-maximal in (γ, β). Define linearly independent solutions u_1 and u_2 by the equations*

$$u_j(x) = k_{j1}w_1(x) + k_{j2}w_2(x) \qquad (j = 1, 2)$$

where $k_{11}k_{22} - k_{12}k_{21} > 0$. Then $x_{k-1} < \xi_k < x_k$ $(k = 1, 2, \ldots)$ where $x_0 = \gamma$ and x_k, ξ_k denote the kth zeros of u_1, u_2, respectively in (γ, β).

Proof   As in Theorem 1.38, we may assume that w_1, w_2, u_1, and u_2 are all positive in some interval $(\gamma, \delta]$ to the right of γ. Since w_1 is zero-maximal, the quantity ω in (1.88) is zero, and it follows as in the proof of Theorem 1.38 that $W(w_1, w_2; x) < 0$. Thus

$$W(u_1, u_2; x) = (k_{11}k_{22} - k_{12}k_{21})W(w_1, w_2; x) < 0,$$

and the proof is completed along the lines of Theorem 1.38.

Example 2   Let $J_m(x)$ and $Y_m(x)$ denote the standard Bessel functions of the first and second kinds, which constitute linearly independent solutions of Eq. (1.89). Define

$$C_m(x, \theta) = J_m(x) \cos \theta - Y_m(x) \sin \theta,$$

$0 < x < \infty$, $0 \le \theta < \pi$. As shown in Example 1, $w_1(x) = J_m(x)$ is zero-maximal in $(0, \infty)$. If we define

$$w_2(x) = -Y_m(x), \qquad u_1(x) = C_m(x, \theta), \qquad u_2(x) = C_m(x, \varphi),$$

for $0 \le \theta < \varphi < \pi$, then in the notation of Theorem 1.40,

$$k_{11}k_{22} - k_{12}k_{21} = \cos \theta \sin \varphi - \sin \theta \cos \varphi = \sin(\varphi - \theta) > 0.$$

Hence the kth positive zero of $C_m(x, \theta)$ exceeds that of $C_m(x, \varphi)$ for $m \ge 0$, $0 \le \theta < \varphi < \pi$.

Example 3   For $m > 0$ $(m \ne 1, 2, \ldots)$ let j_{mk}, j_{-mk}, and y_{mk} denote respectively the kth positive zeros of $J_m(x)$, $J_{-m}(x)$, and $Y_m(x)$ $(k = 1, 2, \ldots)$. Then $j_{mk} > j_{-mk}$ and $j_{mk} > y_{mk}$ since $J_m(x)$ is zero-maximal by Example 1 and $J_m(x)$ and $J_{-m}(x)$ are linearly independent when m is not an integer [44]. We shall use the identity [44, Vol. 2, p. 4(4)]

$$J_{-m}(x) = J_m(x) \cos m\pi - Y_m(x) \sin m\pi$$

and set

$$w_1(x) = J_m(x), \qquad w_2(x) = -Y_m(x),$$
$$u_1(x) = J_{-m}(x), \qquad u_2(x) = -Y_m(x),$$

so that, in the notation of Theorem 1.40,

$$k_{11}k_{22} - k_{12}k_{21} = \cos m\pi > 0$$

when $m\pi$ is in the first quadrant. Thus $j_{-mk} > y_{mk}$ in this case ($k = 1, 2, \ldots$). For $m\pi$ in the third quadrant, put $u_1(x) = -J_{-m}(x)$, $u_2(x) = -Y_m(x)$, which are positive near 0. Then

$$k_{11}k_{22} - k_{12}k_{21} = -\cos m\pi > 0,$$

and again $j_{-mk} > y_{mk}$. For $m\pi$ in quadrant I or III the following inequalities have then been established: $j_{mk} > j_{-mk} > y_{mk}$ ($k = 1, 2, \ldots$).

In quadrant II, put $u_1 = -Y_m$, $u_2 = J_{-m}$, and in quadrant IV put $u_1 = -Y_m$, $u_2 = -J_{-m}$. This leads to the result

$$j_{mk} > y_{mk} > j_{-mk} \qquad (k = 1, 2, \ldots)$$

in these quadrants.

Exercises
1. Deduce the result of Example 2 from Theorem 1.38.
2. The solutions of the differential equation

$$u'' + [1 - 2\eta x^{-1} - L(L+1)x^{-2}]u = 0,$$

$$x > 0, \qquad L \geq -\tfrac{1}{2}$$

are called Coulomb wave functions; they are closely related to confluent hypergeometric functions [44]. Show that the solution $F_L(\eta, x)$ which has the limit 0 as $x \to 0+$ (the one commonly used in applications) is zero-maximal in $(0, \infty)$.
3. Show that the kth positive zero of the hypergeometric function $F(\alpha, \beta, \gamma, x)$ [44] (if it exists) exceeds the kth positive zero of $F(\alpha - \gamma + 1, \beta - \gamma + 1, 2 - \gamma, x)$ if $\gamma > 1$, $\gamma \neq 2, 3, \ldots$. In this case, two linearly independent solutions of the hypergeometric differential equation are

$$F(\alpha, \beta, \gamma, x), \qquad x^{1-\gamma}F(\alpha - \gamma + 1, \beta - \gamma + 1, 2 - \gamma, x).$$

4. If n is a nonnegative integer, the Legendre polynomials $P_n(x)$ are solutions of Legendre's equation

$$(1 - x^2)y'' - 2xy' + n(n+1)y = 0,$$

where $P_n(x)$ has a factor of x if n is odd but not if n is even. Show that the Legendre polynomials of odd degree n are zero-maximal in $(0, 1)$ but that those of even degree are not. Since $\lim P_n(x)/Q_n(x) = 0$ ($x \to -1$), where $Q_n(x)$ denotes the second solution of Legendre's equation [44], show that the Legendre polynomial $P_n(x)$ is zero-maximal in $(-1, 1)$ for all n.

5. Show that the Hermite polynomials $H_n(x)$ [44] are zero-maximal in $[0, \infty)$ iff n is odd.

6. Derive zero-maximal properties of associated Legendre functions, associated Laguerre functions, and other special functions of mathematical physics which satisfy differential equations of the form (1.87) [44].

Chapter 2

Oscillation and Nonoscillation Theorems for Second Order Ordinary Equations

1. The Oscillation Criteria of Hille and Nehari

The differential equations under consideration in this section are

$$u'' + c(x)u = 0 \tag{2.1}$$

$$v'' + C(x)v = 0 \tag{2.2}$$

(which are specializations of (1.1), (1.2) to the cases $a(x) \equiv 1$, $A(x) \equiv 1$, respectively) on the half-open interval $[0, \infty)$, where c and C are positive continuous functions on this interval.

Definitions   Equation (2.1) is said to be nonoscillatory in (α, ∞) $(\alpha \geq 0)$ if every nontrivial solution has at most one zero in (α, ∞); it is said to be non-oscillatory (without reference to an interval) if there exists a number α such that it is nonoscillatory in (α, ∞). The equation is said to be oscillatory if it has a nontrivial solution which has an infinite number of zeros in $(0, \infty)$.

Because of the Sturm separation theorem 1.8, Eq. (2.1) is nonoscillatory in (α, ∞) if it has a solution which does not vanish at any point in this interval, and oscillatory iff *every* solution has an infinite number of zeros in $(0, \infty)$.

If (2.1) is not oscillatory, there exists a number α such that no solution of (2.1) has any zeros in (α, ∞), and if (2.1) is not nonoscillatory, there exists a solution with arbitrarily large zeros. Thus, oscillatory and nonoscillatory equations (2.1) are mutually exclusive and exhaustive.

It is an immediate consequence of the Sturm comparison theorem 1.1

44

that (2.1) is nonoscillatory if $c(x) \leq 0$, but it may have this property also if $c(x) > 0$; in fact, the Euler equation

$$u'' + \gamma(x + 1)^{-2}u = 0 \qquad (\gamma = \text{constant}),$$

with the general solution

$$u(x) = \begin{cases} K_1(x + 1)^\rho + K_2(x + 1)^{1-\rho}, & \rho = \tfrac{1}{2} + \tfrac{1}{2}(1 - 4\gamma)^{1/2}, \quad \gamma \neq \tfrac{1}{4} \\ (x + 1)^{1/2}[K_1 + K_2 \ln(x + 1)], & \gamma = \tfrac{1}{4} \end{cases}$$

is nonoscillatory if $\gamma \leq \tfrac{1}{4}$ (and oscillatory if $\gamma > \tfrac{1}{4}$). With this example in mind, Kneser [95] proved in 1893 that equation (2.1) is oscillatory if $\omega > \tfrac{1}{4}$, and nonoscillatory if $\omega < \tfrac{1}{4}$, where

$$\omega = \lim_{x \to \infty} x^2 c(x). \tag{2.3}$$

There is an extensive literature [see the bibliography] on the topic of oscillation criteria, i.e., conditions on $c(x)$ which imply that (2.1) is oscillatory (or nonoscillatory). Since Kneser's result, Bellman [16], Fite [45], Hartman [62–78], Hille [81], Leighton [112–115], Levinson [122], Moore [134], Nehari [143], Potter [152], Wintner [69–78, 211–218], and others have contributed to the subject. Wintner and Leighton proved, in particular, that (2.1) is oscillatory if

$$\int_0^\infty c(t) \, dt = \infty,$$

and hence the integral is finite if (2.1) is nonoscillatory. Very general oscillation criteria were developed by Hille [81] and Nehari [143], which contain the criteria of Wintner, Leighton, Kneser, and others as special cases. Hille stated his results in terms of the function g defined by

$$g(x) = x \int_x^\infty c(t) \, dt \tag{2.4}$$

and the numbers g_* and g^* defined by

$$g_* = \lim_{x \to \infty} \inf g(x), \qquad g^* = \lim_{x \to \infty} \sup g(x). \tag{2.5}$$

If the integral in (2.4) is not finite, the previously stated result of Wintner and Leighton applies, and in this case we set $g_* = g^* = \infty$. Hille obtained the following result, which will follow as a special case of our subsequent theorems.

Theorem 2.1 *The conditions $g_* \leq \tfrac{1}{4}$, $g^* \leq 1$ are necessary conditions and $g^* < \tfrac{1}{4}$ is a sufficient condition for Eq. (2.1) to be nonoscillatory; $g_* > \tfrac{1}{4}$ is a sufficient condition for (2.1) to be oscillatory.*

In particular this shows that $g^* \geq \frac{1}{4}$ if (2.1) is oscillatory and that (2.1) is oscillatory if the integral in (2.4) is not finite. To deduce Kneser's result (cited above) from Theorem 2.1 we obtain from (2.3) that, for given $\varepsilon > 0$, there is a number $x_0 > 0$ such that

$$\left| c(x) - \frac{\omega}{x^2} \right| < \frac{\varepsilon}{x^2}$$

provided $x > x_0$. Hence

$$|g(x) - \omega| = x \left| \int_x^\infty \left[c(t) - \frac{\omega}{t^2} \right] dt \right| < \varepsilon x \int_x^\infty \frac{dt}{t^2} = \varepsilon.$$

Thus $g^* = g_* = \omega$ and Theorem 2.1 shows that Eq. (2.1) is oscillatory if $\omega > \frac{1}{4}$ and nonoscillatory if $\omega < \frac{1}{4}$.

In 1957 Nehari [143] discovered a connection between the oscillatory behavior of the solutions of (2.1) and the eigenvalue problem

$$u'' + \lambda c(x)u = 0, \qquad u(\alpha) = u'(\beta) = 0. \tag{2.6}$$

(See Theorem 2.2 below.) Actually this is the same as the problem (1.54) of Chapter 1, Section 5 in the special case that $a(x)$, $c(x)$, $k(x)$, $p_\alpha[u]$, and $p_\beta[u]$ in (1.54) are replaced by 1, 0, $c(x)$, $u(\alpha)$, and $u'(\beta)$, respectively. The associated quadratic functional (1.51) becomes

$$j_\alpha[u] = \int_\alpha^\beta u'^2 \, dx, \qquad u \in \mathfrak{D}_\alpha,$$

where $\mathfrak{D}_\alpha = \{u \in \mathscr{C}^1[\alpha, \beta] : u(\alpha) = 0\}$. Courant's minimum principle (Theorem 1.22) states that if λ_0 is the smallest eigenvalue of (2.6), then

$$\lambda_0 \|y\|^2 \leq j_\alpha[y] \qquad \text{for all real} \quad y \in \mathfrak{D}_\alpha. \tag{2.7}$$

In fact, this is even true for all real $y \in \mathscr{C}^1[\alpha, \beta]$ satisfying the weaker condition

$$\lim_{x \to \alpha+} \frac{y^2(x)}{x - \alpha} = 0.$$

The proof follows from the identity

$$0 \leq \int_{\alpha+\varepsilon}^\beta \left(y' - \frac{u'}{u} y \right)^2 dx$$

$$= \int_{\alpha+\varepsilon}^\beta y'^2 \, dx - 2 \int_{\alpha+\varepsilon}^\beta \frac{u'}{u} yy' \, dx + \int_{\alpha+\varepsilon}^\beta \frac{u'^2}{u^2} y^2 \, dx$$

$$= \int_{\alpha+\varepsilon}^\beta y'^2 \, dx + \int_{\alpha+\varepsilon}^\beta \frac{u''}{u} y^2 \, dx - \left[\frac{u'}{u} y^2 \right]_{\alpha+\varepsilon}^\beta$$

upon integration of the middle term by parts, valid for all $u \in \mathscr{C}^1(\alpha, \beta)$ which do not vanish in (α, β), and $0 < \varepsilon < \beta - \alpha$. If u is an eigenfunction of (2.6) corresponding to the smallest eigenvalue λ_0, and hence free of zeros in (α, β) by Theorem 1.26, then in the limit $\varepsilon \to 0$:

$$0 \le \int_\alpha^\beta y'^2 \, dx - \lambda_0 \int_\alpha^\beta c(x) y^2(x) \, dx,$$

which is (2.7).

Theorem 2.2 (Nehari) *Let λ_0 denote the smallest eigenvalue of* (2.6). *Then Eq.* (2.1) *is nonoscillatory in* (α, ∞) *if and only if $\lambda_0 > 1$ for all β satisfying $\beta > \alpha$.*

Proof If (2.1) is nonoscillatory in (α, ∞) and y is a solution of (2.1) such that $y(\alpha) = 0$ and $y'(\alpha) > 0$, then we assert that $y'(x) > 0$ for all $x \ge \alpha$. In fact

$$y'(x_2) - y'(x_1) = -\int_{x_1}^{x_2} c(x) y(x) \, dx < 0$$

for $\alpha \le x_1 < x_2 < \infty$. Then $y'(x)$ is never increasing for $\alpha < x$ and the graph of $y = y(x)$ is concave downwards. Since the graph lies below the tangent line at each point and does not intersect the x-axis for $x > \alpha$, it follows that $y'(x) > 0$ for all $x > \alpha$.

Let u be a positive eigenfunction of (2.6) in $(\alpha, \beta]$ corresponding to λ_0. Then

$$0 < u(\beta) y'(\beta) = -\int_\alpha^\beta (yu'' - uy'') \, dx = (\lambda_0 - 1) \int_\alpha^\beta cuy \, dx. \qquad (2.8)$$

Since c, u, and y are positive in (α, β), $\lambda_0 > 1$.

Conversely, if $\lambda_0 > 1$, (2.8) shows that y cannot have a zero to the right of α; for if β is the first such zero, (2.8) implies that $y'(\beta) > 0$, an impossibility.

Theorem 2.3 (Nehari) *If* (2.1) *is nonoscillatory in* (α, ∞), *then*

$$(x - \alpha)^{1-q} \int_\alpha^x (t - \alpha)^q c(t) \, dt + (x - \alpha)^{1-p} \int_x^\infty (t - \alpha)^p c(t) \, dt$$

$$\le \frac{q - p}{4} \left[1 + \frac{1}{(q - 1)(1 - p)} \right] \qquad (2.9)$$

for arbitrary numbers p and q satisfying $0 \le p < 1, q > 1$.

Proof Since (2.1) is nonoscillatory, $\lambda_0 > 1$ by Theorem 2.2, and hence Courant's minimum principle (2.7) yields

$$\int_\alpha^\beta c(x) y^2(x) \, dx < \int_\alpha^\beta y'^2(x) \, dx, \qquad \beta > \alpha \qquad (2.10)$$

for all $y \in \mathscr{C}^1[\alpha, \beta]$ such that $\lim(x - \alpha)^{-1}y^2(x) = 0$ $(x \to \alpha+)$. With the particular choice

$$y(x) = \begin{cases} (x - \alpha)^{q/2}(x_0 - \alpha)^{-q/2} & \text{if } \alpha \le x \le x_0 \\ (x - \alpha)^{p/2}(x_0 - \alpha)^{-p/2} & \text{if } x \ge x_0, \end{cases}$$

where $\alpha < x_0 < \beta$, (2.10) becomes

$$(x_0 - \alpha)^{-q} \int_\alpha^{x_0} (x - \alpha)^q c(x) \, dx + (x_0 - \alpha)^{-p} \int_{x_0}^\beta (x - \alpha)^p c(x) \, dx$$

$$\le \frac{q^2}{4(q - 1)(x_0 - \alpha)} + \frac{p^2[(x_0 - \alpha)^{p-1} - (\beta - \alpha)^{p-1}]}{4(1 - p)(x_0 - \alpha)^p},$$

and (2.9) follows in the limit $\beta \to \infty$ since

$$\frac{q^2}{4(q - 1)} + \frac{p^2}{4(1 - p)} = \frac{q^2 - p^2 + pq(p - q)}{4(q - 1)(1 - p)}$$

$$= \frac{(q - p)(q + p + pq)}{4(q - 1)(1 - p)}$$

$$= \frac{q - p}{4}\left[1 + \frac{1}{(q - 1)(1 - p)}\right].$$

Since both terms on the left side of (2.9) are nonnegative, the following inequalities are obtained when $p = 0$ and $q = 2$, respectively:

$$(x - \alpha)^{1-q} \int_\alpha^x (t - \alpha)^q c(t) \, dt \le \frac{q^2}{4(q - 1)}, \qquad q > 1, \tag{2.11}$$

$$(x - \alpha)^{1-p} \int_x^\infty (t - \alpha)^p c(t) \, dt \le \frac{(2 - p)^2}{4(1 - p)}, \qquad 0 \le p < 1.$$

Hence

$$\limsup_{x \to \infty} x^{1-q} \int_\alpha^x t^q c(t) \, dt \le \frac{q^2}{4(q - 1)}, \qquad q > 1, \tag{2.12}$$

$$\limsup_{x \to \infty} x^{1-p} \int_x^\infty t^p c(t) \, dt \le \frac{(2 - p)^2}{4(1 - p)}, \qquad 0 \le p < 1. \tag{2.13}$$

In particular (2.11) shows that $x^p c(x)$ $(0 \le p < 1)$ is integrable in (α, ∞) if (2.1) is nonoscillatory in (α, ∞), which is Leighton and Wintner's result [112, 211] in the case $p = 0$. Also, the first necessary condition $g^* \le 1$ of Hille's theorem 2.1 follows from (2.13) in the special case $p = 0$, where g^* is defined by (2.4) and (2.5).

Nehari also gives the following formulation of Theorem 2.3 by introducing the function σ defined by

$$\sigma(x) = (x - \alpha)^{1-p} \int_x^\infty (t - \alpha)^p c(t) \, dt, \qquad 0 \le p < 1. \tag{2.14}$$

Theorem 2.4 *If* (2.1) *is nonoscillatory in* (α, ∞), *then*

$$(x - \alpha)^{1-q} \int_\alpha^x (t - \alpha)^{q-2} \sigma(t) \, dt \le \frac{1}{4} + \frac{1}{4(q-1)(1-p)} \tag{2.15}$$

for arbitrary p *and* q *satisfying* $0 \le p < 1, q > 1$.

Proof If we define

$$\varphi(x) = \int_\alpha^x (t - \alpha)^q c(t) \, dt,$$

Theorem 2.3 states that

$$(x - \alpha)^{1-q} \varphi(x) + \sigma(x) \le \frac{q-p}{4} \left[1 + \frac{1}{(q-1)(1-p)} \right]. \tag{2.16}$$

However, integration by parts yields

$$
\begin{aligned}
\varphi(x) &= \int_\alpha^x (t - \alpha)^{q-p} (t - \alpha)^p c(t) \, dt \\
&= -\int_\alpha^x (t - \alpha)^{q-p} \, d[(t - \alpha)^{p-1} \sigma(t)] \\
&= -(x - \alpha)^{q-1} \sigma(x) + (q - p) \int_\alpha^x (t - \alpha)^{q-2} \sigma(t) \, dt.
\end{aligned}
$$

Substitution of this into (2.16) then gives the result (2.15).

Theorem 2.5   (Nehari) *If* (2.1) *is nonoscillatory, then*

$$\liminf_{x \to \infty} x^{1-p} \int_x^\infty t^p c(t) \, dt \le \frac{1}{4(1-p)}, \qquad 0 \le p < 1. \tag{2.17}$$

Proof By hypothesis there exists a number α such that (2.1) is nonoscillatory in (α, ∞), and hence we may apply Theorem 2.4. If x_0 is a number such that $\alpha < x_0 < x$, (2.15) can be written in the form

$$(x - \alpha)^{1-q} \int_\alpha^{x_0} (t - \alpha)^{q-2} \sigma(t) \, dt + (x - \alpha)^{1-q} \int_{x_0}^x (t - \alpha)^{q-2} \sigma(t) \, dt$$

$$\le \frac{1}{4} + \frac{1}{4(q-1)(1-p)}.$$

The first term of the left member tends to zero as $x \to \infty$ and the second term is bounded from below by $m(q-1)^{-1}$, where $m = \min \sigma(t)$. Hence

$$\inf_{x_0 \le t < \infty} \sigma(t) \le \frac{q-1}{4} + \frac{1}{4(1-p)}.$$

Since the left member is independent of q [cf. (2.14)], $q-1$ is an arbitrarily small positive number, and since x_0 is arbitrarily large, this proves (2.17).

   In particular, for $p = 0$, Theorem 2.5 reduces to Hille's necessary condition $g_* \le \frac{1}{4}$, where g_* is defined by (2.4) and (2.5). Both necessary conditions of Hille's theorem 2.1 have then been established as special cases of Nehari's results (2.13) and (2.17). The proof of the sufficiency condition $g^* < \frac{1}{4}$ will be deferred to the next section.

   The bound $g_* \le \frac{1}{4}$ of Hille's theorem is "sharp" in the sense that there exists a nonoscillatory equation for which $g_* = \frac{1}{4}$. Indeed, the Euler equation,

$$u'' + \tfrac{1}{4}(x+1)^{-2}u = 0 \tag{2.18}$$

considered at the beginning of this section is nonoscillatory and

$$g_* = \lim_{x \to \infty} \inf x \int_x^\infty \tfrac{1}{4}(t+1)^{-2}\, dt = \tfrac{1}{4}.$$

Theorem 2.6   (Nehari)   *If* (2.1) *is nonoscillatory in* (α, ∞) *and if* $0 \le c(x) \le m^2$ *in this interval, then there exists a universal constant* γ_0 *such that the inequality*

$$\int_\alpha^\infty c(x)\, dx \le \gamma m$$

holds for $\gamma = \gamma_0$ *but not, in general, for* $\gamma < \gamma_0$. *The universal constant* γ_0 *is a number in the interval*

$$\tfrac{1}{2} \le \gamma_0 \le 3^{3/4}2^{-1/2} = 1.61 \dots.$$

Proof Let

$$y(x) = \left(\int_\alpha^x c(t)\, dt \right)^\nu, \qquad \alpha \le x \le x_0, \quad \nu > \tfrac{1}{2}$$

$$= \left(\int_\alpha^{x_0} c(t)\, dt \right)^\nu, \qquad x_0 \le x \le \beta$$

in (2.10) and there results†

$$\frac{1}{2v+1}\left(\int_\alpha^{x_0} c(t)\,dt\right)^{2v+1} + \left(\int_\alpha^{x_0} c(t)\,dt\right)^{2v} \int_{x_0}^\beta c(t)\,dt$$

$$< v^2 \int_\alpha^{x_0} c^2(x)\left(\int_\alpha^x c(t)\,dt\right)^{2v-2} dx$$

$$\le v^2 m^2 \int_\alpha^{x_0} c(x)\left(\int_\alpha^x c(t)\,dt\right)^{2v-2} dx$$

$$= \frac{v^2 m^2}{2v-1}\left(\int_\alpha^{x_0} c(t)\,dt\right)^{2v-1}. \tag{2.19}$$

Since (2.1) is nonoscillatory, $c(x)$ is integrable in (α, ∞) by Wintner's theorem (or (2.11) with $p = 0$), and hence the function ψ defined by

$$\psi(x) = \int_\alpha^x c(t)\,dt, \qquad \alpha \le x < \infty,$$

is strictly increasing from 0 to a finite limit as x varies from α to ∞. Clearly $(2v + 1)/4v < 1$ by the hypothesis $v > \frac{1}{2}$, and since ψ must assume every value in its range, there exists a number x_0 such that

$$\psi(x_0) = \int_\alpha^{x_0} c(t)\,dt = \frac{2v+1}{4v}\int_\alpha^\infty c(t)\,dt,$$

and consequently

$$\int_{x_0}^\infty c(t)\,dt = \frac{2v-1}{4v}\int_\alpha^\infty c(t)\,dt.$$

Then (2.19) yields in the limit $\beta \to \infty$.

$$\left[\frac{1}{2v+1}\left(\frac{2v+1}{4v}\right)^2 + \frac{2v+1}{4v}\left(\frac{2v-1}{4v}\right)\right]\left[\int_\alpha^\infty c(t)\,dt\right]^2 \le \frac{v^2 m^2}{2v-1},$$

or

$$\left[\int_\alpha^\infty c(t)\,dt\right]^2 \le \frac{8v^3 m^2}{4v^2-1} \equiv m^2 f(v),$$

which defines $f(v)$, $v > \frac{1}{2}$. The best upper bound available by this method is,

† Although y' fails to exist at x_0, it is easy to see that (2.7) and (2.10) are still valid.

of course, the minimum of $f(v)$ times m^2, which is easily found by elementary calculus to be $m^2 f(\sqrt{3}/2) = 3\sqrt{3}\,m^2/2$. Thus

$$\int_\alpha^\infty c(x)\,dx \le 3^{3/4}2^{-1/2}m,$$

which shows that $\gamma_0 \le 3^{3/4}2^{-1/2}$.

The nonoscillatory example (2.18), in which

$$\int_\alpha^\infty c(x)\,dx = \frac{1}{4}\int_\alpha^\infty (x+1)^{-2}\,dx = \frac{1}{4(\alpha+1)} = \frac{1}{2}\,m,$$

yields the lower bound $\frac{1}{2}$ for γ_0. This completes the proof of Theorem 2.6.

2. Conditionally Oscillatory Equations

The Euler equation

$$u'' + \gamma(x+1)^{-2}u = 0$$

considered at the beginning of Section 1 is nonoscillatory if $\gamma \le \frac{1}{4}$ and oscillatory if $\gamma > \frac{1}{4}$. In general there exists a positive number μ such that the equation

$$u'' + \lambda c(x)u = 0, \qquad c(x) > 0 \quad \text{in } (\alpha, \infty) \tag{2.20}$$

is nonoscillatory for $\lambda < \mu$ and oscillatory for $\lambda > \mu$; in fact, if (2.20) is oscillatory for $\lambda = \lambda_1$, it is also oscillatory for all $\lambda > \lambda_1$ by the Sturm comparison theorem 1.1, and furthermore if (2.20) is nonoscillatory for $\lambda = \lambda_2$, it is also nonoscillatory for all $\lambda < \lambda_2$. Since oscillatory and nonoscillatory equations are mutually exhaustive, the g.l.b. of all λ for which (2.20) is oscillatory is equal to the l.u.b. of all λ for which it is nonoscillatory.

In general μ will be referred to as the *oscillation constant of* $c(x)$. If $\mu = 0$ (2.20) is oscillatory for all positive values of λ, and Eq. (2.1) is said to be *strongly oscillatory*. If $\mu = \infty$, (2.20) is nonoscillatory for all positive λ, and (2.1) is said to be *strongly nonoscillatory*. If $0 < \mu < \infty$, (2.1) is said to be *conditionally oscillatory*. In 1957 Nehari [143] obtained the following theorem, in which the oscillatory behavior of Eq. (2.1) is compared with that of a conditionally oscillatory equation (2.2) with known oscillation constant. The sufficient condition $g^* < \frac{1}{4}$ as well as the necessary condition $g_* \le \frac{1}{4}$ of Hille's theorem 2.1 follow as special cases of the theorem.

Theorem 2.7   (Nehari) *Let $c(x)$ and $C(x)$ be continuous and nonnegative in $0 \le x < \infty$ and let μ $(0 < \mu < \infty)$ denote the oscillation constant of $C(x)$.*

Then Eq. (2.1) is oscillatory if $h_* > \mu$ and nonoscillatory if $h^* < \mu$, where

$$h(x) = \int_x^\infty c(t)\, dt \bigg/ \int_x^\infty C(t)\, dt, \qquad (2.21)$$

$$h_* = \lim_{x \to \infty} \inf h(x), \qquad h^* = \lim_{x \to \infty} \sup h(x). \qquad (2.22)$$

Proof Let w be a nonnegative eigenfunction of the problem

$$w'' + \nu C(x)w = 0, \qquad w(\alpha) = w'(\beta) = 0. \qquad (2.23)$$

corresponding to the smallest eigenvalue ν. Since $w'(\alpha) > 0$, the proof of Theorem 2.2 shows that $w'(x) \geq 0$, $\alpha \leq x \leq \beta$. By Courant's minimum principle (Theorem 1.22),

$$\nu \int_\alpha^\beta C(x)w^2(x)\, dx = \int_\alpha^\beta [w'(x)]^2\, dx. \qquad (2.24)$$

If (2.1) is nonoscillatory, it is nonoscillatory in (α, ∞) for some α and (2.10) yields

$$\int_\alpha^\beta c(x)w^2(x)\, dx < \int_\alpha^\beta [w'(x)]^2\, dx. \qquad (2.25)$$

By the definitions (2.21), (2.22), and partial integration we obtain

$$\int_\alpha^\beta c(x)w^2(x)\, dx = -\int_\alpha^\beta \left[h(x) \int_x^\infty C(t)\, dt \right]' w^2(x)\, dx$$

$$= -h(\beta)w^2(\beta) \int_\beta^\infty C(t)\, dt + \int_\alpha^\beta h(x) \left[\int_x^\infty C(t)\, dt \right] [w^2(x)]'\, dx$$

$$\geq -h(\beta)w^2(\beta) \int_\alpha^\infty C(t)\, dt + (h_* - \varepsilon) \int_\alpha^\beta \left[\int_x^\infty C(t)\, dt \right] [w^2(x)]'\, dx$$

$$= [h_* - h(\beta) - \varepsilon]w^2(\beta) \int_\beta^\infty C(t)\, dt + (h_* - \varepsilon) \int_\alpha^\beta C(x)w^2(x)\, dx$$

for arbitrary $\varepsilon > 0$ provided α is sufficiently large, where the facts that $w(\alpha) = 0$ and $w'(x) \geq 0$ have been used. However by (2.22) there are arbitrarily large values of β for which $h(\beta) \leq h_* + \varepsilon$, and hence for such β

$$\int_\alpha^\beta c(x)w^2(x)\, dx \geq -2\varepsilon w^2(\beta) \int_\beta^\infty C(t)\, dt + (h_* - \varepsilon) \int_\alpha^\beta C(x)w^2(x)\, dx.$$

It follows from (2.24) and the fact that

$$w^2(\beta) = \left(\int_\alpha^\beta w'(x)\, dx \right)^2 \leq (\beta - \alpha) \int_\alpha^\beta w'^2(x)\, dx$$

(Schwarz inequality) that

$$\int_\alpha^\beta c(x)w^2(x)\,dx \geq -2\varepsilon(\beta-\alpha)\int_\beta^\infty C(t)\,dt \int_\alpha^\beta w'^2(x)\,dx$$

$$+ \frac{h_* - \varepsilon}{v}\int_\alpha^\beta w'^2(x)\,dx.$$

Combining this with (2.25) we obtain the inequality

$$1 \geq -2\varepsilon(\beta-\alpha)\int_\beta^\infty C(t)\,dt + \frac{h_* - \varepsilon}{v}.$$

Since μ is the oscillation constant of $C(x)$, the equation

$$u'' + (\mu - \varepsilon)C(x)u = 0, \qquad \varepsilon > 0$$

is nonoscillatory and the special case (2.11) of Theorem 2.3 yields (with $p = 0$)

$$(\mu - \varepsilon)(\beta - \alpha)\int_\beta^\infty C(t)\,dt \leq 1,$$

and therefore

$$1 \geq -\frac{2\varepsilon}{\mu - \varepsilon} + \frac{h_* - \varepsilon}{v}. \qquad (2.26)$$

The eigenvalue problem (2.23) can be written in the form

$$w'' + \left(\frac{v}{\mu + \varepsilon}\right)(\mu + \varepsilon)C(x)w = 0, \qquad w(\alpha) = w'(\beta) = 0,$$

of the form (2.6) considered in Theorem 2.2. Since μ is the oscillation constant of $C(x)$, the equation

$$u'' + (\mu + \varepsilon)C(x)\mu = 0, \qquad \varepsilon > 0,$$

is oscillatory, and Theorem 2.2 shows that $v(\mu + \varepsilon)^{-1} \leq 1$ if b is sufficiently large. Hence (2.26) implies the inequality

$$1 \geq -\frac{2\varepsilon}{\mu - \varepsilon} + \frac{h_* - \varepsilon}{\mu + \varepsilon}.$$

Since ε is arbitrarily small, this shows that $h_* \leq \mu$ if (2.1) is nonoscillatory. Hence (2.1) is oscillatory if $h_* > \mu$.

To prove the second assertion of Theorem 2.7, let μ_0 be the oscillation constant of $c(x)$. Then the equation

$$u'' + (\mu_0 - \varepsilon)c(x)u = 0, \qquad \varepsilon > 0 \qquad (2.27)$$

is nonoscillatory. By the first part of the theorem with (2.1) replaced by (2.27), and h_* replaced by $(\mu_0 - \varepsilon)h_*$, we conclude that $(\mu_0 - \varepsilon)h_* \leq \mu$, and since ε is arbitrary,

$$\mu_0 h_* \leq \mu. \tag{2.28}$$

Since

$$\lim_{x \to \infty} \inf \left[\int_x^\infty C(t)\, dt \Big/ \int_x^\infty c(t)\, dt \right] = 1/h^*$$

by (2.21) and (2.22), we can interchange the rôles of $C(t)$ and $c(t)$ to conclude from (2.28) that

$$\mu/h^* \leq \mu_0.$$

If (2.1) is oscillatory then $\mu_0 \leq 1$ by Theorem 2.2 and therefore $\mu \leq \mu_0 h^* \leq h^*$. This completes the proof of Theorem 2.7.

Corollary *Let $c(x)$ and $C(x)$ be continuous and nonnegative in $(0, \infty)$ and let μ_0, μ be the oscillation constants of $c(x)$, $C(x)$, respectively, $0 < \mu$, $\mu_0 < \infty$. Then $\mu_0 h_* \leq \mu$ where h_* is defined by (2.21), (2.22).*

In the special case $C(x) = (x + 1)^{-2}$, then $\mu = \frac{1}{4}$, as pointed out at the beginning of this section,

$$\int_x^\infty C(t)\, dt = (x + 1)^{-1} \qquad (x \geq 0),$$

and $h_* = g_*$, $h^* = g^*$ where Hille's quantities g_* and g^* are defined by (2.4) and (2.5). Thus $g_* \leq \frac{1}{4}$ is a necessary condition and $g^* < \frac{1}{4}$ is a sufficient condition for (2.1) to be nonoscillatory. Since the necessary condition, $g^* \leq 1$ was established in Section 1, the proof of Hille's theorem 2.1 is complete.

In 1960, Howard [84] obtained the following modification of Theorem 2.7, which also contains Hille's sufficient condition $g^* < \frac{1}{4}$ and Hille's necessary condition $g_* \leq \frac{1}{4}$ for nonoscillation as special cases. The proof is deleted.

Theorem 2.8 (Howard) *Let c be a positive continuous function in $[0, \infty)$ and let f be a positive nonincreasing function of class $\mathscr{C}^1(\alpha, \infty)$ $(\alpha \geq 0)$ such that*

$$\int_\alpha^\infty x^{-2} f(x) < \infty.$$

Then Eq. (2.1) is nonoscillatory or oscillatory according as

$$\lim_{x \to \infty} \sup \left(\int_x^\infty c(t) f(t)\, dt \right) \left(\int_x^\infty t^{-2} f(t)\, dt \right)^{-1} < \frac{1}{4}$$

or

$$\lim_{x \to \infty} \inf \left(\int_x^\infty c(t) f(t)\, dt \right) \left(\int_x^\infty t^{-2} f(t)\, dt \right)^{-1} > \frac{1}{4}.$$

In the special case $f(x) \equiv 1$, these reduce to Hille's conditions

$$g^* = \lim_{x \to \infty} \sup x \int_x^\infty c(t)\, dt < \frac{1}{4}$$

$$g_* = \lim_{x \to \infty} \inf x \int_x^\infty c(t)\, dt > \frac{1}{4}$$

respectively.

On the basis of Hille's theorem, Nehari found the following necessary and sufficient conditions for strongly oscillatory and strongly nonoscillatory equations.

Theorem 2.9   (Nehari)   *Equation* (2.1) *is strongly oscillatory iff* $g^* = \infty$ *and strongly nonoscillatory iff* $\lim g(x) = 0$ $(x \to \infty)$.

Proof   If (2.1) is strongly oscillatory, (2.20) is oscillatory for all $\lambda > 0$ and hence $\lambda g^* \geq \frac{1}{4}$ for all $\lambda > 0$ by Theorem 2.1, which shows that $g^* = \infty$. Conversely, if $g^* = \infty$ then $\lambda g^* > 1$ for all positive λ and (2.1) is oscillatory for all such λ.

If (2.1) is strongly nonoscillatory, the inequality $\lambda g^* \leq 1$ holds for all $\lambda > 0$ by Theorem 2.1 and hence $g^* = 0$. Conversely, if $g^* = 0$, $\lambda g^* < \frac{1}{4}$ is obvious and so (2.1) is strongly nonoscillatory.

3. Nehari's Comparison Theorems [143]

Comparison theorems will be obtained for the eigenvalue problems

$$u'' + \lambda c(x)u = 0, \qquad u'(\alpha) = u(\beta) = 0, \tag{2.29}$$

$$v'' + \mu C(x)v = 0, \qquad v'(\alpha) = v(\beta) = 0, \tag{2.30}$$

related to the differential equations (2.1), (2.2), respectively. The results are similar to special cases of those derived in Chapter 1, but the hypotheses are slightly different.

Theorem 2.10   (Nehari)   *Let* $c(x)$ *be nonnegative and continuous and let* $C(x)$ *be continuous on* $[\alpha, \beta]$. *Suppose that*

$$\int_\alpha^x c(t)\, dt \leq \int_\alpha^x C(t)\, dt, \qquad \alpha < x < \beta. \tag{2.31}$$

If λ_0, μ_0 *are the smallest eigenvalues of* (2.29), (2.30), *respectively, then* $\mu_0 \leq \lambda_0$, *equality holding iff* $c(x) \equiv C(x)$.

Proof Multiplication of (2.29) by u' and integration from α to β yields

$$\int_\alpha^\beta u'^2 \, dx = -\int_\alpha^\beta uu'' \, dx = \lambda_0 \int_\alpha^\beta cu^2 \, dx$$

$$= \lambda_0 \int_\alpha^\beta \left[\int_\alpha^x c(t) \, dt \right]' u^2 \, dx$$

$$= \lambda_0 \left[u^2(x) \int_\alpha^x c(t) \, dt \right]_\alpha^\beta - \lambda_0 \int_\alpha^\beta \left[\int_\alpha^x c(t) \, dt \right] [u^2(x)]' \, dx$$

$$= -\lambda_0 \int_\alpha^\beta \left[\int_\alpha^x c(t) \, dt \right] [u^2(x)]' \, dx. \tag{2.32}$$

Since λ_0 is the smallest eigenvalue of (2.29), there exists an eigenfunction u corresponding to λ_0 with only positive values in (α, β) by Theorem 1.26. It follows from (2.29) on account of the hypothesis $c(x) \geq 0$ and the fact that $\lambda_0 > 0$ (see Chapter 1, Section 5) that $u''(x) \leq 0$. Since $u'(\alpha) = 0$, $u'(x) \leq 0$ throughout (α, β). Combining this with (2.31) we obtain

$$-\int_\alpha^\beta \left[\int_\alpha^x c(t) \, dt \right] [u^2(x)]' \, dx \leq -\int_\alpha^\beta \left[\int_\alpha^x C(t) \, dt \right] [u^2(x)]' \, dx$$

$$= \left[u^2(x) \int_\alpha^x C(t) \, dt \right]_\alpha^\beta + \int_\alpha^\beta C(x)u^2(x) \, dx$$

$$= \int_\alpha^\beta C(x)u^2(x) \, dx.$$

Hence (2.32) gives the inequality

$$\int_\alpha^\beta [u'(x)]^2 \, dx \leq \lambda_0 \int_\alpha^\beta C(x)u^2(x) \, dx. \tag{2.33}$$

However, Courant's minimum principle (2.7) applied to the system (2.30) shows that the smallest eigenvalue μ_0 of (2.30) satisfies

$$\mu_0 \int_\alpha^\beta C(x)u^2(x) \, dx \leq \int_\alpha^\beta [u'(x)]^2 \, dx, \tag{2.34}$$

equality holding iff u is an eigenfunction of (2.30). Thus if u is an eigenfunction of (2.29) (with only positive values in (α, β)) corresponding to the smallest eigenvalue, (2.33) and (2.34) together imply that $\mu_0 \leq \lambda_0$, equality iff u is also an eigenfunction of (2.30) corresponding to the same eigenvalue λ_0, i.e.,

$$\int_\alpha^\beta [c(x) - C(x)]u^2(x) \, dx = 0,$$

or

$$c(x) \equiv C(x).$$

Actually the conclusion of Theorem 2.10 is still true if (2.31) is replaced by the more general condition

$$\int_\alpha^x c(t)f(t)\,dt \le \int_\alpha^x C(t)f(t)\,dt, \qquad \alpha < x < \beta,$$

where f is an arbitrary positive, nondecreasing function of class $\mathscr{C}^1[\alpha, \beta]$. This is easily proved by multiplying and dividing (2.32) by f and noting that $-(u^2/f)' \ge 0$ in (α, β). Howard [84] obtained the analog of this result when the boundary conditions in (2.29) and (2.30) are replaced by

$$u(\alpha) = u'(\beta) = 0 \qquad \text{and} \qquad v(\alpha) = v'(\beta) = 0,$$

respectively. In this case the conclusion of Theorem 2.10 remains true if (2.31) is replaced by

$$\int_x^\beta c(t)f(t)\,dt \le \int_x^\beta C(t)f(t)\,dt, \qquad \alpha < x < \beta,$$

where f is now an arbitrary, positive, *nonincreasing* function of class $\mathscr{C}^1[\alpha, \beta]$. The proof is virtually the same as that given above.

Howard [84] also obtained an analog of Theorem 2.10 for the eigenvalue problems

$$[a(x)u']' + \lambda c(x)u = 0, \qquad u(\alpha) = u'(\beta) = 0 \tag{2.29'}$$

$$[A(x)v']' + \mu c(x)v = 0, \qquad v(\alpha) = v'(\beta) = 0. \tag{2.30'}$$

Theorem 2.10′   (Howard) *Let* a, A, *and* c *be positive functions of class* $\mathscr{C}^2$, $\mathscr{C}^2$, *and* $\mathscr{C}$, *respectively, on* $[\alpha, \beta]$. *Suppose that*

$$\int_\alpha^x A(t)f(t)\,dt \le \int_\alpha^x a(t)f(t)\,dt, \qquad \alpha < x < \beta,$$

where f *is a positive function of class* $\mathscr{C}^1[\alpha, \beta]$ *such that* $a^2(t)f(t)$ *is nondecreasing on* $[\alpha, \beta]$. *If* λ_0, μ_0 *denote the smallest eigenvalues of* (2.29′), (2.30′), *respectively, then* $\mu_0 \le \lambda_0$.

The proof is left as an exercise. The following interesting comparison theorem can be deduced from Theorem 2.10′.

Theorem 2.10″   (Howard) *Let* a *and* c *be positive functions of class* $\mathscr{C}^2$ *and* $\mathscr{C}$, *respectively in* $[\alpha, \infty)$. *Suppose that*

$$\lim_{x \to \infty} \sup \left(\int_\alpha^x f(t)\,dt \right) \left(\int_\alpha^x a(t)f(t)\,dt \right)^{-1} < 1,$$

where f is a positive function of class $\mathscr{C}^1[\alpha, \infty]$ such that $a^2(t)f(t)$ is non-decreasing in $[\alpha, \infty)$. Then the equation $v'' + c(x)v = 0$ is oscillatory if $[a(x)u']'$ $+ c(x)u = 0$ is oscillatory.

Theorem 2.11 (Nehari) *Let $c(x)$ be nonnegative and continuous and let $C(x)$ be continuous on $[\alpha, \beta]$. Suppose that (2.1) has a solution u for which $u'(\alpha) = u(\beta) = 0$, and that (2.2) has a solution v for which $v(\alpha) > 0$ and $v'(\alpha) \le 0$. If $c(x) \not\equiv C(x)$ and (2.31) holds for $\alpha < x < \beta$, then at least one of the functions v, v' changes sign in (α, β).*

Proof It follows from (2.1) and (2.2) that

$$v(\beta)u'(\beta) + u(\alpha)v'(\alpha) = \left[vu' - uv' \right]_\alpha^\beta$$

$$= \int_\alpha^\beta (vu'' - uv'')\, dx$$

$$= \int_\alpha^\beta (C - c)uv\, dx$$

$$= \int_\alpha^\beta \left[\int_\alpha^x (C(t) - c(t))\, dt \right]' uv\, dx.$$

Integrating by parts and noting that the integrated part is zero we obtain

$$v(\beta)u'(\beta) + u(\alpha)v'(\alpha) = \int_\alpha^\beta \left[\int_\alpha^x (C(t) - c(t))\, dt \right](vu' + uv')\, dx. \quad (2.35)$$

To prove Theorem 2.11, suppose to the contrary that neither v nor v' changes its sign in (α, β), Since $v(\alpha) > 0$, $v'(\alpha) \le 0$, then $v(x) \ge 0$, $v'(x) \le 0$ in (α, β). There is no loss of generality in assuming that $u(x)$ does not change sign in (α, β), since otherwise β could be replaced by the first zero of $u(x)$ to the right of α. Also we may assume that $u(x)$ is nonnegative in the interval. Then $u'(x) \le 0$ by the argument used in the proof of Theorem 2.10. It follows from (2.35) and the hypothesis (2.31) that

$$v(\beta)u'(\beta) + u(\alpha)v'(\alpha) > 0,$$

which is a contradiction since $v(\beta) \ge 0$, $u(\alpha) > 0$, $u'(\beta) < 0$, and $v'(\alpha) \le 0$. Therefore either v or v' changes sign in (α, β).

As an application of Theorem 2.10, consider the case that

$$C(x) = c(x) + k(1 - 3x^2) \qquad (k = \text{constant}),$$

$$\alpha = 0, \quad \beta = 1, \quad k > 0, \quad c(x) = c(-x).$$

Since

$$\int_0^x C(t)\, dt = \int_0^x c(t)\, dt + kx(1 - x^2),$$

(2.31) is fulfilled and Theorem 2.10 gives $\mu_0 < \lambda_0$, where λ_0 and μ_0 are the lowest eigenvalues of the problems

$$u'' + \lambda c(x) u = 0, \qquad u(\pm 1) = 0,$$
$$v'' + \mu[c(x) + k(1 - 3x^2)]v = 0, \qquad v(\pm 1) = 0,$$

respectively. In particular, if $c(x) = x^2$ and $k = \frac{1}{3}$ then $C(x) = \frac{1}{3}$. Hence $\mu = 3\pi^2/4$ and the above result is that $\lambda_0 > 3\pi^2/4$, where λ_0 is the smallest eigenvalue of $u'' + \lambda x^2 u = 0$, $u(\pm 1) = 0$. This is an improvement on the result $\lambda > \pi^2/4$ obtained by comparing $u'' + \lambda x^2 u = 0$ with $v'' + \lambda v = 0$ by the Sturm comparison theorem.

4. The Hille–Wintner Comparison Theorem

If Eq. (2.1) is known to be nonoscillatory the comparison theorem of this section gives sufficient conditions on the coefficient $C(x)$ in (2.2), in comparison with $c(x)$ in (2.1), for (2.2) also to be nonoscillatory. Besides being of independent interest, the comparison theorem can be used as the basis of an alternative proof of Nehari's theorem 2.7. Actually Hille first obtained the sufficient condition $g^* < \frac{1}{4}$ of Theorem 2.1 by comparing (2.2) with the nonoscillatory Euler equation $u'' + u/4x^2 = 0$. The following notation will be used:

$$f(x) = \int_x^\infty c(t)\, dt, \qquad F(x) = \int_x^\infty C(t)\, dt.$$

Theorem 2.12   (Hille–Wintner) *Let c, C be continuous functions in $(0, \infty)$ such that the integrals $f(x)$, $F(x)$ converge (possibly only conditionally) and $0 \le F(x) \le f(x)$ for $x \ge \alpha > 0$. If (2.1) is nonoscillatory, then also (2.2) is nonoscillatory; if (2.2) is oscillatory, then also (2.1) is oscillatory.*

Hille [81] first obtained this result under the additional hypotheses that $c(x)$ and $C(x)$ are positive. The proof of Wintner [216] given below does not require positivity.

Proof Suppose that (2.1) is nonoscillatory. Then, if u is a solution of (2.1), there exists a number $x_0 \ge \alpha$ such that $u(x))$ has no zero in (x_0, ∞). Then $v = u'/u$ is well defined in this interval and satisfies the Riccati equation

$$v'(x) + v^2(x) = -c(x). \tag{2.36}$$

Hence

$$v(X) - v(x) + \int_x^X v^2(t)\, dt = -\int_x^X c(t)\, dt. \tag{2.37}$$

Since the right side has a limit as $X \to \infty$, so does

$$v(X) + \int_x^X v^2(t)\, dt. \tag{2.38}$$

If the integral diverges, then $v(X) \to -\infty$, which contradicts the fact that (2.38) has a limit. Thus the integral converges and hence $\lim v(X) = 0\,(X \to \infty)$ so that (2.37) gives, in the limit $X \to \infty$,

$$v(x) = V(x) + f(x),$$

where

$$V(x) = \int_x^\infty v^2(t)\, dt.$$

This implies the identity

$$[V(x) + f(x)]^2 + V'(x) = 0.$$

Since $F(x) \le f(x)$ by hypothesis,

$$p(x) \equiv -[V(x) + F(x)]^2 - V'(x) \ge 0$$

(defining the continuous function p), which can be written in the form

$$V'(x) + V^2(x) + 2F(x)V(x) + [F^2(x) + p(x)] = 0, \qquad p(x) \ge 0. \tag{2.39}$$

This nonlinear differential equation has the solution

$$V(x) = \int_x^\infty v^2(t)\, dt.$$

by the above construction, and thus, by direct calculation, the function y defined by

$$y(x) = \exp\left(\int_{x_0}^x V(t)\, dt\right)$$

satisfies the linear differential equation

$$y'' + 2F(x)y' + [F^2(x) + p(x)]y = 0. \tag{2.40}$$

It then follows from Sturm's comparison theorem that

$$z'' + 2F(x)z' + F^2(x)z = 0 \tag{2.41}$$

is nonoscillatory in (x_0, ∞); for if a solution z had more than one zero in

(x_0, ∞) then every solution of (2.40) would have a zero in (x_0, ∞) since $p(x) \geq 0$, which is a contradiction.

Finally, we need to prove that $v'' + C(x)v = 0$ is nonoscillatory. For a nontrivial solution z of (2.41), define

$$v(x) = z(x) \exp \int_{x_0}^{x} F(t)\, dt. \tag{2.42}$$

An easy calculation shows that v satisfies $v'' + C(x)v = 0$, and since the exponential factor in (2.42) has no zeros, the zeros of v are the same as the zeros of the corresponding solution z of (2.41). This proves that (2.2) is non-oscillatory. The second statement of Theorem 2.12 is an obvious consequence (contrapositive implication) of the first.

The sufficiency condition $G^* < \frac{1}{4}$ for (2.1) to be nonoscillatory (proved before in Section 2 from Nehari's theorem 2.7) is an easy consequence of Theorem 2.12. In fact, the Euler equation

$$u'' + \tfrac{1}{4}x^{-2}u = 0,$$

of the type discussed in Section 1, is nonoscillatory and in this case

$$f(x) = \int_{x}^{\infty} \tfrac{1}{4}t^{-2}\, dt = \tfrac{1}{4}x^{-1}.$$

By Theorem 2.12, (2.2) is nonoscillatory if $F(x) \leq f(x) = \frac{1}{4}x^{-1}$, and since

$$G^* = \lim_{x \to \infty} \sup \, xF(x),$$

in particular if $G^* < \frac{1}{4}$.

Taam [198] proved the following extension of Theorem 2.12 to the more general differential equations (1.1) and (1.2). The proof will not be given here.

Theorem 2.12′   (Taam)   *Let c and C be integrable functions in $(0, \infty)$ such that $|F(x)| \leq f(x)$ for $x \geq \alpha > 0$, where $f(x)$ and $F(x)$ are defined above Theorem 2.12. Let a and A in (1.1) and (1.2) be differentiable functions such that $A(x) \geq a(x) > 0$ and $a(x) \leq k$ ($k = constant$) on $[\alpha, \infty)$. Then (1.2) is nonoscillatory if (1.1) is nonoscillatory.*

It is an open question whether or not this theorem remains true without the condition $a(x) \leq k$. Taam also considered some related matters in his papers [198–200].

Theorem 2.13   (Wintner)   *For large positive x let c be a real-valued continuous function for which $f(x)$ converges. If $f(x) > \gamma/x$ for some $\gamma > \frac{1}{4}$, then Eq. (2.1) is oscillatory.*

(The fact that $\frac{1}{4}$ is the best possible lower bound is shown by the nonoscillatory Euler equation (2.1), where $c(t) \equiv \frac{1}{4}t^{-2}$.)

To prove this, take $C(t) = \gamma/t^2$, $\gamma > \frac{1}{4}$, so $F(x) = \gamma/x$. In this case (2.2) is an oscillatory Euler equation. Hence the hypothesis $f(x) > \gamma/x = F(x)$ implies by Theorem 2.12 that Eq. (2.1) is oscillatory.

Likewise, Wintner [216] gave the following criterion for (2.1) to be non-oscillatory.

Theorem 2.14   (Wintner)   *If c is a real-valued continuous function for which $f(x)$ converges and $0 \leq f(x) \leq \frac{1}{4}x^{-1}, 0 < x < \infty$, then Eq. (2.1) is nonoscillatory.*

In this case we take $C(t) = \frac{1}{4}t^{-2}$, $F(x) = \frac{1}{4}x^{-1}$, so $f(x) \leq F(x)$. Interchanging the roles of $f(x)$ and $F(x)$, we see from Theorem 2.12 that (2.1) is nonoscillatory since (2.2) is a nonoscillatory Euler equation.

Theorem 2.15   (Wintner [215])   *Equation (2.1) is nonoscillatory iff there exists a function $v \in \mathscr{C}^1$ which satisfies the inequality*

$$v'(x) + v^2(x) \leq -c(x)$$

for sufficiently large x.

Proof   If (2.1) is nonoscillatory and $u(x)$ is a nontrivial solution of (2.1), there exists a number x_0 such that $u(x)$ has no zero on $[x_0, \infty)$, and hence $v = u'/u$ satisfies (2.36). Conversely, if there exists a function v satisfying

$$-C(x) \equiv v'(x) + v^2(x) \leq -c(x), \qquad x \geq x_0$$

(defining $C(x)$) then

$$u(x) = \exp\left[\int_{x_0}^x v(t)\, dt\right]$$

satisfies $u'' + C(x)u = 0$. Since $c(x) \leq C(x)$ on $x_0 \leq x < \infty$, it follows from Sturm's theorem 1.1 that no solution of $u'' + c(x)u = 0$ can have more than one zero on $[x_0, \infty)$.

More generally Wintner proved [215] that if I is an arbitrary interval (open or closed, bounded or unbounded), no solution of (2.1) has more than one zero on I iff there exists a function $v \in \mathscr{C}^1(I)$ satisfying $v' + v^2 \leq -c$ throughout I.

Hartman [62] obtained the following result in 1948 in connection with the problem of determining conditions for a nonoscillatory equation (2.1) to have exactly one solution of class $\mathscr{L}^2(0, \infty)$, i.e., for (2.1) to be of limit point type in Weyl's classification [35].

Theorem 2.16   (Hartman)   *Every nonoscillatory equation* (2.1) *has a solution u such that*

$$\int^{\infty} u^{-2}(t)\, dt$$

is finite and a nontrivial solution v such that

$$\int^{\infty} v^{-2}(t)\, dt = \infty.$$

Proof   Let w be a solution of (2.1) such that $w(x) > 0$ for $x > x_0$, and define a second solution by

$$u(x) = w(x) \int_{x_0}^{x} w^{-2}(t)\, dt, \qquad x > x_0.$$

Then the Wronskian $u(x)w'(x) - w(x)u'(x) = -1$. Since $u(x) > 0$ for $x > x_0$, it follows that the ratio w/u is differentiable for $x > x_0$ and $(w/u)' = -1/u^2$. Hence for $x_0 < x_1 \le x < \infty$,

$$\frac{w(x)}{u(x)} = \frac{w(x_1)}{u(x_1)} - \int_{x_1}^{x} \frac{dt}{u^2(t)}.$$

If the integral did not approach a finite limit as $x \to \infty$, then $w(x)/u(x)$ would approach $-\infty$, contrary to the fact that both $u(x)$ and $w(x)$ are positive for $x \ge x_1$.

To prove the second statement of the theorem, define another solution by

$$v(x) = u(x) \int_{x}^{\infty} u^{-2}(t)\, dt, \qquad x > x_0.$$

Then $v(x)/u(x) \to 0$ as $x \to \infty$ since u^{-2} is integrable. As a consequence of the identity $(u/v)' = 1/v^2$ we obtain

$$\frac{u(x)}{v(x)} = \frac{u(x_1)}{v(x_1)} + \int_{x_1}^{x} \frac{dt}{v^2(t)}, \qquad x_0 < x_1 \le x,$$

and hence

$$\int_{x_1}^{x} v^{-2}(t)\, dt \to \infty \qquad \text{as} \quad x \to \infty.$$

Corollary 1   *If Eq.* (2.1) *is nonoscillatory then*

$$\int_{0}^{\infty} \frac{dx}{u^2(x) + v^2(x)} < \infty$$

for every pair of linearly independent solutions u, v of (2.1).

Indeed the zeros of u and v separate each other by Theorem 1.8. Hence the denominator $u^2(x) + v^2(x)$ is everywhere positive and the integral exists over every finite interval. Furthermore, every solution w of (2.1) has the form $w = \alpha u + \beta v$ for some constants α and β, and hence, if (2.1) is nonoscillatory,

$$\int_{x_0}^{x} \frac{dt}{w^2(t)} \geq \frac{1}{2\gamma^2} \int_{x_0}^{x} \frac{dt}{u^2(t) + v^2(t)},$$

where $\gamma = \max(|\alpha|, |\beta|)$ and x_0 is chosen so that $w(x) \neq 0$ for $x \geq x_0$. If (2.1) is nonoscillatory, Theorem 2.16 shows that the left member has a finite limit as $x \to \infty$ for some w, and hence the integral on the right side also has a finite limit as $x \to \infty$.

The proof of the following consequence of Corollary 1 is left as an exercise.

Corollary 2   *If Eq.* (2.1) *is nonoscillatory then some solution of* (2.1) *must fail to be* $O(x^{1/2})$ *as* $x \to \infty$, *i.e., there exists a solution* u *such that the inequality* $|u(x)| \leq kx^{1/2}$ *on* $x_0 \leq x < \infty$ *does not hold for any constants* x_0 *and* k.

The Euler equation $u'' + (2x)^{-2}u = 0$, with linearly independent solutions $x^{1/2}$, $x^{1/2} \log x$, shows that every solution of a nonoscillatory equation can be $O(x^{1/2} \log x)$. However, the example $u'' - u = 0$ shows that this is not necessary.

Exercises
1. Hartman and Wintner [70, p. 209] gave the following alternative proof of Corollary 1: The equations $u = y \cos z$, $v = y \sin z$ determine a unique positive function y and, if $0 \leq z(0) < 2\pi$, a unique continuous $z = z(x)$ for $0 \leq x < \infty$. With the normalization $uv' - vu' = 1$, $y^2 z' = 1$, and hence

$$\int_{0}^{x} y^{-2}(t)\, dt$$

has a finite limit iff Eq. (2.1) is nonoscillatory. Verify the validity of all the statements made in this proof.
2. Let $N_u(x)$ denote the number of zeros of a solution u of (2.1) on the interval $[0, x]$, $x > 0$. If u and v are nontrivial solutions of (2.1) show by Sturm's separation theorem that

$$|N_u(x) - N_v(x)| \leq 1, \qquad 0 \leq x < \infty.$$

Show that $|z(x)/\pi - N(x)| \leq 1$, where $z(x)$ is given in Exercise 1, and hence that

$$\lim_{x \to \infty} \inf x^{-2} z(x) < \infty$$

is implied by

$$\lim_{x \to \infty} \inf x^{-2} N_u(x) < \infty.$$

3. (Hartman and Wintner [70]). In the notation of the previous exercises, show that

$$\int_0^\infty dx/z'(x) = \infty \qquad \text{if} \ \lim_{x \to \infty} \inf x^{-2} N_u(x) \ \text{is finite.}$$

Outline of proof Since z' is continuous and positive,

$$\left[x^{-1} \int_\alpha^{\alpha+x} dt/z'(t) \right]^{-1} \le x^{-1} \int_\alpha^{\alpha+x} z'(t) \, dt$$

for $0 \le \alpha < \alpha + x$, and hence

$$\int_\alpha^{\alpha+x} dt/z'(t) \ge x^2 [z(\alpha + x) - z(\alpha)]^{-1}.$$

Therefore

$$\int_\alpha^\infty dt/z'(t) \ge \lim_{x \to \infty} \sup[x^{-2} z(x)]^{-1},$$

and the result is obtained by letting $\alpha \to \infty$ and using Exercise 2.
4. Deduce from Exercise 3 that (2.1) cannot have two linearly independent square integrable solutions on $(0, \infty)$ if $N(x) = O(x^2)$ as $x \to \infty$. (The subscript u on $N(x)$ can be deleted on account of Exercise 2.)
5. If u and v are linearly independent solutions of (2.1) with Wronskian $uv' - vu' = 1$, show that

$$\pi N(x) = \int_0^x \frac{dt}{u^2(t) + v^2(t)} + O(1)$$

as $x \to \infty$ by using the results of Exercises 1 and 2. In the oscillatory case show that this implies the asymptotic formula

$$\pi N(x) \sim \int_0^x \frac{dt}{u^2(t) + v^2(t)},$$

where the symbol $\sim$ means that the ratio of the two quantities has limit 1 as $x \to \infty$.
6. Use Exercise 5 to give yet another proof that the condition of Corollary 1 is both necessary and sufficient for Eq. (2.1) to be nonoscillatory.
7. Prove Corollary 2.

Theorem 2.17   (Wintner)   *If c is a real-valued continuous function for which f(x) converges and*

$$\int^\infty \exp\left\{-2 \int^t \left[\int_u^\infty c(s)\, ds\right] du\right\} dt \qquad (2.43)$$

is finite, then Eq. (2.1) is oscillatory.

Proof   Suppose to the contrary that (2.1) is nonoscillatory. Let u be any solution and let $v = u'/u$. Since $f(x)$ converges, the integral

$$\int^\infty v^2(t)\, dt$$

also converges by (2.37), (2.38), and $v(t) \to 0$ as $t \to \infty$. Also,

$$\frac{d}{dt} \log u(t) = v(t) = \int_t^\infty [v^2(s) + c(s)]\, ds$$

$$> \int_t^\infty c(s)\, ds.$$

We can assume without loss of generality that $u(t) > 0$ for $t \geq t_0$ ($t_0 > 0$) (since $-u(t)$ is a solution along with $u(t)$). Then by the hypothesis (2.43)

$$\int^\infty [u(t)]^{-2}\, dt = \int^\infty \exp\left\{-2 \int^t v(u)\, du\right\} dt$$

$$< \int^\infty \exp\left\{-2 \int^t \left[\int_u^\infty c(s)\, ds\right] du\right\} dt$$

$$< \infty,$$

which contradicts Hartman's theorem 2.16 that every nonoscillatory equation (2.1) has a solution u for which

$$\int^\infty u^{-2}(t)\, dt = \infty.$$

The proofs of the following related theorems of Wintner [215] are omitted.

Theorem 2.18   (Wintner)   *If (2.1) is nonoscillatory, if f(x) converges, and if*

$$\int^\infty \exp\left\{2 \int^t \left[\int_u^\infty c(s)\, ds\right] du\right\} dt = \infty,$$

then (2.1) cannot have an eigensolution, i.e., a solution u satisfying

$$\int^\infty {}^2 u(t)\, dt < \infty.$$

Theorem 2.19   (Wintner)   *A nonoscillatory equation cannot have an eigen-solution if $f(x)$ converges and*

$$x \int_x^\infty c(t) \, dt \geq -\tfrac{1}{2}, \qquad x \geq x_0 \,.$$

Thus (2.1) cannot have an eigensolution if $f(x)$ converges and

$$\tfrac{1}{4} \geq x \int_x^\infty c(t) \, dt \geq -\tfrac{1}{2}, \qquad x \geq x_0 \,.$$

Theorem 2.20   (Wintner)   *Equation (2.1) is nonoscillatory if $f(x)$ converges and*

$$-\tfrac{3}{4} \leq x \int_x^\infty c(t) \, dt \leq \tfrac{1}{4}.$$

Theorem 2.21   (Wintner)   *Equation (2.1) is nonoscillatory if $f(x)$ converges and*

$$\left[\int_x^\infty c(t) \, dt \right]^2 \leq \tfrac{1}{4} c(x), \qquad 0 < x < \infty.$$

The physical interpretation of square integrability of solutions of differential equations and related matters can be found in standard works on quantum mechanics, e.g., [176].

5. Hille's Necessary and Sufficient Condition for Nonoscillatory Equations

Hille obtained his version of Theorem 2.12 in 1948 (for positive functions c and C) by appealing to the following interesting necessary and sufficient condition for oscillatory equations.

Theorem 2.22   (Hille)   *Equation (2.1) is nonoscillatory iff the nonlinear integral equation*

$$v(x) = \int_x^\infty v^2(t) \, dt + \int_x^\infty c(t) \, dt \qquad (2.44)$$

has a solution for sufficiently large x.

The theorem will be proved with the aid of the following lemma.

Lemma 2.23 *If (2.1) is nonoscillatory and $u(x)$ is a solution of (2.1) such that $u(x) \neq 0$ for $x \geq \alpha$, then*

$$0 < (x + d)v(x) \leq 1, \qquad x \geq \alpha, \tag{2.45}$$

where

$$v(x) = u'(x)/u(x), \qquad d = -\alpha + 1/v(\alpha).$$

Proof If $u(x) > 0$ for $x \geq \alpha$, the proof of Theorem 2.2 shows that also $u'(x) > 0$ for $x \geq \alpha$, and hence $v(x) > 0$ for $x \geq \alpha$. Similarly $v(x) > 0$ if $u(x) < 0$ for $x \geq \alpha$. This proves the left part of the inequality (2.45). Since u satisfies (2.1), v satisfies the Riccati equation (2.36):

$$v'(x) + v^2(x) + c(x) = 0, \qquad x \geq \alpha. \tag{2.36}$$

Since $c(x) > 0$, $v'(x) + v^2(x) \leq 0$, and hence

$$\frac{d}{dx}\left[-\frac{1}{v(x)} + x \right] \leq 0.$$

Thus

$$-1/v(x) + x \leq -1/v(\alpha) + \alpha, \qquad \alpha \leq x,$$

which is equivalent to (2.45).

Proof of Theorem 2.22 If (2.1) is nonoscillatory, then $v = u'/u$ satisfies (2.36) as pointed out before. Integration of (2.36) from x to β gives

$$v(\beta) - v(x) + \int_x^\beta v^2(t)\, dt + \int_x^\beta c(t)\, dt = 0.$$

Since (2.1) is nonoscillatory, Lemma 2.23 shows that the first integral tends to a finite limit as $\beta \to \infty$ and also that $v(\beta) \to 0$ as $\beta \to \infty$. It follows that the last integral also tends to a finite limit as $\beta \to \infty$ (which is Wintner and Leighton's result, stated below (2.11)), and that v satisfies the integral equation (2.44).

Conversely, if there exists a finite α such that (2.44) has a solution v for $x \geq \alpha$, it follows from the form of the equation that $v^2(x)$ is integrable in (α, ∞) and v is a positive, monotone decreasing, differentiable function. Differentiation of (2.44) with respect to x shows that $v(x)$ satisfies (2.36). Hence

$$u(x) = \exp\left[\int_\alpha^x v(t)\, dt \right]$$

satisfies (2.1) for $x \geq \alpha$, and since $u(x) \geq 1$, (2.1) is nonoscillatory.

Actually Hille [81] generalized the necessity part of Theorem 2.22 as follows: If φ is a positive nondecreasing function such that $x^{-2}\varphi(x)$ is integrable in $(1, \infty)$ and if (2.1) is nonoscillatory, then $c(x)\varphi(x)$ also is integrable in $(1, \infty)$.

Hille proved Theorem 2.12 (for positive functions c and C) by constructing a solution of the integral equation (2.44) by the method of successive approximations and then using both the necessity and the sufficiency of the condition in Theorem 2.22.

6. Leighton's Oscillation Criteria [115]

The differential equation under consideration is

$$[a(x)u']' + c(x)u = 0 \qquad (1.1)$$

in the interval $0 < x < \infty$, where a, a', and c are continuous functions and $a(x) > 0$ in this interval. The following notations will be used:

$$a_\infty = \lim_{x \to \infty} \int_1^x \frac{dt}{a(t)}, \qquad c_\infty = \lim_{x \to \infty} \int_1^x c(t)\, dt. \qquad (2.46)$$

Theorem 2.24   (Leighton) *Equation (1.1) is oscillatory in $(1, \infty)$ if $a_\infty = c_\infty = \infty$.*

In the case that $a(x) \equiv 1$, this reduces to Wintner's result mentioned earlier (special case of Theorem 2.1): Equation (2.1) is oscillatory if $c_\infty = \infty$. Note that $c(x)$ is not required to be positive for these theorems.

Proof Suppose to the contrary that no solution of (1.1) has arbitrarily large zeros. If $u(x)$ is a positive solution for $x \geq x_1$, define $w(x) = -a(x)u'(x)/u(x)$ for $x \geq x_1$. Then

$$w'(x) = -\frac{u(x)[a(x)u'(x)]' - a(x)u'^2(x)}{u^2(x)} = c(x) + \frac{w^2(x)}{a(x)},$$

and hence

$$w(x) - w(x_1) \geq \int_{x_1}^x c(t)\, dt \to +\infty$$

as $x \to \infty$ by hypothesis. Then $w(x) \to +\infty$, which implies that $u'(x) < 0$ for large x and consequently $\lim u(x)$ $(x \to \infty)$ is finite. Now let u_1 and u_2 be linearly independent solutions of (1.1) which are positive for $x \geq x_1$. It then follows from (1.1) that

$$\frac{d}{dx}[a(u_1 u_2' - u_2 u_1')] = 0,$$

so that

$$a(u_1 u_2' - u_2 u_1') = k \neq 0.$$

The constant k cannot be zero since the Wronskian $u_1 u_2' - u_2 u_1'$ of linearly independent solutions never vanishes. Define y and z to be the principal solutions of the equations

$$y^2 = u_1^2 + u_2^2, \qquad z = \tan^{-1}(u_2/u_1).$$

Then

$$z' = (u_1 u_2' - u_2 u_1')/(u_1^2 + u_2^2) = k/ay^2$$

exists and is positive on $[x_1, \infty)$ (where u_1 is free of zeros), and hence

$$z(x) = k \int_{x_1}^x \frac{dt}{a(t)y^2(t)} \to +\infty$$

as $x \to \infty$ since $a_\infty = \infty$ and $y^2(t)$ has a finite limit as $t \to \infty$ along with $u_1(t)$ and $u_2(t)$. This contradicts the fact that $z < \pi/2$ and establishes Theorem 2.24.

Theorem 2.25   (Leighton) *If $c(x)$ is a positive monotone function, a necessary condition for Eq. (2.1) to be oscillatory is*

$$\int_1^\infty c^{1/2}(x)\, dx = \infty. \tag{2.47}$$

Proof Consider the associated differential equation

$$(xz')' + x^{-1}[x^2 c(x) - \tfrac{1}{4}]z = 0, \tag{2.48}$$

obtained from (2.1) by the substitution $u = x^{1/2}z$. Suppose that the integral in (2.47) is finite, so that $\lim[xc^{1/2}(x)] = 0 \ (x \to \infty)$. Then the coefficient of z in (2.48) would eventually become negative and remain negative, and (2.48) would be nonoscillatory, implying also that (2.1) is nonoscillatory.

Condition (2.47) is not sufficient for (2.1) to be oscillatory, as shown by the nonoscillatory example $u'' + u/4x^2 = 0$.

Theorem 2.26   (Leighton) *If ac is a positive monotone function, a necessary condition for (1.1) to be oscillatory in $(1, \infty)$ is*

$$\lim_{x \to \infty} \int_1^x \left[\frac{c(x)}{a(x)}\right]^{1/2} dx = \infty. \tag{2.49}$$

Proof The substitution

$$t = \int_1^x a^{-1}(s)\, ds = g(x)$$

transforms (1.1) into

$$\frac{d^2u}{dt^2} + a(x)c(x)u = 0. \tag{2.50}$$

Note that t is a strictly monotone function of x since $a(t) > 0$, and hence $a[x(t)]c[x(t)]$ is a monotone function of t. Let $\lambda = \lim g(x)/(x \to \infty)$ and observe that $0 < \lambda \le \infty$. Thus (1.1) is oscillatory in $(1, \infty)$ iff (2.50) is oscillatory in $(0, \lambda)$.

Case 1 If $\lambda = \infty$, it follows from Theorem 2.25 that a necessary condition for (2.50) to be oscillatory is

$$\int_0^\infty \{a[x(t)]c[x(t)]\}^{1/2} \, dt = \infty, \tag{2.51}$$

which is equivalent to (2.49) under the substitution

$$t = \int_1^x a^{-1}(s) \, ds.$$

Case 2 $\lambda < \infty$ Equation (2.1) is oscillatory in $(1, \infty)$ iff every solution of (2.50) has an infinite number of zeros in $(0, \lambda)$. Since $a[x(t)]c[x(t)]$ is monotone, the assumption that the integral in (2.51) is finite would imply that

$$\lim_{t \to \lambda-} (\lambda - t)^2 a[x(t)]c[x(t)] = 0. \tag{2.52}$$

As in the proof of Theorem 2.25, we transform Eq. (2.50) by the substitution $y = (\lambda - t)^{1/2}z$ to obtain

$$\frac{d}{dt}\left[(\lambda - t)\frac{dz}{dt}\right] + \frac{1}{\lambda - t}[(\lambda - t)^2 a[x(t)]c[x(t)] - \tfrac{1}{4}]z = 0.$$

The coefficient of z would be negative near $t = \lambda-$ on account of (2.52), and hence the solutions could not be oscillatory in $(\lambda/2, \lambda)$. It follows that (2.1) would be nonoscillatory in $(1, \infty)$, contrary to the hypothesis of Theorem 2.26.

An application of the theorem to Eq. (2.48) yields the following corollary:

Corollary 2.27 *If the function b defined by*

$$b(x) = [x^2c(x) - \tfrac{1}{4}]^{1/2}$$

is a positive monotone function, a necessary condition for Eq. (2.1) to be oscillatory is

$$\int_1^\infty [b(x)/x] \, dx = \infty.$$

Corollary 2.28 *If ac is a positive monotone function and both of the integrals*

$$\int_1^\infty \frac{dx}{a(x)}, \qquad \int_1^\infty c(x)\,dx$$

are finite, then Eq. (1.1) *is nonoscillatory.*

Proof The Schwarz inequality

$$\int_1^X \left[\frac{c(x)}{a(x)}\right]^{1/2} dx \le \int_1^X \frac{dx}{a(x)} \int_1^X c(x)\,dx$$

implies by the hypotheses that

$$\lim_{X \to \infty} \int_1^X \left[\frac{c(x)}{a(x)}\right]^{1/2} dx < \infty$$

and Theorem 2.26 shows that (1.1) is nonoscillatory.

In 1955, Moore [134, p. 135] refined this result as follows: *Equation* (1.1) *is nonoscillatory if both*

$$\int_1^\infty a^{-1}(x)\,dx < \infty \qquad \text{and} \qquad \lim_{x \to \infty} \sup \left| \int_1^x c(t)\,dt \right| < \infty.$$

Moore also obtained the following refinements of the oscillation criteria stated earlier:

1. *Suppose that* $a(x)c(x) \le k$ $(0 < x < \infty)$ *for some constant* k. *Then a sufficient condition for* (1.1) *to be oscillatory is*

$$\lim_{x \to \infty} \sup \int_1^x c(t)\,dt = +\infty,$$

and a necessary condition for (1.1) *to be oscillatory is*

$$\int_1^\infty a^{-1}(x)\,dx = \infty.$$

2. *Equation* (1.1) *is oscillatory if*

$$\int_1^\infty \frac{dx}{a(x)} = \infty \qquad \text{and} \qquad \int_1^\infty c(x)g^n(x)\,dx = \infty$$

for some $n < 1$, *where*

$$g(x) = 1 + \int_1^x a^{-1}(t)\,dt.$$

3. *Equation* (1.1) *is oscillatory if*

$$\int_1^\infty \frac{dx}{a(x)} < \infty \qquad and \qquad \int_1^\infty c(x)h^m(x)\,dx = \infty$$

for some $m > 1$, *where*

$$h(x) = \int_x^\infty a^{-1}(t)\,dt.$$

Moore found other oscillation criteria and related results in the paper cited.

Exercises

1. Show that an alternative proof of Theorem 2.24 in the case that $c(x)$ is positive for large x can be made as follows: If Eq. (1.1) is nonoscillatory, there is a nontrivial solution u of (1.1) such that $u(x) > 0$ on $k \le x < \infty$ for some constant k. Multiplication of (1.1) and integration by parts over (k, x) yields

$$\frac{a(x)u'(x)}{u(x)} = \frac{a(k)u'(k)}{u(k)} - \int_k^x a(t)\frac{u'^2(t)}{u^2(t)}\,dt - \int_k^x c(t)\,dt.$$

Deduce that $u'(x) < 0$ for sufficiently large x and also that

$$u'(x) < a(k)u'(k)/a(x) < 0, \qquad k < x < \infty$$

for sufficiently large k. Integrate from k to x to obtain the contradiction that $u(x)$ eventually becomes negative. This is the argument first given by Leighton in 1950 [114].

2. Use a similar argument to prove that Eq. (1.1) is oscillatory in the interval $(0, 1)$ if $c(x)$ is positive in this interval and if

$$\int_0^1 \frac{dt}{a(t)} = \int_0^1 c(t)\,dt = \infty.$$

3. Find analogs of Theorems 2.25 and 2.26 and Corollaries 2.27 and 2.28 for the interval $(0, 1)$.

4. Let l be the differential operator defined by (1.1), where a, a' and c are continuous and $a(x) > 0$ in $(0, \infty)$. If y and z are functions of class $\mathscr{C}^2(0, \infty)$ and

$$u_1(x) = y(x)\cos z(x), \qquad u_2(x) = y(x)\sin z(x), \qquad (2.53)$$

show that

$$lu_1 = f\cos z - g\sin z, \qquad lu_2 = g\cos z + f\sin z$$

where
$$f = (ay')' + cy - ayz'^2,$$
$$g = 2ay'z' + ayz'' + a'yz'.$$

Hence show that u_1 and u_2 satisfy (1.1) iff y and z satisfy the differential equations
$$ay^3[(ay')' + cy] = k^2$$
$$ay^2z' = k$$

where k is a constant. Show in addition from (2.53) that
$$a(u_1u_2' - u_2u_1') = ay^2z' = k$$

and hence that u_1 and u_2 are linearly independent iff $k \neq 0$.

5. Prove that the equation $u'' + q^{-4}(x)u = 0$ (which is (1.1) with $a(x) \equiv 1$ and $c(x) = q^{-4}(x)$) has a pair of linearly independent solutions of the form $q \cos z$ and $q \sin z$ iff there exists a constant k such that $1 + q^3q'' = k^2$ and $q^2z' = k$.

6. Suppose $A(x) = a(x)$ in Eq. (1.2). Prove that $\lim_{x \to \infty} W[u, v; x]$ cannot be zero for every pair of solutions u, v of (1.1), (1.2), respectively, where
$$W[u, v; x] = a(x)[u(x)v'(x) - v(x)u'(x)].$$

Outline of Proof   Consider the solutions u_1, u_2 of (1.1) given by (2.53) and corresponding solutions U_1, U_2 of (1.2) defined by
$$U_1(x) = Y(x) \cos Z(x), \qquad U_2(x) = Y(x) \sin Z(x),$$

where $y(x) > 0$, $Y(x) > 0$, and
$$a(x)y^2(x)z'(x) = a(x) Y^2(x)Z'(x) = 1.$$

Then
$$W[u_1, U_1] + W[u_2, U_2] = f \cos(z - Z) + g \sin(z - Z),$$
$$W[u_2, U_1] + W[u_1, U_2] = g \cos(z - Z) - f \sin(z - Z),$$

where
$$f = a(y Y' - Yy'), \qquad g = (y/Y) + (Y/y).$$

The assumption that $W[u, U] \to 0$ $(x \to \infty)$ for all solutions u, U of (1.1), (1.2), respectively then leads to the contradiction $g \to 0$.

7. Prove: *If $\lim W[u, v; x]$ $(x \to \infty)$ exists (finite or infinite) and is not zero for a pair of solutions u, v of (1.1), (1.2), respectively, then the zeros of $u(x)$ and $v(x)$ are interlaced for large x.*

Outline of Proof   Since $W[u, v; x]$ has a limit $\neq 0$ as $x \to \infty$, it has constant sign for large x, and hence $u(x)v'(x)$ is eventually positive or eventually negative at the zeros of $v(x)$. Since the zeros of solutions of

(1.2) are simple, $v'(x)$ is alternatively positive and negative at the zeros of $v(x)$, and hence $u(x)$ has the same property. Thus for sufficiently large x, $u(x)$ has a zero between every pair of zeros of $v(x)$. By interchanging the roles of u and v we see also that $v(x)$ has a zero between adjacent zeros of $u(x)$.

8. Show that the equation $u'' + (1 + \lambda x^{-2})u = 0$ is oscillatory for all numbers λ.

9. Show that the equation $[(k + \sin x)u']' + (\frac{1}{2} + \sin x)u = 0$ $(k > 1)$ is oscillatory.

10. Decide whether the following equations are oscillatory or not:
   (a) $(xy')' + y/x = 0$;
   (b) $y'' + y'/x + y = 0$;
   (c) $xy'' + (1 - x)y' + ny = 0$ ($n = $ constant); this is Laguerre's equation;
   (d) $y'' - 2xy' + 2ny = 0$ ($n = $ constant); this is Hermite's equation;
   (e) $xy'' + (2n + 1)y' + xy = 0$ ($n = $ constant);
   (f) $x^2y'' + kxy' + ny = 0$ ($k, n = $ constants);
   (g) $x^2y'' + xy' + (x^2 - m^2)y = 0$ ($m = $ constant); this is Bessel's equation.

11. Prove Osgood's theorem: *Suppose $c \in \mathscr{C}^1$, $c(x) > 0$, and $c'(x) \geq 0$ in Eq. (2.1). If u is any solution of (2.1) such that u' has consecutive zeros at α and β $(0 \leq \alpha < \beta)$, then $|u(\beta)| \leq |u(\alpha)|$, i.e., the amplitude of the oscillation of a solution never increases as x increases.*
   Hint: Multiply (2.1) by $2u'(x)$ and integrate by parts.

12. Prove that the conclusion of Osgood's theorem is also true for the more general equation (1.1) if $a \in \mathscr{C}^1$, $c \in \mathscr{C}^1$, $a(x) > 0$, $c(x) > 0$, and $[a(x)c(x)]' \geq 0$. *Hint:* Transform (1.1) by Leighton's substitution

$$t = \int_0^x \frac{ds}{a(s)}$$

to obtain the differential equation

$$\frac{d^2u}{dt^2} + [a(x)c(x)]u = 0,$$

and apply Exercise 11.

7. Potter's Oscillation Criteria [152]

In 1953 Ruth Lind Potter obtained various modifications and refinements of the earlier oscillation criteria of Leighton, Hartman, Wintner, and others, as described in the previous sections. In connection with these results, she obtained criteria for the boundedness of solutions of Eqs. (1.1) and (2.1) for large x.

Consider first the case that $c(x) = h^{-2}(x)$ in Eq. (2.1), where h is a positive function of class $\mathscr{C}^2$ in $(0, \infty)$. Then (2.1) becomes

$$u'' + h^{-2}(x)u = 0. \tag{2.54}$$

To study the oscillation of solutions of (2.54), Potter considered the auxiliary equations

$$[h^2(x)v']' + v = 0, \tag{2.55}$$

$$[h(x)w']' + H_1(x)w = 0, \tag{2.56}$$

$$[h(x)y']' + H_2(x)y = 0, \tag{2.57}$$

where

$$H_1(x) = \frac{1}{h(x)} - \frac{h'^2(x)}{4h(x)} + \frac{h''(x)}{2} \tag{2.58}$$

and

$$H_2(x) = \frac{1}{h(x)} - \frac{h'^2(x)}{4h(x)} - \frac{h''(x)}{2}. \tag{2.59}$$

Any two of the four equations (2.54)–(2.57) are oscillatory or nonoscillatory together, for, as is easily verified, the derivative of a solution of (2.54) is a solution of (2.55), Eq. (2.56) is obtained from (2.54) by the substitution $w = h^{-1/2}(x)u$, and (2.57) is obtained from (2.55) by the substitution $y = h^{1/2}(x)v$.

Theorem 2.29 (Potter) *Equation (2.54) is nonoscillatory if either $H_1(x) \leq 0$ or $H_2(x) \leq 0$ for large x. Equation (2.54) is oscillatory if either*

$$\int_1^\infty \frac{dx}{h(x)} = \int_1^\infty H_1(x) \, dx = +\infty \tag{2.60}$$

or

$$\int_1^\infty H_2(x) \, dx = +\infty. \tag{2.61}$$

Proof The first statement is an immediate consequence of Sturm's theorem 1.1 in view of the remark made prior to the theorem. If (2.60) holds, Leighton's theorem 2.24 shows that Eq. (2.56) is oscillatory, and hence (2.54) also is oscillatory. If (2.61) holds, then the integral

$$\int_1^\infty h^{-1}(x) \, dx$$

cannot be finite, for in that case (2.59) and (2.61) imply that $h'(x) \to -\infty$, and $h(x)$ could not be positive everywhere in $(0, \infty)$. Hence

$$\int_1^\infty h^{-1}(x)\, dx = \infty$$

and Leighton's theorem again shows that (2.54) is oscillatory.

The following theorem gives a modification of Hille's necessary condition $g^* \geq \frac{1}{4}$ for oscillatory equations (Theorem 2.1).

Theorem 2.30　　*If h is a positive monotone function, a necessary condition for* (2.54) *to be oscillatory is that*

$$\int_1^\infty \frac{dx}{h(x)} = \infty. \tag{2.62}$$

This can be deduced from Theorem 2.1, but the following procedure is easier. Suppose to the contrary that the integral in (2.62) is finite. Then for arbitrary $\varepsilon > 0$, there exists a number $x_0 > 0$ such that $h^{-1}(x) < \sqrt{\varepsilon}\, x^{-1}$ for $x \geq x_0$. Since the Euler equation

$$v'' + \varepsilon x^{-2} v = 0$$

is nonoscillatory for $\varepsilon \leq \frac{1}{4}$ (as pointed out in Section 1), Sturm's theorem 1.1 shows that (2.54) also is nonoscillatory for such ε. This contradiction establishes Theorem 2.30.

Theorem 2.31　　(Potter)　*If*

$$\int_1^\infty H_1(x)\, dx = +\infty,$$

Eq. (2.54) *is oscillatory iff*

$$\int_1^\infty \frac{dx}{h(x)} = \infty. \tag{2.62}$$

Proof　The sufficiency of the condition is contained in Theorem 2.29. To prove the necessity, suppose to the contrary that the integral in (2.62) is finite. Then the hypothesis

$$\int_1^\infty H_1(x)\, dx = +\infty$$

shows on account of (2.58) that $h'(x) \to +\infty$, and hence $h(x)$ is monotone for large x. It follows from Theorem 2.30 that Eq. (2.54) is nonoscillatory, contrary to the hypothesis.

Theorem 2.32 (Potter) *Equation* (2.54) *is oscillatory if* (2.62) *holds and* $h'^2(x) \le k$ *for large* x, *where* $0 < k < 4$.

Proof By hypothesis

$$\lim_{x \to \infty} \int_1^x H_1(x)\, dx \ge \lim_{x \to \infty} \left\{ \tfrac{1}{2}[h'(x) - h'(1)] \right.$$
$$\left. + \left(1 - \frac{k}{4}\right) \int_1^x \frac{dt}{h(t)} \right\}$$
$$= \infty,$$

and hence the conclusion follows from Theorem 2.31.

Theorem 2.33 (Potter) *If* hH_2 *is a positive monotone function,* (2.62) *is a necessary condition for* (2.54) *to be oscillatory.*

Proof Suppose to the contrary that the integral in (2.62) is finite. Since

$$\int_1^x H_2(t)\, dt = \int_1^x \frac{dt}{h(t)} - \int_1^x \frac{h'^2(t)\, dt}{4h(t)} - \tfrac{1}{2}[h'(x) - h'(1)]$$

and $H_2(t)$ is positive, the limit of the left member must be finite, for otherwise $h'(x) \to -\infty$ and $h(x)$ would not be everywhere positive. Since both of the integrals

$$\int_1^\infty \frac{dx}{h(x)}, \qquad \int_1^\infty H_2(x)\, dx$$

are finite, Corollary 2.28 shows that (2.57) and hence also (2.54) would be nonoscillatory.

Theorem 2.34 (Hartman–Wintner–Potter) *If* $\lim h'(x) = L$ $(x \to \infty)$ *exists, then Eq.* (2.54) *is oscillatory if* $L < 2$ *and nonoscillatory if* $L > 2$.

Proof For arbitrary $\varepsilon > 0$ there is a number $x_0 > 0$ such that $L - \varepsilon \le h'(t) \le L + \varepsilon$ for all $t \ge x_0$. Integration yields

$$(L - \varepsilon)(x - x_0) + h(x_0) \le h(x) \le (L + \varepsilon)(x - x_0) + h(x_0).$$

In the case of Eq. (2.54), Kneser's number ω (defined by (2.3)) is given by

$$\frac{1}{\omega} = \lim_{x \to \infty} \frac{h^2(x)}{x^2},$$

and hence $(L - \varepsilon)^2 < 1/\omega < (L + \varepsilon)^2$. Since ε is arbitrary, $\omega = 1/L^2$. Then $\omega > \tfrac{1}{4}$ if $L < 2$ and $\omega < \tfrac{1}{4}$ if $L > 2$, and the result follows from Kneser's theorem (stated above (2.3)).

The example

$$\frac{d^2u}{dx^2} + \left[\frac{1}{4x^2} + \frac{\gamma}{x^2 \log^2 x}\right] u = 0,$$

shows that Eq. (2.54) can be either oscillatory or nonoscillatory if $L = 2$. In fact,

$$h(x) = 2x \log x/(\log^2 x + 4\gamma)^{1/2}$$

and $L = \lim h'(x) = 2$ while the general solution

$$u(x) = x^{1/2}[K_1(\log x)^\zeta + K_2(\log x)^{1-\zeta}],$$
$$\zeta = \tfrac{1}{2} + \tfrac{1}{2}(1 - 4\gamma)^{1/2}$$

is oscillatory of $\gamma > \tfrac{1}{4}$ and nonoscillatory if $\gamma \le \tfrac{1}{4}$.

The oscillatory criterion $L < 2$ of Theorem 2.34 is contained in a theorem of Hartman and Wintner [69]. In view of the definition $c(x) = h^{-2}(x)$, this criterion is equivalent to

$$\lim_{x \to \infty} \frac{-c'(x)}{c^{3/2}(x)} < 4.$$

The paper of Hartman and Wintner cited explores some interesting related questions regarding the boundedness of solutions of Eq. (2.54).

Theorem 2.35   (Potter)   *If* (2.62) *holds and* $H_1(x)$ *and* $H_2(x)$ *are nonnegative and not identically zero for large* x, *a necessary condition for* (2.54) *to be nonoscillatory is* $\lim h'(x) = 2$ ($x \to \infty$).

Proof   Theorem 2.29 shows that both of the integrals

$$\int_1^\infty H_1(x)\, dx, \qquad \int_1^\infty H_2(x)\, dx$$

exist and are finite. Since

$$\int_1^x H_1(x)\, dx = \frac{1}{2}[h'(x) - h'(1)] + \frac{1}{4}\int_1^x \frac{4 - h'^2(x)}{h(x)}\, dx$$

and

$$\int_1^x H_2(x)\, dx = -\frac{1}{2}[h'(x) - h'(1)] + \frac{1}{4}\int_1^x \frac{4 - h'^2(x)}{h(x)}\, dx,$$

$\lim h'(x)$ exists since the limit of the difference of the two integrals exists. Furthermore the hypotheses imply that

$$0 < \int_1^x [H_1(x) + H_2(x)]\, dx$$

and hence $\lim h'^2(x) \le 4$. Then Theorem 2.34 shows that $\lim h'(x) = 2$ as required.

Theorem 2.34 will now be extended to the more general equation (1.1).

Theorem 2.36   (Potter) *Suppose that the functions a and c in Eq. (1.1) are of class $\mathscr{C}^1(0, \infty)$, a is positive and c is nonnegative in $(0, \infty)$, and*

$$\int_1^\infty \frac{dx}{a(x)} = \infty.$$

If $L = \lim a(x)\{[a(x)c(x)]^{-1/2}\}'$ $(x \to \infty)$ exists, then (1.1) is oscillatory if $L < 2$ and nonoscillatory if $L > 2$.

Proof Leighton's substitution

$$t = \int_1^x a^{-1}(s)\, ds$$

transforms (1.1) into (2.50), which has the form (2.54). The conclusion is then obtained upon application of Theorem 2.34.

Example As an example of the foregoing theorems, consider the generalized Airy equation

$$u'' + \alpha^2 x^n u = 0, \qquad 0 \le x < \infty, \quad \alpha > 0, \tag{2.63}$$

whose solutions can be expressed in terms of modified Bessel functions of order $1/(n + 2)(n \ne -2)$ [194]. In this case,

$$h'(x) = -(n/2\alpha)x^{-(n+2)/2}.$$

If $n > -2$, then $L = \lim h'(x) = 0$ and Theorem 2.34 shows that the equation is oscillatory. If $n < -2$, $L = \infty$ and Theorem 2.34 shows that the equation is nonoscillatory. If $n = -2$, then $L = 1/\alpha$, and the equation is oscillatory if $\alpha > \frac{1}{2}$ and nonoscillatory if $\alpha < \frac{1}{2}$. Theorem 2.34 gives no information if $n = -2$ and $\alpha = \frac{1}{2}$. However, in this case,

$$h(x) = 2x, \qquad h'(x) = 2, \qquad h''(x) = 0$$

and Eq. (2.58) reduces to $H_1(x) \equiv 0$. Thus (2.63) is nonoscillatory by Theorem 2.29. If $n = -2$ these results are obvious, of course, since (2.63) reduces to an Euler equation.

We remark that in the event x and u in Eq. (2.63) are complex variables, the author and Headley have characterized the zero-free sectors of solutions of (2.63) in the complex x-plane [194].

Theorem 2.37   (Potter) *Suppose that a, a', and c are continuous and a is positive in* $(0, \infty)$, *and* $c(x)$ *is positive for sufficiently large x. A necessary and sufficient condition for a nonoscillatory equation* (1.1) *to have all of its solutions bounded is that*

$$\int_1^\infty a^{-1}(x) \, dx$$

be finite.

Proof Let $u(x)$ be a nonoscillatory solution of (1.1) such that $u(x) > 0$ and $u'(x) \neq 0$ for $x \geq \alpha$, where α has been chosen large enough so that $p(x) > 0$ for $x \geq \alpha$. (It is sufficient to consider only solutions which are eventually positive since the negative of a solution is also a solution.) Then the function w defined by $w(x) = a(x)u'(x)/u(x)$ satisfies the Riccati equation.

$$w'(x) = -c(x) - w^2(x)/a(x), \qquad x \geq \alpha. \tag{2.64}$$

Since $c(x) > 0$, $w'(x)/w^2(x) < -1/a(x)$, $x \geq \alpha$ and hence

$$\frac{1}{w(x)} > \int_\alpha^x \frac{dt}{a(t)} + \frac{1}{w(\alpha)}. \tag{2.65}$$

If

$$\int_1^\infty a^{-1}(x) \, dx$$

is finite, we are to prove that $u(x)$ is bounded as $x \to \infty$. Since $u'(x) < 0$ obviously implies that $u(x)$ is bounded, we may assume that $u'(x) > 0$ for $x \geq \alpha \geq 1$, and hence, in particular, $w(\alpha) > 0$. Then (2.65) is equivalent to

$$\frac{u'(x)}{u(x)} < \frac{1}{a(x)} \left[\int_\alpha^x \frac{dt}{a(t)} + \frac{1}{w(\alpha)} \right]^{-1},$$

or

$$[\log u(x)]' < [\log z(x)]'$$

where

$$z(x) = \int_\alpha^x \frac{dt}{a(t)} + \frac{1}{w(\alpha)}.$$

Then $u(x)/u(\alpha) < z(x)/z(\alpha)$, and since $z(x)$ is bounded, so is $u(x)$.
    Conversely, if

$$\int_1^\infty a^{-1}(x) \, dx = \infty,$$

it follows from (2.64) and (2.65) that w is a positive, monotone decreasing function with limit 0 as $x \to \infty$. Hence

$$\lim_{x \to \infty} \frac{a(x)u'(x)}{u(x)} = 0 \tag{2.66}$$

for all solutions $u(x)$ of (1.1). If u_1 and u_2 are linearly independent solutions of (1.1), then

$$a(x)[u_1(x)u_2'(x) - u_2(x)u_1'(x)] = k$$

for some nonzero constant k, as shown in the proof of Theorem 2.24, and therefore

$$\frac{a(x)u_2'(x)}{u_2(x)} - \frac{a(x)u_1'(x)}{u_1(x)} = \frac{k}{u_1(x)u_2(x)}.$$

Since the limit of each term on the left side is zero by (2.66), either $u_1(x)$ or $u_2(x)$ is unbounded. Hence all of the solutions of (1.1) cannot be bounded unless

$$\int_1^\infty a^{-1}(x)\,dx \qquad \text{is finite.}$$

Theorem 2.38   (Potter)   *With a and c as in Theorem 2.37, Eq. (1.1) is nonoscillatory and all of its solutions are bounded if either* (1) *ac is monotone decreasing and*

$$\int_1^\infty a^{-1}(x)\,dx$$

is finite; or (2) *ac is monotone increasing and*

$$\int_1^\infty c(x)\,dx$$

is finite.

Proof   If ac is (positive) monotone decreasing it is certainly bounded, and hence

$$\int_1^x \left[\frac{c(t)}{a(t)}\right]^{1/2} dt = \int_1^x [a(t)c(t)]^{1/2}\, \frac{dt}{a(t)}$$

tends to a finite limit as $x \to \infty$. Then Theorem 2.26 shows that (1.1) is non-oscillatory and Theorem 2.37 shows that all of its solutions are bounded. The second assertion follows similarly from the identity

$$\int_1^x \left[\frac{c(t)}{a(t)}\right]^{1/2} dt = \int_1^x [a(t)c(t)]^{-1/2} c(t)\, dt.$$

Theorem 2.39   *If*

$$\int_1^\infty a^{-1}(x)\, dx = \infty,$$

all positive nonoscillatory solutions of (1.1) *are monotone increasing.*

Proof   As stated in the proof of Theorem 2.37, the hypothesis implies that $w = au'/u$ is positive for every nonoscillatory solution u of (1.1).

Theorem 2.40   *If*

$$\int_1^\infty c(x)\, dx = \infty,$$

all positive nonoscillatory solutions of (1.1) *are eventually monotone decreasing.*

Proof   Equation (2.64) shows under the hypothesis

$$\int_1^\infty c(x)\, dx = \infty$$

that $w = au'/u$ eventually becomes negative for every nonoscillatory solution of (1.1).

Exercises
1. Show from Theorem 2.29 that the differential equation

$$u'' + (x^{-2}/4 + e^{-x})u = 0$$

is nonoscillatory.
2. Show that $\lim h'(x) = 2$ $(x \to \infty)$ for the equation

$$u'' + \tfrac{1}{4}x^{-2} \log^{-1}x(1 + \log x)u = 0,$$

so that Theorem 2.34 gives no information. Show that

$$\int_1^\infty H_2(x)\, dx = \infty$$

and hence the equation is oscillatory by Theorem 2.29.

3. Show that the theorems of this section give no information on the oscillatory or nonoscillatory character of the equation

$$u'' + [\tfrac{1}{4}x^{-2} + \gamma x^{-2} \log^{-2}x]u = 0.$$

The reader is advised to be patient, however, since Hille's theorem 2.42 of the next section shows that this equation is oscillatory if $\gamma > \tfrac{1}{4}$ and nonoscillatory if $\gamma < \tfrac{1}{4}$.

4. Prove the following analog of Theorem 2.36: If a and c are positive functions of class $\mathscr{C}^1(0,\infty)$,

$$\int_1^\infty c(x)\,dx = \infty,$$

and $M = \lim c^{-1}(x)\,d\sqrt{ac}/dx\ (x \to \infty)$ exists, then Eq. (1.1) is oscillatory if $M < 2$ and nonoscillatory if $M > 2$.

   Hint: If $u(x)$ is a solution of (1.1), then $z(x) = a(x)u'(x)$ is a solution of the differential equation

$$\left[\frac{1}{c(x)}z'\right]' + \frac{1}{a(x)}z = 0.$$

Proceed as in the proof of Theorem 2.36.

5. Develop the following counterexample to show that Theorem 2.37 is false without the hypothesis that Eq. (1.1) is nonoscillatory: Consider the equation

$$(xu')' + x^{-1}u = 0,$$

with general solution

$$u(x) = K_1 \sin \log |x| + K_2 \cos \log |x|.$$

All solutions are bounded even though

$$\int_1^\infty a^{-1}(x)\,dx = \lim_{x\to\infty} \log |x| = \infty$$

6. Prove that Eq. 2.1 must have at least one unbounded solution if it is nonoscillatory. (Apply Theorem 2.37 with $a(x) \equiv 1$.)

8. Hille's Kneser-Type Oscillation Criteria

The following oscillation criterion of Hille [81] is a slight extension of Kneser's theorem (proved in Section 1 below the statement of Theorem 2.1).

Theorem 2.41   (Hille–Kneser)   *Let*

$$\omega^* = \lim_{x\to\infty}\sup x^2c(x), \qquad \omega_* = \lim_{x\to\infty}\inf x^2c(x).$$

Then Eq. (2.1) is oscillatory if $\omega_* > \frac{1}{4}$ and nonoscillatory if $\omega^* < \frac{1}{4}$, but it can be either oscillatory or nonoscillatory if either ω_* or ω^* equals $\frac{1}{4}$.

Proof If $\omega_* > \frac{1}{4}$, there exists a number $\gamma > \frac{1}{4}$ and a positive number x_0 such that $c(x) - \gamma x^{-2} > 0$ for $x \ge x_0$. Since the Euler equation $v'' + \gamma x^{-2}v = 0$

is oscillatory for $\gamma > \frac{1}{4}$, the Sturm comparison theorem 1.1 shows that every solution of (2.1) has arbitrarily large zeros.

If $\omega^* < \frac{1}{4}$, there exists a number $\gamma < \frac{1}{4}$ and a number $x_0 > 0$ such that $c(x) - \gamma x^{-2} < 0$ for $x \geq x_0$. If a solution of (2.1) had arbitrarily large zeros, then every solution of $v'' + \gamma x^{-2}v = 0$ ($\gamma < \frac{1}{4}$) would have arbitrarily large zeros by Sturm's comparison theorem. The contradiction shows that (2.1) is nonoscillatory.

To prove the last statement of Theorem 2.41, consider the example

$$u'' + c(x)u = 0, \qquad c(x) = \frac{1}{4x^2} + \frac{\delta}{(x \log x)^2}, \qquad (2.67)$$

with general solution

$$u(x) = x^{1/2}[K_1(\log x)^{\zeta} + K_2(\log x)^{1-\zeta}],$$

where

$$\zeta = \tfrac{1}{2} + \tfrac{1}{2}(1 - 4\delta)^{1/2}.$$

In this case $\omega_* = \omega^* = \frac{1}{4}$ and the solutions are oscillatory if $\delta > \frac{1}{4}$ but non-oscillatory if $\delta \leq \frac{1}{4}$,

Theorem 2.42   (Hille) *Let*

$$\left.\begin{array}{c}\omega_1{}^* \\ \omega_{1*}\end{array}\right\} = \lim_{x \to \infty} \frac{\sup}{\inf}(x \log x)^2\left[c(x) - \frac{1}{4x^2}\right].$$

Then Eq. (2.1) is oscillatory if $\omega_{1*} > \frac{1}{4}$, nonoscillatory if $\omega_1{}^* < \frac{1}{4}$, and no conclusion can be drawn if either $\omega_1{}^*$ or ω_{1*} equals $\frac{1}{4}$.

The proof follows along the lines of the proof of the previous theorem by means of the Sturm comparison theorem with (2.67) as a comparison equation.

Actually, Theorems 2.41 and 2.42 form the beginning of an infinite sequence of comparison theorems, obtained by comparison of (2.1) with an infinite sequence of differential equations of which the Euler equation $v'' + \gamma x^{-2}v = 0$ and (2.67) are the first two members. Define

$$L_0(x) = x, \qquad L_n(x) = L_{n-1}(x) \log_n x, \qquad n = 1, 2, \ldots,$$

where

$$\log_2 x = \log \log x, \qquad \log_n x = \log \log_{n-1} x,$$

and further define

$$S_n(x) = \sum_{k=0}^{n} [L_k(x)]^{-2}, \qquad n = 1, 2, \ldots,$$

$$e_1 = e, \qquad e_n = \exp(e_{n-1}).$$

One can then show by direct calculation that the differential equation

$$u'' + c(x)u = 0, \qquad c(x) = \tfrac{1}{4}S_{n-1}(x) + \delta[L_n(x)]^{-2} \tag{2.68}$$

has the general solution

$$u(x) = [L_{n-1}(x)]^{1/2}[K_1(\log_n x)^{\zeta} + K_2(\log_n x)^{1-\zeta}] \tag{2.69}$$

for $x > e_{n-1}$, where $\zeta = \tfrac{1}{2} + \tfrac{1}{2}(1 - 4\delta)^{1/2}$.

Theorem 2.43   (Hille) *Let*

$$\left.\begin{array}{r}\omega_n{}^* \\ \omega_{n*}\end{array}\right\} = \lim_{x \to \infty} \begin{array}{c}\sup \\ \inf\end{array} [L_n(x)]^2[c(x) - \tfrac{1}{4}S_{n-1}(x)],$$

$n = 1, 2, \ldots.$ *Then Eq. (2.1) is oscillatory if $\omega_{n*} > \tfrac{1}{4}$, nonoscillatory if $\omega_n{}^* < \tfrac{1}{4}$, and no conclusion is possible if either $\omega_n{}^*$ or ω_{n*} equals $\tfrac{1}{4}$.*

The proof is obtained similarly to that of Theorem 2.25 by comparing (2.1) with (2.68) by Sturm's theorem 1.1.

Theorem 2.44   (Hille) *Equation (2.1) is nonoscillatory if there exists a positive integer n such that*

$$\int_x^\infty c(t)\, dt \le \tfrac{1}{4}\int_x^\infty S_n(t)\, dt$$

for x sufficiently large.

Proof   In the comparison theorem 2.12, take

$$C(x) = \tfrac{1}{4}S_{n-1}(x) + \tfrac{1}{4}[L_n(x)]^{-2} \equiv \tfrac{1}{4}S_n(x).$$

Then Eq. (2.2) (which is the same as (2.68) in this case) is nonoscillatory, and if

$$\int_x^\infty c(t)\, dt \le \int_x^\infty C(t)\, dt,$$

Theorem 2.12 shows that (2.1) also is nonoscillatory. (The roles of c and C are interchanged.)

Some extensions of Theorem 2.44 were obtained by Taam [198, p. 496].

Exercises
1. Prove Theorems 2.42 and 2.43 by appealing to Sturm's comparison theorem.
2. Verify that (2.67) has the general solution given in the text.
3. Show that (2.68) has the general solution (2.69) and hence that (2.68) is oscillatory if $\delta > \tfrac{1}{4}$ and nonoscillatory if $\delta \le \tfrac{1}{4}$.

4. Write out Theorem 2.43 explicitly in the case $n = 2$.
5. Verify the statement: Theorem 2.42 shows that Eq. (2.67) is oscillatory if $\delta > \frac{1}{4}$ but nonoscillatory if $\delta < \frac{1}{4}$, while Kneser's theorem gives no information.

9. Nonoscillation Theorems of Hartman and Wintner

Hartman and Wintner [70–77] developed several oscillation criteria in the early 1950's which have a somewhat different character from those considered in the preceeding sections. These depend in part on an interesting comparison theorem given by the same authors in 1949 [71], which in turn depends on a classical result of Knesere [95]. The latter may be stated as follows:

Theorem 2.45   (Kneser) *If c is a nonnegative continuous function in $[0, \infty)$, then the differential equation $u'' - c(x)u = 0$ has a positive nonincreasing solution in $[0, \infty)$.*

Proof Let u be the solution satisfying $u(0) = u'(0) = 1$. Then $u'(x)$ is never decreasing, $u'(x) \geq 1$, and $u(x) \geq x$ for all x in $[0, \infty)$. Hence the function u_1 defined by

$$u_1(x) = u(x) \int_x^\infty \frac{dt}{u^2(t)}, \qquad 0 \leq x < \infty,$$

exists, satisfies the differential equation $u'' = c(x)u$, and is positive and nonincreasing in $[0, \infty)$. In fact, since $u'(x)$ is nondecreasing,

$$u_1'(x) = -\frac{1}{u(x)} + u'(x) \int_x^\infty \frac{dt}{u^2(t)}$$

$$\leq -\frac{1}{u(x)} + \int_x^\infty \frac{u'(t)\, dt}{u^2(t)}$$

$$= 0$$

and

$$u_1''(x) - c(x)u_1(x) = [u''(x) - c(x)u(x)] \int_x^\infty \frac{dt}{u^2(t)}$$

$$= 0.$$

It is easy to extend this theorem to the general second order linear equation

$$Lu \equiv a(x)u'' + b(x)u' - c(x)u = 0, \qquad 0 \leq x < \infty, \qquad (2.70)$$

as shown by Hartman and Wintner [70] in the following theorem:

Theorem 2.46   *If a, b, and c are real-valued continuous functions in* $[0, \infty)$ *such that a is positive and c is nonnegative in this interval, then the differential equation* (2.70) *has a positive nonincreasing solution in* $[0, \infty)$. *The same assertions remain true if* $[0, \infty)$ *is replaced by* $(0, \infty)$, $[0, \alpha)$ *or* $(0, \alpha)$, $\alpha < \infty$.

Proof   The idea of the proof is to reduce Eq. (2.70) to the simple form $u'' = c(x)u$ and then apply Theorem 2.45. The reduction will be accomplished in two steps:

(1)   Multiplication of (2.70) by $p(x)/a(x)$, where

$$p(x) = \exp\left\{\int_0^x [b(t)/a(t)] \, dt\right\}$$

yields the identity

$$\frac{p(x)}{a(x)} Lu = \frac{d}{dx}\left[p(x)\frac{du}{dx}\right] - \frac{c(x)p(x)}{a(x)} u;$$

(2)   Under the transformation

$$s = \varphi(x) = \int_0^x \frac{dt}{p(t)}, \tag{2.71}$$

which defines φ as a strictly increasing function of x, it follows that $d/ds = p(x) \, d/dx$, and hence

$$\frac{p^2(x)}{a(x)} Lu = \frac{d^2u}{ds^2} - \frac{c(x)p^2(x)}{a(x)} u.$$

Since $p(x) > 0$ and $a(x) > 0$, u satisfies $Lu = 0$ iff u (as a function of s) satisfies

$$\frac{d^2u}{ds^2} - c_1(s)u = 0, \tag{2.72}$$

where

$$c_1(s) = c[\varphi^{-1}(s)]p^2[\varphi^{-1}(s)]/a[\varphi^{-1}(s)] \geq 0,$$

with φ^{-1} the inverse of the (monotone) function φ. Equation (2.72) has a positive nonincreasing solution $u = f(s)$ by Kneser's theorem 2.45, and since $s = \varphi(x)$ is strictly increasing, it follows that (2.70) also has a positive nonincreasing solution.

   If $[0, \infty)$ is replaced by $(0, \infty)$ in the hypotheses of Theorem 2.46, we can use the above reasoning to show that there exists a positive nonincreasing solution of (2.70) in $[\varepsilon, \infty)$ for each $\varepsilon > 0$, and then let $\varepsilon \to 0$. The proofs for intervals $[0, \alpha)$ and $(0, \alpha)$, $\alpha < \infty$, are virtually the same and will be omitted.

If a is differentiable and $b = a'$, (2.70) reduces to the self-adjoint equation

$$[a(x)u']' - c(x)u = 0,$$

and thus Theorem 2.46 includes the self-adjoint case if we assume that $a \in \mathscr{C}^1$.

As a consequence of Theorem 2.46, Hartman and Wintner [70] obtained the following theorem on completely monotone functions, i.e., functions f such that $(-1)^m f(x) \geq 0$ for $m = 0, 1, 2, \ldots; 0 < x < \infty$.

Theorem 2.47   (Hartman and Wintner)   *If a', b, and c are completely monotone and $a > 0$ in $(0, \infty)$, then the differential equation (2.70) has a nontrivial completely monotone solution in $(0, \infty)$. The solution can be represented in the form*

$$u(x) = \int_0^\infty e^{-xt}\, d\sigma(t),$$

where σ is monotone nondecreasing in $[0, \infty)$ but not necessarily bounded.

For the proof we refer the reader to the literature [70, 76].

Next, a comparison theorem for nonoscillatory equations (2.1) will be obtained with the aid of Theorem 2.46.

Theorem 2.48   (Hartman and Wintner [71])   *Suppose that c and C in (2.1), (2.2), respectively, are continuous functions satisfying $c(x) \geq C(x)$ in $0 \leq x < \infty$. If (2.1) is nonoscillatory, then for every solution u of (2.1) there corresponds a solution v of (2.2) such that*

$$v(x) = O(|u(x)|) \qquad as \quad x \to \infty.$$

Proof We remark first that the order symbol O means as usual that there are constants x_0 and K such that $v(x) \leq K|u(x)|$ for $x_0 \leq x < \infty$. Observe also that (2.2) is nonoscillatory as well as (2.1) under the hypothesis $c(x) \geq C(x)$ because of Sturm's theorem 1.1.

For every nontrivial solution u of (2.1) there exists a number x_0 such that $|u(x)| > 0$ in $x_0 \leq x < \infty$ since (2.1) is nonoscillatory. Suppose first that $u(x) > 0$ in this interval. We shall seek a solution v of (2.2) in the form

$$v(x) = z(x)u(x), \tag{2.73}$$

where $z(x)$ is to be determined. Substitution of (2.73) into (2.2) leads to the following differential equation for z:

$$u(x)z'' + 2u'(x)z' - [c(x) - C(x)]u(x)z = 0 \tag{2.74}$$

since $u''(x) = -c(x)u(x)$. This equation has the form (2.70) where the co-efficients u, $2u'$, and $(c - C)u$ are continuous, u is positive, and $(c - C)u$ is nonnegative by hypothesis in $[x_0, \infty)$. Hence Theorem 2.46 shows that this equation has a positive nonincreasing solution $z(x)$ in $[x_0, \infty)$, and in particular there exists a constant K such that $z(x) \le K$ in this interval. Thus the function v defined by (2.73) is a solution of (2.2) in $[x_0, \infty)$ and satisfies $v(x) < Ku(x)$ in this interval.

If $u(x) < 0$ in $[x_0, \infty)$, then $-u(x)$ is a positive solution and the foregoing proof shows that there is a solution $v(x)$ of (2.2) satisfying $v(x) < - Ku(x)$, $x_0 \le x < \infty$.

Example   As an example of Theorem 2.48, consider the case that (2.1) is the Euler equation

$$u'' - \gamma x^{-2} u = 0, \qquad \gamma > 0$$

in $1 \le x < \infty$. This equation has the explicit solution $u(x) = x^{-\lambda}$, where

$$2\lambda = (1 + 4\gamma)^{1/2} - 1 > 0.$$

Thus if $C(x) \le -\gamma x^{-2}$ in $1 \le x < \infty$ for some constant $\gamma > 0$, then Eq. (2.2) has a "small" solution $v(x) = O(x^{-\lambda})$ as $x \to \infty$.

Theorem 2.49   *Under the hypotheses of Theorem 2.48, there exist linearly independent solutions v and V of Eq. (2.2) such that*

$$v(x) \le |u(x)| \le V(x) \tag{2.75}$$

for sufficiently large x.

Proof   As in the proof of Theorem 2.45, Eq. (2.72) has a solution $U(s) \ge s$ in $0 \le s < \infty$, and hence under the strictly increasing transformation $s = \varphi(x)$ given by (2.71), Eq. (2.70) has a solution $U(\varphi(x))$ which is positive and bounded away from zero on $x \ge 1$. For $u(x) > 0$, (2.74) is of the same type as (2.70), and hence (2.74) has a solution $Z(x)$ satisfying $Z(x) \ge 1$ as well as the solution $z(x)$ already found in the proof of Theorem 2.48. Dividing by the constant K if necessary, we may assume that $z(x) \le 1$ in $[x_0, \infty)$. If the solution $v(x)$ of (2.2) is defined by (2.73) and a second solution $V(x)$ is defined by

$$V(x) = Z(x)u(x),$$

then

$$v(x) < z(x)u(x) \le u(x) \le Z(x)u(x) = V(x).$$

This establishes (2.75) if $u(x)$ is positive for $x_0 \le x < \infty$, and the case of negative $u(x)$ is disposed of as in Theorem 2.48.

Theorem 2.50   (Hartman and Wintner [77]) *Suppose $c(x)$ in (2.1) is continuous and*

$$\int^{\infty} c(x)\, dx$$

is finite. If the differential equation

$$v'' + 4f^2(x)v = 0, \qquad f(x) = \int_x^{\infty} c(t)\, dt \tag{2.76}$$

is nonoscillatory, then also (2.1) is nonoscillatory, and corresponding to every nontrivial solution v of (2.76) there exist two linearly independent solutions u_1 and u_2 of (2.1) which satisfy

$$0 < u_1(x) \le |v(x)|^{1/2} \exp\left[\int_0^x f(t)\, dt\right] \le u_2(x)$$

for sufficiently large x.

Proof Since (2.76) is nonoscillatory, $v(x) \ne 0$ for large x and we may assume without loss of generality that $v(x) > 0$ (since $-v(x)$ is a solution along with $v(x)$). For large x define

$$z(x) = v^{1/2}(x) \exp\left[\int_0^x f(t)\, dt\right] > 0. \tag{2.77}$$

Successive differentiation of (2.77) yields

$$z'/z = v'/2v + f = p/2 + f,$$

where $p = v'/v$, and

$$z'' - [\tfrac{1}{2}p' - c + (\tfrac{1}{2}p + f)^2]z = 0. \tag{2.78}$$

Also p satisfies the Riccati equation (compare (2.36))

$$p' + p^2 + 4f^2 = 0.$$

Then (2.78) can be rewritten in the form

$$z'' + [c + (\tfrac{1}{2}p - f)^2]z = 0. \tag{2.79}$$

Since the solution (2.77) of (2.79) is positive for large x, Eq. (2.79) is non-oscillatory. Since

$$c(x) \le c(x) + [\tfrac{1}{2}p(x) - f(x)]^2$$

it follows from Theorem 2.49 that there exist linearly independent solutions u_1 and u_2 of (2.1) such that $u_1(x) \le z(x) \le u_2(x)$. This completes the proof of Theorem 2.50.

In the case $c(x) \geq 0$ it is not known, conversely, whether or not (2.76) must be nonoscillatory if (2.1) is nonoscillatory. However, the following theorem shows that a weakened form of the converse of Theorem 2.50 is true if (2.76) is replaced by

$$v'' + f^2(x)v = 0, \qquad f(x) = \int_x^\infty c(t)\, dt. \qquad (2.80)$$

Theorem 2.51   (Hartman and Wintner) *Suppose $c(x)$ is continuous,*

$$\int^\infty c(x)\, dx$$

is finite, and $f(x)$ is nonnegative for large x. Then the differential equation (2.80) is nonoscillatory if (2.1) is nonoscillatory.

Proof If $u(x)$ is a solution of (2.1) such that $u(x) > 0$ in $[x_0, \infty)$ and if $v(x) = u'(x)/u(x)$, then $v(x) \to 0$ as $x \to \infty$ and

$$v(x) = V(x) + f(x), \qquad V(x) = \int_x^\infty v^2(t)\, dt,$$

as pointed out in the proof of the Hille–Wintner theorem 2.12. Since $f(x)$ and $V(x)$ are nonnegative it follows that $V(x)$ satisfies Riccati's inequality

$$V' + V^2 + f^2 \leq (V + f)^2 + V' = 0.$$

Then Wintner's theorem 2.15 shows that (2.1) is nonoscillatory.

The following analog of the second part of Theorem 2.50 is also valid for Eq. (2.80) when $f(x) \geq 0$.

Theorem 2.52   (Hartman and Wintner) *Suppose $c(x)$ is continuous,*

$$\int^\infty c(x)\, dx$$

is finite, and $f(x)$ is nonnegative for large x. If (2.1) is nonoscillatory, then for every nontrivial solution v of (2.80) there exists a solution u of (2.1) which satisfies

$$|u(x)| \geq |v(x)| \exp\left[\int_0^x f(t)\, dt\right]$$

for large x.

The proof is similar to that of Theorem 2.50 with $v^{1/2}(x)$ replaced by $v(x)$ in (2.77), and will be omitted.

Theorem 2.53   (Hartman and Wintner [77])   *Suppose that $c(x)$ is continuous and nonnegative and that Eq. (2.1) is nonoscillatory. If u is any nontrivial solution of (2.1) and if $v = u'/u$, then there exists a positive number x_0 such that*

(1) $v'(x) \leq 0$ *in* $x_0 \leq x < \infty$,

and

(2) $\displaystyle\int_x^\infty c(t)\,dt \leq v(x) \leq (x - x_0)^{-1}$, $x_0 < x < \infty$.

Proof Since (2.1) is nonoscillatory, there exists $x_0 > 0$ such that $u(x) \neq 0$ for $x \geq x_0$. Then, in the notation of Theorem 2.12,

$$v'(x) = -v^2(x) - c(x) \leq 0, \qquad x_0 \leq x < \infty, \tag{2.81}$$

and

$$v(x) = f(x) + V(x) \geq f(x),$$

where

$$f(x) = \int_x^\infty c(t)\,dt, \qquad V(x) = \int_x^\infty v^2(t)\,dt.$$

This proves (1) and the left inequality of (2). As in the proof of Theorem 2.2, $u'(x) \neq 0$ for all $x \geq x_0$ and $u'(x)$ has the same sign as $u(x)$ for such x. Thus $v(x) > 0$ for $x \geq x_0$ and since $v' + v^2 \leq 0$ by (2.81), we obtain

$$1 + v'/v^2 \leq 0, \qquad x \geq x_0.$$

Hence

$$\int_{x_0}^x \left[1 + \frac{v'(t)}{v^2(t)}\right] dt = x - x_0 - \frac{1}{v(x)} + \frac{1}{v(x_0)} \leq 0,$$

or

$$\frac{1}{v(x)} \geq x - x_0 + \frac{1}{v(x_0)} > x - x_0,$$

which implies the right inequality of (2).

Corollary   *Under the assumptions of Theorem 2.53, $v(x) \to 0$ as $x \to \infty$ and*

$$\int^\infty v^2(x)\,dx$$

converges.

A large number of additional oscillation criteria and related topics, generally of special character, can be found in the references to the work of Hartman and Wintner listed in the bibliography. Some disconjugacy criteria of Barrett [7] and asymptotic properties of Mařík and Ráb [129] also have connections with the results of this section.

Since the original studies of Lyapunov, there has arisen an immense literature on *stability criteria* for differential equations, i.e., in the case of linear differential equations, criteria for every solution to be bounded in $[0, \infty)$. A detailed treatment of stability problems for both linear and non-linear equations together with an extensive bibliography may be found in the monograph by Cesari [29]. A typical result is the following criterion of Gusarov [58]: *If the function c in* (2.1) *is absolutely continuous and the derivative c' is of bounded variation in* $[0, \infty)$, *and if* $0 < \alpha^2 \leq c(x) \leq \beta^2$ *for some constants* α *and* β, *then every solution of* (2.1) *together with its first derivative is bounded in* $[0, \infty)$.

Hukuhara and Nagumo [87] and Caccioppoli [25] established the following result: *If c is a real-valued continuous function in* $[0, \infty)$ *such that*

$$\int_0^\infty |c(x) - \rho|\, dx < \infty$$

for some number $\rho > 0$, *then every solution of* (2.1) *is bounded in* $[0, \infty)$. For this theorem it is not necessary that $c(x) \to \rho$ as $x \to \infty$ or even that the limit of $c(x)$ exist. Furthermore, it has been proved by Caligo [26], Bellman [15], and others that the continuity hypothesis on c can be weakened to measurability of c. Extensions to nth order differential equations and systems have been obtained by Hukuhara [85] and others. (See Chapter 4, Section 5.)

10. Asymptotic Estimates for the Number of Zeros of a Solution of (1.1) or (2.1)

As in Section 7 we shall first consider the case that $c(x) = h^{-2}(x)$ in Eq. (2.1), where h is a positive differentiable function in $(0, \infty)$. Let $N(\alpha, x)$ denote the number of zeros of a solution u of (2.1) in the interval $(\alpha, x]$, $\alpha > 0$. Since we shall be concerned with oscillatory equations in this section, and since the number $N(\alpha, x)$ differs by at most one for all solutions of a given equation, the asymptotic behavior of $N(\alpha, x)$ depends only on the differential equation, i.e., the function h. If (2.1) is oscillatory and $\lim h'(x) = 0$ $(x \to \infty)$, a classic result of Wiman [219] states that

$$N(\alpha, x) \sim \frac{1}{\pi} \int_\alpha^x \frac{ds}{h(s)}, \tag{2.82}$$

where the symbol $\sim$ means that the ratio of the two quantities tends to 1 as $x \to \infty$. Wiman's result was extended in several directions by Potter [152] and Nehari [143] in the 1950's, and these generalizations will be described in this section.

Let $\alpha_0 = \alpha, \alpha_1, \alpha_2, \ldots, \alpha_n = \beta, \ldots$ $(\alpha_0 < \alpha_1 < \cdots < \alpha_n)$ denote consecutive zeros of a nontrivial solution of (2.1) in $(0, \infty)$. Let H be a positive differentiable function in $[0, \infty)$ and let $C(x) = H^{-2}(x)$. Let $t = \varphi(x)$ be defined by the equation

$$\int_0^t \frac{ds}{H(s)} = \int_\alpha^x \frac{ds}{h(s)}, \tag{2.83}$$

and let $T = \varphi(\beta)$, that is

$$\int_0^T \frac{ds}{H(s)} = \int_\alpha^\beta \frac{ds}{h(s)}.$$

Since $H(s)$ and $h(s)$ are positive, φ is a strictly increasing continuous function which maps $[\alpha, \beta]$ onto $[0, T]$. Consider the eigenvalue problem

$$\frac{d^2v}{dt^2} + \lambda C(t)v = 0, \qquad v(0) = v(T) = 0. \tag{2.84}$$

The following central theorem will be proved at the end of this section.

Theorem 2.54   (Nehari) *If*

$$\left| \frac{dh}{dx} - \frac{dH}{dt} \right| \le 2M \qquad for \quad \alpha \le x \le \beta \quad (t = \varphi(x))$$

then the nth *eigenvalue* λ_n *of the system* (2.84) *satisfies the inequality*

$$|(\lambda_n)^{1/2} - 1| \le M.$$

This result has the character of a comparison theorem. The usefulness of the theorem depends on our knowledge of the eigenvalues of the problem (2.84): the two simplest cases are those for which $C(t) = 1$ and $C(t) = \gamma^2(t + 1)^{-2}$ $(\gamma > 2)$. If $C(t) = 1$, (2.84) reduces to $v'' + \lambda v = 0$, $v(0) = v(T) = 0$, and the corresponding eigenvalues are given by

$$(\lambda_n)^{1/2} = \frac{n\pi}{T} = n\pi \left[\int_\alpha^\beta \frac{dx}{h(x)} \right]^{-1}.$$

In this case, $H(t) = 1$, $H'(t) = 0$, the hypothesis of Theorem 2.54 reduces to $|h'(x)| \le 2M$ for $\alpha \le x \le \beta$ and the conclusion becomes $|(n\pi/T) - 1| \le M$, or

$$\frac{1 - M}{\pi} \int_\alpha^\beta \frac{dx}{h(x)} \le n \le \frac{1 + M}{\pi} \int_\alpha^\beta \frac{dx}{h(x)}. \tag{2.85}$$

The following theorem is then a consequence of Theorem 2.54.

Theorem 2.55 *Suppose that* $c(x) = h^{-2}(x)$ *in* (2.1) *where h is a positive differentiable function in* $(0, \infty)$. *Let* $\alpha = \alpha_0, \alpha_1, \ldots, \alpha_n = \beta$ $(0 < \alpha_0 < \alpha_1 < \cdots)$ *be* $n + 1$ *consecutive zeros of a nontrivial solution of* (2.1). *If* $|h'(x)| \le 2M$ *for* $\alpha \le x \le \beta$, *then n satisfies the inequalities* (2.85).

Theorem 2.55 contains Wiman's result (2.82) as a special case when $\lim h'(x) = 0$ $(x \to \infty)$. To prove this, observe first that Eq. (2.1) is oscillatory by Theorem 2.34 and hence

$$\int_\alpha^\infty dx/h(x) = \infty$$

by Theorem 2.30. For arbitrary $\varepsilon > 0$ there exist integers m and p_0 $(p_0 > m)$ such that $|h'(x)| < 2\varepsilon$ for $x \ge \alpha_m$, and the inequalities

$$0 < \frac{1}{\pi N(\alpha_m, \alpha_p)} \int_\alpha^{\alpha_m} \frac{dx}{h(x)} < \varepsilon, \tag{2.86}$$

$$\frac{1}{N(\alpha, \alpha_p)} < \frac{1}{N(\alpha_m, \alpha_p)} < \frac{1 + \varepsilon}{N(\alpha, \alpha_p)} \tag{2.87}$$

hold for integers $p \ge p_0$, since $N(\alpha, \alpha_p) \to \infty$ as $p \to \infty$. Applying (2.85) with $M = \varepsilon$ to the interval (α_m, α_p), we find that

$$\frac{1}{1 + \varepsilon} \le \frac{1}{\pi N(\alpha_m, \alpha_p)} \int_{\alpha_m}^{\alpha_p} \frac{dx}{h(x)} \le \frac{1}{1 - \varepsilon},$$

and hence from (2.86) and (2.87) that

$$\frac{1}{(1 + \varepsilon)^2} < \frac{1}{\pi N(\alpha, \alpha_p)} \int_\alpha^{\alpha_p} \frac{dx}{h(x)} < \frac{1}{1 - \varepsilon} + \varepsilon.$$

Since ε is arbitrary this means that

$$\lim_{p \to \infty} \frac{1}{\pi N(\alpha, \alpha_p)} \int_\alpha^{\alpha_p} \frac{dx}{h(x)} = 1. \tag{2.88}$$

Since $N(\alpha, x) = N(\alpha, \alpha_p)$ for $\alpha_p \le x < \alpha_{p+1}$, it follows without difficulty from (2.88) that

$$\lim_{x \to \infty} \frac{1}{\pi N(\alpha, x)} \int_\alpha^x \frac{dt}{h(t)} = 1,$$

which is equivalent to Wiman's formula (2.82).

As a second example of Theorem 2.54 consider the case that $C(t) = \gamma^2(t + 1)^{-2}$ $(\gamma > \frac{1}{2})$ in (2.84). The eigenvalues of (2.84) are then found by direct calculation to be

$$\lambda_n = \frac{1}{4\gamma^2} + \left[\frac{\pi n}{\gamma \log(T + 1)}\right]^2, \qquad n = 1, 2, \dots. \tag{2.89}$$

Since $H(t) = \gamma^{-1}(t + 1)$ in this case, and hence $H'(t) = \gamma^{-1}$, the hypothesis of Theorem 2.54 reduces to

$$|h'(x) - \gamma^{-1}| \le 2M, \qquad \alpha \le x \le \beta.$$

The transformation (2.83) reduces to

$$\gamma \log(t + 1) = \gamma \int_0^t \frac{ds}{s + 1} = \int_\alpha^x \frac{ds}{h(s)}.$$

and in particular

$$\gamma \log(T + 1) = \int_\alpha^\beta \frac{ds}{h(s)}.$$

Then (2.89) can be rewritten in the form

$$\lambda_n = (2\gamma)^{-2} + \pi^2 n^2 \left[\int_\alpha^\beta \frac{ds}{h(s)}\right]^{-2}, \qquad n = 1, 2, \dots,$$

and the conclusion of Theorem 2.54 becomes

$$(1 - M)^2 \le (2\gamma)^{-2} + \pi^2 n^2 \left[\int_\alpha^\beta \frac{ds}{h(s)}\right]^{-2} \le (1 + M)^2,$$

or

$$[(1 - M)^2 - \delta^2]\left[\int_\alpha^\beta \frac{ds}{h(s)}\right]^2 \le \pi^2 n^2 \le [(1 + M)^2 - \delta^2]\left[\int_\alpha^\beta \frac{ds}{h(s)}\right]^2, \tag{2.90}$$

where $\delta = 1/2\gamma$. The following theorem has then been established.

Theorem 2.56   (Nehari) *Suppose that $c(x) = h^{-2}(x)$ in (2.1) where h is a positive differentiable function in $(0, \infty)$. Let $\alpha, \alpha_1, \alpha_2, \dots, \alpha_n = \beta$ be $n + 1$ consecutive zeros of a nontrivial solution of (2.1). If*

$$|h'(x) - 2\delta| \le 2M, \qquad 0 < \delta < 1, \quad \alpha \le x \le \beta,$$

then n satisfies the inequalities (2.90).

In the case $\lim h'(x) = 2\delta$ $(x \to \infty)$ this implies the asymptotic formula

$$N(\alpha, x) \sim \frac{(1 - \delta^2)^{1/2}}{\pi} \int_\alpha^x \frac{ds}{h(s)} \qquad (x \to \infty), \tag{2.91}$$

and extends Wiman's formula (2.82). The proof is left as an exercise.

Potter [152] extended the Wiman formula to the general self-adjoint equation (1.1) as follows.

Theorem 2.57   (Potter)   *Suppose that the functions* a *and* c *in* (1.1) *are of class* $\mathcal{C}^1(0, \infty)$, a *is positive and* c *is nonnegative in* $(0, \infty)$, *either* $a_\infty = \infty$ *or* $c_\infty = \infty$ *(see* (2.46) *for the definitions of these quantities), and*

$$\lim_{x \to \infty} a(x) \frac{d}{dx} [a(x)c(x)]^{-1/2} = 0. \tag{2.92}$$

Then the following asymptotic formula for the number of zeros in $(\alpha, x]$ *is valid as* $x \to \infty$:

$$N(\alpha, x) \sim (1/\pi) \int_\alpha^x [c(x)/a(x)]^{1/2} dx. \tag{2.93}$$

Proof   If $a_\infty = \infty$ we apply Leighton's transformation

$$t = \int_\alpha^x \frac{ds}{a(s)} = \varphi(x) \tag{2.94}$$

to (1.1) to obtain

$$\frac{d^2 u}{dt^2} + a(x)c(x)u = 0 \tag{2.95}$$

where $x = \varphi^{-1}(t)$, which is well defined since φ is monotone increasing under the hypothesis that a is positive valued. Since $x \to \infty$ as $t \to \infty$ by the hypothesis $a_\infty = \infty$, it follows from (2.92) that

$$\lim_{t \to \infty} \frac{d}{dt} [a(x)c(x)]^{-1/2} = \lim_{x \to \infty} a(x) \frac{d}{dx} [a(x)c(x)]^{-1/2} = 0,$$

or $\lim h'(t) = 0$ $(t \to \infty)$, where

$$h(t) = \{a[\varphi^{-1}(t)]c[\varphi^{-1}(t)]\}^{-1/2}.$$

Then the Wiman formula (2.82) yields the result

$$N[0, \varphi(x)] \sim (1/\pi) \int_0^{\varphi(x)} \{a[\varphi^{-1}(s)]c[\varphi^{-1}(s)]\}^{1/2} ds$$

for the number of zeros of $u[\varphi(x)]$ in the interval $(0, \varphi(x)]$. This is equivalent to (2.93) under the transformation (2.94).

If $c_\infty = \infty$, we apply the transformation

$$t = \int_\alpha^x c(t)\, dt$$

to the differential equation

$$\frac{d}{dx}\left[\frac{1}{c(x)}\frac{dz}{dx}\right] + \frac{z}{a(x)} = 0$$

satisfied by $z(x) = a(x)u'(x)$, where $u(x)$ is a solution of (1.1). The result is

$$\frac{d^2z}{dt^2} + \frac{1}{a(x)c(x)}z = 0,$$

of the same type as (2.95). Since the zeros of $u(x)$ and $z(x)$ separate each other, the number of zeros of $z(x)$ in any interval differs by at most one from the number of zeros of $u(x)$ in that interval. The conclusion (2.93) then follows by an argument similar to that used in the first part of the proof (when $a_\infty = \infty$).

Theorem 2.58   (Potter) *In Eq. (2.54) suppose that $h(x)$ is positive and differentiable in $(0, \infty)$, that $g(x) = [x^2 h^{-2}(x) - \frac{1}{4}]^{1/2}$ is real and positive, and that*

$$\lim_{x\to\infty} x[g^{-1}(x)]' = 0. \tag{2.96}$$

Then the following asymptotic formula for the number of zeros of a nontrivial solution of (2.54) is valid as $x \to \infty$:

$$N(\alpha, x) \sim \frac{1}{\pi}\int_\alpha^x \frac{g(s)}{s}\, ds.$$

Proof Under the transformation $u = z x^{1/2}$, Eq. (2.54) goes into

$$(xz')' + g^2(x)x^{-1}z = 0,$$

which has the form of Eq. (1.1) with $a(x) = x$ and $c(x) = g^2(x)x^{-1}$. Then

$$\lim_{x\to\infty} a(x)\frac{d}{dx}[a(x)c(x)]^{-1/2} = \lim_{x\to\infty} x\frac{d}{dx}[g^{-1}(x)] = 0$$

by (2.96) and hence the conclusion follows from Theorem 2.57.

If $\lim h'(x) = 0$ $(x \to \infty)$, then $h(x) - h(0) = xh'(\xi)$, $0 < x < \xi$, by the mean value theorem, and hence $\lim x^{-1}h(x) = 0$ $(x \to \infty)$. A brief calculation gives

$$x[g^{-1}(x)]' = [h'(x) - x^{-1}h(x)][1 - x^{-2}h^2(x)/4]^{-3/2},$$

and hence (2.96) holds whenever the Wiman condition $\lim h'(x) = 0$ $(x \to \infty)$ holds. Furthermore $\lim xh^{-1}(x) = \infty$ under the Wiman condition, and hence

$$g(x)/x \sim xh^{-1}(x)/x = h^{-1}(x).$$

Thus Theorem 2.58 includes the Wiman formula (2.82) as a special case. Since Theorem 2.58 applies to differential equations for which (2.82) is not applicable, and even (2.91) is not applicable, e.g.,

$$\frac{d^2u}{dx^2} + \frac{1 + \log x}{4x^2 \log x} u = 0, \tag{2.97}$$

where $\lim h'(x) = 2$ $(x \to \infty)$, it is a proper generalization of the results obtained before. We remark that Eq. (2.97) is oscillatory by Exercise 2 of Section 7.

If $h(x) \sim mx + b$ as $x \to \infty$, where m and b are constants, then $g(x) \sim [m^{-2} - \frac{1}{4}]^{1/2}$ as $x \to \infty$, and Theorem 2.58 yields the asymptotic formula

$$N(\alpha, x) \sim \frac{1}{\pi} \left(\frac{1}{m^2} - \frac{1}{4} \right)^{1/2} \log x, \qquad 0 < m < 2.$$

This also could have been obtained from (2.91) by setting $m = 2\delta$, $0 < \delta < 1$.

Proof of Theorem 2.54   Let J be the functional defined by

$$J[y] = \int_\alpha^\beta y'^2(x)\,dx \Big/ \int_\alpha^\beta c(x)y^2(x)\,dx$$

for real-valued functions $y \in \mathscr{C}^1[\alpha, \beta]$. If $y = uv$, $u \in \mathscr{C}^1[\alpha, \beta]$, $v \in \mathscr{C}^1[\alpha, \beta]$, this becomes

$$J[uv] = \int_\alpha^\beta (uv' + vu')^2\,dx \Big/ \int_\alpha^\beta cu^2v^2\,dx,$$

which transforms into

$$J[uv] = \int_0^T \left[u\frac{dv}{dx}\left(\frac{dx}{dt}\right)^{1/2} + v\frac{du}{dx}\left(\frac{dx}{dt}\right)^{1/2} \right]^2 dt \Big/ \int_0^T cu^2v^2 \frac{dx}{dt}\,dt$$

under the substitution $t = \varphi(x)$ defined by (2.83). We now choose v to be the positive solution of $v^2 = dx/dt = h(x)/H(t)$. Then

$$2v\frac{dv}{dx}\frac{dx}{dt} = \left(H\frac{dh}{dx}\frac{h}{H} - h\frac{dH}{dt} \right) \Big/ H^2,$$

and hence

$$\frac{dv}{dx}\left(\frac{dx}{dt}\right)^{1/2} = \frac{1}{2v}\left(\frac{dx}{dt}\right)^{-1/2}\frac{h}{H^2}\left(\frac{dh}{dx} - \frac{dH}{dt}\right)$$

$$= \frac{1}{2H}\left(\frac{dh}{dx} - \frac{dH}{dt}\right).$$

It follows that

$$J[uv] = \int_0^T \left[\frac{du}{dx} + \frac{1}{2H}\left(\frac{dh}{dx} - \frac{dH}{dt}\right)u\right]^2 dt \bigg/ \int_0^T Cu^2\, dt. \qquad (2.98)$$

We use the hypothesis $|dh/dx - dH/dt| \leq 2M$ and the Schwarz inequality to obtain

$$I[u]J[uv] \leq \int_0^T u'^2\, dt + 2M \int_0^T H^{-1}|uu'|\, dt + M^2 I[u]$$

$$\leq \int_0^T u'^2\, dt + 2MI^{1/2}[u]\left(\int_0^T u'^2\, dt\right)^{1/2} + M^2 I[u]$$

where the prime denotes differentiation with respect to x, and $I[u]$ is defined by

$$I[u] = \int_0^T Cu^2\, dt = \int_0^T H^{-2}u^2\, dt.$$

Hence

$$J[y] = J[uv] \leq \left\{\left(I^{-1}[u]\int_0^T u'^2\, dt\right)^{1/2} + M\right\}^2,$$

or with the notation

$$J_1[u] = I^{-1}[u]\int_0^T u'^2\, dt = \int_0^T u'^2\, dt \bigg/ \int_0^T Cu^2\, dt,$$

$$J^{1/2}[y] \leq J_1^{1/2}[u] + M. \qquad (2.99)$$

We shall now show in addition to (2.99) that

$$J^{1/2}[y] \geq J_1^{1/2}[u] - M \qquad (2.100)$$

which together with (2.99) establishes the inequality

$$|J^{1/2}[y] - J_1^{1/2}[u]| \leq M. \qquad (2.101)$$

To prove (2.100) we may assume that $J_1^{1/2}[u] > M$ since otherwise (2.100) holds trivially. Then, if we use the abbreviation $g = \frac{1}{2}(dh/dx - dH/dt)$,

$$0 < J_1^{1/2}[u] - M \leq J_1^{1/2}[u] - \left(\int_0^T Cg^2u^2\, dt/I[u]\right)^{1/2}$$

by the hypothesis of Theorem 2.54, and hence

$$(J_1^{1/2} - M)^2 \le J_1 - 2\left(J_1 \int_0^T Cg^2u^2 \, dt/I[u]\right)^{1/2} + \int_0^T Cg^2u^2 \, dt/I[u]$$

$$\le J_1 - 2\int_0^T C^{1/2} |guu'| \, dt/I[u] + \int_0^T Cg^2u^2 \, dt/I[u]$$

$$\le \int_0^T (u' + C^{1/2}gu)^2 \, dt/I[u]$$

$$= J[uv] = J[y]$$

by (2.98). This proves (2.100) and hence also (2.101).

The conclusion of Theorem 2.54 is now obtained as a consequence of Courant's maximum-minimum principle [39, p. 405]. Indeed the nth eigenvalue λ_n of (2.84) is given by max min $J_1[w]$, where the minimum is taken over all $w \in \mathscr{C}^1(0, T)$ such that $w(0) = w(T) = 0$ and w is orthogonal to $n - 1$ functions $g_i \in \mathscr{C}^1(0, T)$ satisfying $g_i(0) = g_i(T) = 0$, and the maximum is taken over all such g_i. Likewise, the nth eigenvalue Λ_n of the system

$$\frac{d^2u}{dx^2} + \Lambda c(x)u = 0, \qquad u(\alpha) = u(\beta) = 0 \qquad (2.102)$$

is given by $\Lambda_n = $ max min $J[w]$ among similarly defined admissible functions w. It is easy to verify [143] that admissible functions for $J[w]$ are carried into admissible functions for $J_1[w]$ by the transformation $t = \varphi(x)$ given by (2.83), and hence it follows from (2.101) and the max min characterization of eigenvalues that

$$|\lambda_n^{1/2} - \Lambda_n^{1/2}| \le M. \qquad (2.103)$$

(The reader is referred to Courant and Hilbert [39] for a discussion of the maximum-minimum principle and its consequences.) It follows in particular from the max min principle that the nth eigenvalue Λ_n^* for a proper subdomain I^* of $I = [\alpha, \beta]$ is strictly less than Λ_n. From this it follows that a (nontrivial) eigenfunction u_n corresponding to Λ_n has precisely $n + 1$ zeros on $[\alpha, \beta]$, including those at α and β; for if u_n had more than $n - 1$ interior zeros, then an eigenvalue problem of the form (2.102) on a subinterval I^* of I would have $\Lambda_n^* = \Lambda_n$, contradicting the statement just made; and if u_n had *less* than $n - 1$ interior zeros, Sturm's comparison theorem would be violated.

By the hypotheses of Theorem 2.54, Eq. (2.1) has a solution u which has exactly $n + 1$ zeros on $[\alpha, \beta]$, including those at α and β, and hence $\Lambda_n = 1$. In view of (2.103), Theorem 2.54 finally has been proved.

Exercises
1. Verify that (2.82) follows from (2.88).
2. In the case $C(t) = \gamma^2(t+1)^{-2}$, show that the eigenvalues of (2.84) are given by
$$\lambda_n = (2\gamma)^{-2} + \pi^2 n^2 \gamma^{-2}[\log(T+1)]^{-2}, \qquad \gamma > \tfrac{1}{2}, \qquad n = 1, 2, \dots .$$
3. Derive the asymptotic formula (2.91) in the case that $\lim h'(x) = 2\delta$ $(x \to \infty)$, $0 \le \delta < 1$, and show that this result includes Wiman's formula (2.82). Also prove that Eq. (2.1) is oscillatory in this case.
4. Give the details of the proof of Theorem 2.57 in the case $c_\infty = \infty$.
5. Prove the maximum-minimum principle stated in the text and examine some of its consequences. This is a large project and probably will require some references, e.g., [39, 131].
6. It is a problem of current interest to extend Wiman's formula (2.82) to *partial* differential equations, e.g., $\nabla^2 u + cu = 0$, in unbounded domains. Some recent references are [39, 49, 50]. This problem was solved by Weyl [39] in the case of bounded domains. The physical interpretation is discussed, for example, in [39] and [176].

11. Nonoscillation Criteria for Hill's Equation

Hill's equation has the form
$$u'' + [-k + mq(x)]u = 0, \tag{2.104}$$
where k and m are real constants and q is a nontrivial real-valued continuous *periodic* function with period 1, i.e.,
$$q(x+1) = q(x), \qquad -\infty < x < \infty.$$
The classical problem of Hill [135] is to find the values of a and b for which (2.104) has periodic solutions. For each m, the largest value of k, say $k_0 = \varphi(m)$, for which (2.104) has a periodic solution, has the following property: All solutions are oscillatory if $k < k_0$ and nonoscillatory if $k \ge k_0$. This was proved by Hamel in 1912. Detailed references are given in [50, 135].

Theorem 2.59   (Moore [135])   *If a nontrivial solution of (2.104) is nonoscillatory, it has at most one zero in* $(-\infty, \infty)$.

Proof If a nontrivial solution u had zeros at α and β, say $\alpha < \beta$, then the function v defined by $u(x+n) = v(x)$, where n is an integer, would be a solution with zeros at $\alpha - n$, $\beta - n$. Hence u would vanish on every interval $[\alpha - n, \beta - n]$, $n = \pm 1, \pm 2, \dots$, by Sturm's separation theorem 1.8 and therefore u would be oscillatory.

Theorem 2.60   (Moore)   *Let c and C be continuous in $[x_0, \infty)$. If (2.1) and (2.2) are nonoscillatory, then so is the equation*

$$u'' + [(1 - \lambda)c(x) + \lambda C(x)]u = 0, \qquad 0 \le \lambda \le 1. \tag{2.105}$$

Proof   Since the cases $\lambda = 0$ and $\lambda = 1$ are self-contained, we may assume $0 < \lambda < 1$. By hypothesis there exists a solution u_1 of (2.1) and a number x_1, $x_1 \ge x_0$, such that $u_1(x) > 0$ for $x_1 < x$. Under the substitution $u = u_1 z$, Eqs. (2.2) and (2.105) are respectively transformed into

$$[u_1{}^2(x)z']' + u_1{}^2(x)[C(x) - c(x)]z = 0,$$

$$\lambda^{-1}[u_1{}^2(x)z']' + u_1{}^2(x)[C(x) - c(x)]z = 0.$$

The first of these equations is nonoscillatory by hypothesis and the second is nonoscillatory iff (2.105) is nonoscillatory. However, the Sturm–Picone theorem 2.2 shows, since $\lambda^{-1} > 1$ by hypothesis, that every solution of the first equation has a zero between consecutive zeros of the second equation. Hence the second equation is nonoscillatory along with the first, and also (2.105) is nonoscillatory.

Let R denote the set of all points in the km-plane for which Eq. (2.104) is nonoscillatory. This set is nonempty: for example, it contains the sector defined by

$$\begin{cases} k \ge [\max q(x)]m, & m \ge 0 \\ k \ge [\min q(x)]m, & m \le 0, \end{cases}$$

for $-k + mq(x) \le 0$ within this sector for all x. Some properties of R are given in the following theorem.

Theorem 2.61   (Moore)   *R is closed and convex, and except for the origin, is entirely contained in the half-plane $k > 0$.*

Proof   The convexity of R follows from Theorem 2.60. To prove the closure, let (k_0, m_0) be a limit point of points in R. Then for arbitrary $\varepsilon > 0$ the differential equation (2.104) is nonoscillatory for some k_1, m_1 satisfying $|k_1 - k_0| < \varepsilon$, $|m_1 - m_0| < \varepsilon$. Let u be a nontrivial solution of (2.104) for $(k, m) = (k_0, m_0)$. If $u(x)$ has no zero then $(k_0, m_0) \in R$ and we are finished. If $u(x_0) = 0$ at some point x_0, let v be the solution of the initial value problem

$$v'' + [-k_1 + m_1 q(x)]v = 0, \qquad v(x_0) = 0, \qquad v'(x_0) = u'(x_0),$$

(which is known to exist and be unique [35]). Since this equation is nonoscillatory, it has no zero other than x_0 by Theorem 2.59. Furthermore, $v(x)$ uniformly approximates $u(x)$ on an arbitrarily large interval of the form $|x - x_0| \le \Delta$ since $|k_1 - k_0| < \varepsilon$, $|m_1 - m_0| < \varepsilon$ for arbitrary $\varepsilon > 0$ [35]. Hence $u(x)$ can change sign only at x_0, and (2.104) is nonoscillatory at (k_0, m_0).

To prove the last statement of Theorem 2.61, it is enough to show that Eq. (2.104) is oscillatory for all $k \leq 0$, $(k, m) \neq (0, 0)$. Let v be a periodic function such that $v''(x) = q(x)$. Then the substitution $u = ze^{-mv(x)}$ transforms (2.104) into

$$(e^{-2mv(x)}z')' + [-k + m^2 v'^2(x)]e^{-2mv(x)}z = 0. \qquad (2.106)$$

Since v is a nonconstant periodic function and $k \leq 0$, $(k, m) \neq (0, 0)$, it follows that

$$\lim_{x \to \infty} \int_1^x e^{2mv(t)}\, dt = \infty, \qquad \lim_{x \to \infty} \int_1^x [-k + m^2 v'^2(t)]e^{-2mv(t)}\, dt = \infty.$$

These conditions are sufficient for (2.106), and hence (2.104), to be oscillatory by Leighton's theorem 2.24.

Corollary *Let $k = \varphi(m)$ be the boundary of R, i.e., the smallest value of k for which (2.104) is nonoscillatory. Then φ is convex, $\varphi(0) = 0$, and φ is increasing in $(0, \infty)$ and decreasing in $(-\infty, 0)$.*

The following theorem of Moore gives bounds on $\varphi(m)$ when $q(x)$ in (2.104) satisfies quite general inequalities. The proof in Moore [135] will not be given here.

Theorem 2.62   (Moore) *Let x_0, x_1 be, respectively, numbers at which the maximum q_0, minimum q_1 of $q(x)$ is attained. Suppose there exist positive numbers α, β, λ, and μ such that the inequalities*

$$q_0 - |\alpha(x - x_0)|^\lambda \leq q(x) \leq q_1 + |\beta(x - x_1)|^\mu$$

hold for all x. Then the boundary function φ of R is bounded from below as follows:

$$\begin{aligned}
\varphi(m) &> q_0 m - 2(\pi^2 \alpha^2/4)^{\lambda\sigma}m^{2\sigma}, & m &> 0 \\
\varphi(m) &> q_1 m - 2(\pi^2 \beta^2/4)^{\mu\zeta}(-m)^{2\zeta}, & m &< 0,
\end{aligned} \qquad (2.107)$$

where $\sigma = 1/(\lambda + 2)$, $\zeta = 1/(\mu + 2)$.

A special case of interest is that in which $q(x) = q_0$ for $|x - x_0| \leq \delta$, $\delta > 0$. Then the hypotheses of the theorem are satisfied if $\alpha = 1/\delta$ and λ is sufficiently large. Hence (2.107) yields

$$\varphi(m) \geq q_0 m - \pi^2/2\delta^2, \qquad m > 0.$$

Since φ is convex by the corollary of Theorem 2.61, this implies that there exists a positive number d such that

$$\lim_{m \to \infty} [q_0 m - d - \varphi(m)] = 0.$$

Hence the boundary curve $k = \varphi(m)$ of R has an asymptote in the half-plane $m > 0$ if the set $\{x : q(x) = q_0\}$ contains an interval. Likewise $k = \varphi(m)$ has an asymptote in the half-plane $m < 0$ if the set $\{x : q(x) = q_1\}$ contains an interval. Moore also gave the following partial converses to the statements just made.

Theorem 2.63   (Moore)   *If the set of points on the interval* $[0, 1]$ *where* $q(x)$ *attains its absolute maximum (minimum) has measure zero, then the curve given by* $k = \varphi(m)$ *has no asymptote in the half-plane* $m > 0$ $(m < 0)$.

Define $q^+(x) = \max[q(x), 0]$, and $q^-(x) = -\min[q(x), 0]$. In addition to (2.104) consider a second equation of the same type:

$$v'' + [-k + mQ(x)]v = 0. \tag{2.108}$$

Moore [135] gave the following comparison theorem for the boundary functions φ, Φ associated with $q(x)$, $Q(x)$, i.e., (2.104), (2.108), respectively.

Theorem 2.64   (Moore)   *Let* φ, Φ *be the boundary functions associated with the nontrivial, continuous, periodic functions* q, Q *respectively. If* $q^+(x) \geq Q^+(x)$ *and* $q^-(x) \geq Q^-(x)$, *then* $\varphi(m) \geq \Phi(m)$ *for all* m. *In particular, an upper bound for* $\varphi(m)$ *is an upper bound for* $\Phi(m)$, *and a lower bound for* $\Phi(m)$ *is a lower bound for* $\varphi(m)$.

Proof   By hypothesis (2.104) is nonoscillatory if $k = \varphi(m)$, and $mq(x) \geq mQ(x)$ for all m (positive or nonpositive). Then, if $k = \varphi(m)$ in (2.108), that equation also is nonoscillatory by Sturm's comparison theorem. Thus the smallest value $\Phi(m)$ of k in (2.108) for which (2.108) is nonoscillatory does not exceed $\varphi(m)$. The other statements are obvious.

Example 1   Consider the period function q_n defined as follows:

$$q_n(x) = 1 - |4x|^n \qquad \text{if} \quad |x| \leq \tfrac{1}{4}$$

$$q_n(x + \tfrac{1}{2}) = -q_n(x), \qquad -\infty < x < \infty.$$

Theorem 2.62 is applicable with

$$q_0 = \max q_n(x) = q_n(0) = 1,$$

$$\alpha = 4, \quad \lambda = n, \quad \sigma = 1/(n+2),$$

and the conclusion (2.107) reduces to

$$\varphi(m) > m - 2(4\pi^2)^{n\sigma}m^{2\sigma}, \qquad m > 0. \tag{2.109}$$

In particular, $\varphi(m) - m = -O(m^{2\sigma})$, $m > 0$.

Example 2   As an application of the comparison Theorem 2.64, consider the celebrated Mathieu equation

$$u'' + (-k + m \cos 2\pi x)u = 0.$$

In this case

$$\cos{}^+ 2\pi x = \cos 2\pi x \qquad \text{if} \quad 0 \le x \le \tfrac{1}{4}, \ \tfrac{3}{4} \le x \le 1$$
$$= 0 \qquad \text{if} \quad \tfrac{1}{4} \le x \le \tfrac{3}{4}$$
$$\cos{}^- 2\pi x = 0 \qquad \text{if} \quad 0 \le x \le \tfrac{1}{4}, \ \tfrac{3}{4} \le x \le 1$$
$$= \cos 2\pi x \qquad \text{if} \quad \tfrac{1}{4} \le x \le \tfrac{3}{4}.$$

We shall compare $\cos 2\pi x$ with $q_2(x)$, the latter defined in Example 1. Since

$$q_2{}^+(x) = 1 - 4x^2 \qquad \text{if} \quad 0 \le x \le \tfrac{1}{4}, \ \tfrac{3}{4} \le x \le 1$$
$$= 0 \qquad \text{if} \quad \tfrac{1}{4} \le x \le \tfrac{3}{4},$$
$$q_2{}^-(x) = 0 \qquad \text{if} \quad 0 \le x \le \tfrac{1}{4}, \ \tfrac{3}{4} \le x \le 1$$
$$= 1 - 4x^2 \qquad \text{if} \quad \tfrac{1}{4} \le x \le \tfrac{3}{4},$$

and since

$$\frac{d^2}{dx^2} \cos 2\pi x \bigg|_{x=0} = -4\pi^2 < -8 = q_2''(0),$$

it follows that $\cos{}^+ 2\pi x \le q_2{}^+(x)$ and $\cos{}^- 2\pi x \le q_2{}^-(x)$. If Φ denotes the boundary function for the Mathieu equation, it is a consequence of Theorem 2.64 that

$$\Phi(m) \ge \varphi(m) > m - 2(4\pi^2)^{1/2} m^{1/2}$$

where (2.109) has been used with $n = 2$. Thus

$$\Phi(m) \ge m - 4\pi m^{1/2}.$$

Exercises

1. In Example 2 show that

$$1 - 2\pi^2 x^2 \le \cos 2\pi x \le -1 + 2\pi^2 (x - \tfrac{1}{2})^2,$$

   and apply Theorem 2.62 to obtain the bound

$$\Phi(m) \ge m - \pi^2 (2m)^{1/2}.$$

2. Consider the periodic function q defined by

$$q(x) = 1 - \exp(16 - 1/x^2), \qquad 0 < |x| \le \tfrac{1}{4},$$
$$q(0) = 1,$$
$$q(x + \tfrac{1}{2}) = -q(x), \qquad -\infty < x < \infty,$$

and apply Theorem 2.62 to obtain the result

$$\varphi(m) = m - O(\log m), \qquad m > 0.$$

3. Show that $\varphi(m) = m - O(m/\log m)$, $m > 0$ for the periodic function defined by

$$q(x) = 1 - (\log |4ex|)^{-1}, \qquad 0 < |x| \le \tfrac{1}{4}$$
$$q(0) = 1$$
$$q(x + \tfrac{1}{2}) = -q(x), \qquad -\infty < x < \infty.$$

*4. (Moore [135].) The following companion formula of (2.109) can be obtained:

$$\varphi(m) \le m - ([4(1 + 1/n)]^{n/(n+1)} - 1)m^{n/(n+2)}$$

if $m \ge [4(1 + 1/n)]^{(n+2)/(n+1)}$, relative to the function q_n in Example 1. In particular this shows that

$$\varphi(m) - m = -O(m^{n/(n+2)}), \qquad m > 0.$$

5. Deduce from Example 2 and Exercise 4 that

$$\Phi(m) \le m - (6^{4/3} - 1)m^{1/2}, \qquad m \ge 6^{4/3}.$$

12. Nonoscillation Criteria for Complex Equations

Nonoscillation theorems were obtained by Hille [81], London [125], and Nehari [140] in the case that z and u in the equation

$$u'' + c(z)u = 0 \tag{2.1}$$

are complex variables, and c is an analytic function in a domain (i.e., open connected set) D of the complex z-plane. Equation (2.1) is said to be *disconjugate* in D iff every solution of (2.1) has at most one zero in D. The equation is said to be *nonoscillatory* in D iff every solution has at most a finite number of zeros in D. The proofs of the theorems below are contained in the references cited and will not be given here.

The first theorem of Hille, in the case that D is an (open) sector, gives a sufficient condition for the existence of a solution with no zeros at all in D. The proof makes use of Theorem 2.22 (which is easily extended *verbatim* to the complex case).

Theorem 2.65   (Hille)   *If $c(z)$ is analytic in a sector D: $-\theta_1 < \arg z < \theta_2$ of the complex plane, if the function f given by*

$$f(z) = z \int_z^\infty c(t)\, dt$$

is well defined in D when the integral is taken along a line parallel to the real axis, and if $|f(z)| \leq k < \frac{1}{4}$ for $z \in D$, then (2.1) has a solution $u(z)$ with no zeros in D.

Theorem 2.66   (Nehari)   *If $c(z)$ is analytic in a domain D bounded by an analytic Jordan curve Γ, and if*

$$\int_\Gamma |c(z)\, dz| < \infty,$$

then Eq. (2.1) is nonoscillatory in D. In particular, if $c(z)$ is analytic in the unit disk $|z| < 1$ and if

$$\int_0^{2\pi} |c(e^{i\theta})|\, d\theta < \infty,$$

then (2.1) is nonoscillatory in $|z| < 1$.

Theorem 2.67   (Nehari)   *Let $c(z)$ be analytic and satisfy $|c(x + iy)| \leq x\, \delta(x)$ in the half-strip $0 \leq x < \infty$, $-1 < y < 1$ $(z = x + iy)$, where $\delta(x) \to 0$ as $x \to \infty$. If*

$$\int_0^\infty x\, |c[x \pm i(1 - \varepsilon)]|\, dx < \infty$$

for sufficiently small positive ε, then Eq. (2.1) is nonoscillatory in any half-strip

$$0 \leq x < \infty, \qquad -1 + h \leq y \leq 1 - h \qquad (0 < h < 1).$$

Theorem 2.68   (Hartman–Wintner–Nehari)   *Let $c(z)$ be analytic in the half-strip $0 \leq x < \infty$, $-1 < y < 1$ $(z = x + iy)$, and let $\alpha_n (n = 1, 2, \ldots)$ denote the real parts of the zeros of any nontrivial solution of Eq. (2.1) in this half-strip, $\alpha_1 < \alpha_2 < \cdots$. Then the inequality*

$$|c(x + iy)| \leq Kx^{-\sigma}, \qquad 1 < \sigma < 2, \qquad K = constant$$

cannot hold in the half-strip if $\alpha_n = o(n^\zeta)$ $(n \to \infty)$, where $\zeta = 1/(2 - \sigma)$.

The meaning of this theorem is that a prescription of the asymptotic behavior of $|c(x + iy)|$ for large x and $-1 < y < 1$ restricts the density of the zeros as $n \to \infty$.

Theorem 2.69   (Nehari [140])   *If $c(z)$ is analytic in $|z| < 1$, a sufficient condition for (2.1) to be disconjugate in $|z| < 1$ is:*

$$|c(z)| \leq (1 - |z|^2)^{-2}. \tag{2.110}$$

Hille [82] gave an example to show that this inequality is sharp, i.e., (2.1) can fail to be disconjugate if (2.110) is replaced by

$$|c(z)| \le k(1 - |z|^2)^{-2} \qquad (k > 1).$$

Theorem 2.70   (Pokornyi [151])   *If $c(z)$ is analytic in $|z| < 1$, a sufficient condition for (2.1) to be disconjugate in $|z| < 1$ is*

$$|c(z)| \le 2/(1 - |z|^2).$$

Theorem 2.71   (London)   *If $c(z)$ is analytic in $|z| < 1$, a sufficient condition for (2.1) to be disconjugate in $|z| < 1$ is:*

$$\iint\limits_{|z|<1} |c(z)| \, dx \, dy \le \pi.$$

It is not known whether or not the bound π is sharp.

Corollary   *If $c(z)$ is analytic in D, where D is an open disk or half-plane, a sufficient condition for (2.1) to be disconjugate in D is:*

$$\iint\limits_{D} |c(z)| \, dx \, dy \le \pi.$$

Theorem 2.72   (London)   *If $c(z)$ is analytic in $|z| < 1$, either one of the following two conditions is sufficient for Eq. (2.1) to be nonoscillatory in $|z| < 1$:*

(1) $\displaystyle \iint\limits_{|z|<1} |c(z)| \, dx \, dy < \infty,$

or

(2) $\displaystyle \int_0^{2\pi} |c(e^{i\theta})| \, d\theta < \infty,$

where the last integral is defined as the limit as $r \to 1$ of the nondecreasing function

$$R(r) = \int_0^{2\pi} |c(re^{i\theta})| \, d\theta.$$

Theorem 2.73   (London)   *If $c(z)$ is analytic in a domain D bounded by an analytic Jordan curve, a sufficient condition for (2.1) to be nonoscillatory in D is:*

$$\iint\limits_{D} |c(z)| \, dx \, dy < \infty.$$

Theorem 2.74   *If $c(z)$ is analytic in $|z| < 1$, a sufficient condition for* (2.1) *to be nonoscillatory in $|z| < 1$ is:*

$$\int_0^{2\pi} |c(e^{i\theta})|\, d\theta \le 4\pi,$$

where the integral is defined in Theorem 2.72.

It is not known whether or not the constant 4π is the best possible. However, the example $c(z) = \pi^2/4$, for which

$$\int_0^{2\pi} |c(e^{i\theta})|\, d\theta = \pi^3/2 = (4.9348\cdots)\pi$$

shows that it cannot be improved very much.

Wend [207] obtained a general nonoscillation theorem for Eq. (1.1) in the case that a and c are complex-valued functions in $[0, \infty)$, where $a \in \mathscr{C}^1$, $c \in \mathscr{C}$, $a(x) \ne 0$, and $a(x)$ has the additional property that

$$\left| \int_\alpha^\beta \frac{dx}{a(x)} \right| < \left| \int_\alpha^\gamma \frac{dx}{a(x)} \right| \quad \text{and} \quad \left| \int_\beta^\gamma \frac{dx}{a(x)} \right| < \left| \int_\alpha^\gamma \frac{dx}{a(x)} \right|$$

for all numbers α, β, γ satisfying $0 \le \alpha < \beta < \gamma < \infty$.

Theorem 2.75   (Wend)   *Under the above assumptions on a and c, define*

$$\lambda = \int_0^\infty |c(x)| \int_0^x \frac{dt}{|a(t)|}\, dx, \qquad \mu = \int_0^\infty |c(x)| \int_x^\infty \frac{dt}{|a(t)|}\, dx.$$

Then Eq. (1.1) *is nonoscillatory if either λ or μ is finite, and disconjugate in $[0, \infty)$ if either of these numbers is less than* 1.

In the case that $a(x)$ and $c(x)$ are real, Theorem 2.75 compares with the oscillation criteria of Leighton [115], Moore [134], and Potter [152] already stated in previous sections of this chapter.

Chapter 3

Fourth Order Ordinary Equations

1. Introduction

The investigation of the oscillatory behavior or solutions of fourth order linear equations probably originated with the vibrating rod problem of mathematical physics. If the rod is clamped at its two endpoints $x = \alpha$ and $x = \beta$, it is well known (Courant and Hilbert [39]) that the deflection of the rod at time zero is an eigenfunction for the problem

$$[a(x)u'']'' - \lambda c(x)u = 0,$$
$$u(\alpha) = u'(\alpha) = u(\beta) = u'(\beta) = 0, \tag{3.1}$$

where a and c are positive functions of class $\mathscr{C}^2$ and $\mathscr{C}$, respectively. In particular u has a double zero at $x = \alpha$ and at $x = \beta$. In the case that the rod is supported instead of clamped, the boundary conditions are replaced by $u(\alpha) = u''(\alpha) = u(\beta) = u''(\beta) = 0$. Other homogeneous boundary conditions are possible—two at each endpoint—in accordance with the physical conditions at the ends of the rod.

The general properties of (3.1) listed below, in analogy with those for second order eigenvalue problems, have been developed by Courant, Hilbert [39], Friedrichs [46], Pleijel [150], and others with the aid of the theory of linear integral equations and functional analysis. We state them without proof in order to avoid departure from the theme of this book.

Theorem 3.1 *The problem* (3.1) *has a denumerable sequence of positive eigenvalues* λ_n, $\lambda_1 < \lambda_2 < \cdots$ *with no finite limit point and corresponding nontrivial orthogonal eigenfunctions* u_n *on* (α, β), *i.e.,*

$$\langle u_n, u_m \rangle \equiv \int_\alpha^\beta u_n(x)\bar{u}_m(x)c(x)\, dx = 0,$$

113

$m, n = 1, 2, \ldots$; $n \neq m$. The smallest eigenvalue λ_1 is the minimum of the "Rayleigh quotient"

$$J[w] = \int_\alpha^\beta a(w'')^2 \, dx \Big/ \int_\alpha^\beta cw^2 \, dx$$

among all "admissible" functions w, i.e., all functions satisfying the boundary conditions in (3.1) and having piecewise continuous second derivatives on $[\alpha, \beta]$. The nth eigenvalue λ_n is characterized by Courant's maximum-minimum principle:

$$\lambda_n = \max \min J[w],$$

where the minimum is taken over all admissible functions w which are orthogonal to $n - 1$ admissible functions $g_1, g_2, \ldots, g_{n-1}$, i.e., $\langle w, g_i \rangle = 0$, $i = 1, 2, \ldots, n - 1$; and the maximum is taken over all such sets of g_i's.

Theorem 3.1 is the basis by which comparison and oscillation theorems for the differential equations

$$[a(x)u'']'' - c(x)u = 0, \qquad a(x) > 0, \quad c(x) > 0 \tag{3.2}$$
$$[A(x)v'']'' - C(x)v = 0, \qquad A(x) > 0, \quad C(x) > 0 \tag{3.3}$$

were obtained by Leighton and Nehari [117], Howard [84], Kreith [104], the author [191], and others. Before the definitive article of Leighton and Nehari appeared in 1958, only a few isolated results were known (e.g., by Cimmino [33], Reynolds [173], Švec [186], Sternberg [183], and Whyburn [210]). The considerable progress made since 1957 will be summarized in this chapter.

2. Separation Theorems

Leighton and Nehari made use of the following lemma for Eq. (3.2).

Lemma 3.2 Let a and c be positive functions of class $\mathscr{C}^2$, $\mathscr{C}$ respectively. If $u(x)$ is a solution of (3.2) such that u, u', u'', and $(au'')'$ are all nonnegative (but at least one of them $\neq 0$) at α, then they are all positive at x for all $x > \alpha$ at which the hypotheses on a and c are fulfilled.

Proof We remark that at least one of the initial values must be $\neq 0$ in order to guarantee that the (unique) solution of the initial value problem will be nontrivial [35]. In view of the assumptions either $u(\alpha) > 0$ or the first non-vanishing derivative of u at α is positive. In all cases, therefore, $u(x) > 0$ in some open interval (α, β). If the conclusion of the lemma were false, there would exist $\beta > \alpha$ such that $u(\beta) = 0$ and $u(x) > 0$ in (α, β). Then (3.2) would show that

$$a(x)u''(x) = a(\alpha)u''(\alpha) + (x - \alpha)[(au'')'(\alpha)] + \int_\alpha^x (x - t)c(t)u(t) \, dt.$$

Since the right side is positive and increasing for $\alpha < x < \beta$, $u''(x)$ and $[a(x)u''(x)]'$ are positive in this interval. Since $u'(\alpha) \geq 0$, $u'(x) > 0$ in (α, β) and we obtain the contradiction $0 \leq u(\alpha) < u(\beta) = 0$. This proves that $u'(x)$, $u''(x)$, and $[a(x)u''(x)]'$ as well as $u(x)$ are positive for all $x > \alpha$.

Lemma 3.2 shows that Eq. (3.2) always has at least one nonoscillatory solution, i.e., solution with only a finite number of zeros in $(0, \infty)$. However, (3.2) may have oscillatory solutions as well, as shown by the example $u^{(4)} - u = 0$ with solutions $u_1 = \sin x$ and $u_2 = \cos x$ (in particular). In this respect, therefore, the situation for fourth order equations differs from that for second order equations, where the solutions are all oscillatory or all nonoscillatory.

The following analog of Lemma 3.2 is obtained by the substitution $x = \alpha + \gamma - t$ into (3.2) and application of Lemma 3.2 at $t = \gamma$ ($\gamma > 0$).

Lemma 3.3 *With a, c as in Lemma 3.2 and $\alpha > 0$, let $u(x)$ be a solution of (3.2) such that u, $-u'$, u'', and $-(au'')'$ are nonnegative at α, with at least one of these numbers $\neq 0$. Then these 4 functions are all positive at any x in the interval $0 < x < \alpha$.*

Lemma 3.4 *With a, c as in Lemma 3.2, if $u(x)$ is a nontrivial solution of (3.2) such that $u(\alpha) = u(\beta) = u(\gamma) = 0$ for $0 < \alpha < \beta < \gamma$, then $u'(\beta) \neq 0$.*

Proof If $u(\beta) = u'(\beta) = 0$, we may assume without loss of generality that $u''(\beta) \geq 0$. If $(au'')'$ is nonnegative at β, then $u(x) > 0$ for all $x > \beta$, by Lemma 3.2, contradicting the hypothesis $u(\gamma) = 0$. Likewise a contradiction is obtained on the basis of Lemma 3.3 if $(au'')'$ is nonpositive at β.

The following are easy consequences of the foregoing lemmas.

Lemma 3.5 *With a, c as in Lemma 3.2, if u is a nontrivial solution of (3.2) such that $u(\beta) = u'(\beta) = 0$ ($\beta > 0$), then all of the functions u, u', u'', and $(au'')'$ are different from zero in at least one of the two intervals $(0, \beta)$ and (β, ∞).*

Lemma 3.6 *The conclusion of Lemma 3.5 remains valid if the conditions $u(\beta) = u'(\beta) = 0$ are replaced by $u''(\beta) = u'''(\beta) = 0$.*

The following uniqueness theorem holds for the solutions of Eq. (3.2):

Theorem 3.7 (Leighton and Nehari) *A pair of linearly independent solutions of (3.2) cannot have three common zeros.*

We note that the positivity of $c(x)$ is essential for the truth of this theorem; indeed, the differential equation $u^{(4)} + 4u = 0$ has linearly independent solutions $u_1 = \sin x \sinh x$, $u_2 = \sin x \cosh x$, with an infinite sequence of common zeros.

Proof   Let u, v be two solutions of (3.2) with common zeros at α, β, γ, and suppose first that $\alpha < \beta < \gamma$. Then Lemma 3.4 shows that $u'(\beta) \neq 0$ and $v'(\beta) \neq 0$. In view of the assumptions, the solution w defined by

$$w(x) = v'(\beta)u(x) - u'(\beta)v(x)$$

satisfies $w(\alpha) = w(\beta) = w'(\beta) = w(\gamma) = 0$, which is impossible by Lemma 3.4 unless $w(x) \equiv 0$, i.e., $v(x)$ is a constant multiple of $u(x)$.

If two of the zeros coincide, say $\alpha = \beta$, define a solution w_1 by

$$w_1(x) = v''(\beta)u(x) - u''(\beta)v(x).$$

Both $u''(\beta)$ and $v''(\beta)$ are different from zero since otherwise Lemma 3.2 would imply that $u(\gamma) \neq 0$, $v(\gamma) \neq 0$. Since

$$w_1(\alpha) = w_1'(\alpha) = w_1''(\alpha) = w_1(\gamma) = 0,$$

$w_1(x) \equiv 0$ by Lemma 3.2, i.e., $v(x)$ is a constant multiple of $u(x)$.

If α is a triple zero, the conclusion follows from the fact that the initial value problem

$$(au'')'' - cu = 0, \qquad u(\alpha) = u'(\alpha) = u''(\alpha) = 0, \qquad u'''(\alpha) = 1$$

has a unique solution.

The preceding results will now be used to obtain analogs of Sturm's separation theorem (1.8).

Theorem 3.8   (Leighton and Nehari)   *If u and v are linearly independent solutions of (3.2) such that $u(\alpha) = u(\beta) = v(\alpha) = v(\beta) = 0$ ($0 < \alpha < \beta$), then the zeros of u and v separate each other in (α, β).*

Proof   By Theorem 3.7, u and v cannot have a common zero in (α, β). If the conclusion of the theorem were false, one of the solutions, say u, would have consecutive zeros γ, δ and v would be different from 0 in $[\gamma, \delta]$, $\alpha < \gamma < \delta < \beta$. Then $vu' - uv'$ would have a zero at some point x_0 in (γ, δ), for otherwise (u/v) would be everywhere increasing or everywhere decreasing in (γ, δ). This implies that $w(x) = u(x) - \lambda v(x)$ has a double zero at x_0, where $\lambda = u(x_0)/v(x_0)$. Since $w(\alpha) = w(x_0) = w'(x_0) = w(\beta) = 0$, Lemma 3.4 is contradicted.

Theorem 3.9 (Leighton and Nehari) *Let u and v be nontrivial solutions of (3.2) such that $u(\alpha) = u(\beta) = v(\alpha) = v(\gamma) = 0$, $0 < \alpha < \beta < \gamma$. If m, n denote the number of zeros of u, v, respectively, in $(\alpha, \beta]$, then $m - 2 \leq n \leq m + 2$.*

Proof Evidently we can assume that γ is the smallest zero of v in (β, ∞). Let w be a solution of (3.2) with zeros at α, β, and γ; it is easily seen to exist as a suitable linear combination of four linearly independent solutions, and is unique except for a constant multiplier by Theorem 3.7. According to Theorem 3.8, the number p of zeros of w in $(\alpha, \beta]$ satisfies the inequality $p - 1 \leq m \leq p + 1$. Likewise by Theorem 3.8, the zeros of v and w separate each other in (α, γ), so also in (α, β), and hence $p - 1 \leq n \leq p + 1$. Thus

$$m - 2 \leq p + 1 - 2 \leq n \leq p + 1 \leq m + 2.$$

Corollary *Under the assumptions of the theorem, there exists a solution w of (3.2) such that $w(\alpha) = 0$ and the zeros of w separate the zeros of both u and v in (α, β).*

Theorem 3.10 (Leighton and Nehari) *Let u and v be nontrivial solutions of (3.2) such that $u(\alpha) = u(\beta) = v(\gamma) = v(\delta) = 0$, where $0 < \gamma < \alpha < \beta < \delta$. If m, n denote the number of zeros of u, v, respectively, on $[\alpha, \beta]$, then $m - 3 \leq n \leq m + 3$.*

This follows from Theorems 3.8 and 3.9 upon construction of solutions w_1, w_2 with zeros at γ, $\alpha\beta$ and α, $\beta\delta$, respectively.

Theorem 3.11 (Leighton and Nehari) *If there exists a nontrivial solution u of (3.2) with a zero at α and at least $n + 3$ zeros in $[\alpha, \infty)$, then there are n points δ_i, and n solutions u_i, $i = 1, 2, \ldots, n$, $\alpha < \delta_1 < \delta_2 < \cdots \delta_n$ such that*

(1) *u_i has double zeros at α and δ_i;*
(2) *u_i has exactly $i + 3$ zeros on $[\alpha, \delta_i]$, where the double zeros are each counted twice;*
(3) *any nontrivial solution u which is not a constant multiple of u_i and vanishes at α has less than $i + 3$ zeros on $[\alpha, \delta_i]$.*

Proof Let $x_1, x_2, \ldots, x_{n+3}$ $(\alpha = x_1)$ denote the first $n + 3$ zeros of $u(x)$ in $[\alpha, \infty)$. We may assume that $x_2 = x_1 = \alpha$, for if $x_2 > \alpha$ we can replace u by the solution v satisfying $v(\alpha) = v'(\alpha) = v(x_{n+3}) = 0$; the zeros of u and v are interlaced by Theorem 3.8 and hence v has at least n zeros in (α, x_{n+3}).

Let w be the solution of (3.2) satisfying the initial conditions $w(\alpha) = w'(\alpha) = w'''(\alpha) = 0$, $w''(\alpha) = 1$, so that $w(x) > 0$ for $x > \alpha$ by Lemma 3.2. If $x_{i+1} = x_{i+3}$, then clearly $u_i = u$ fulfills (1) and (2) of the theorem. If $x_{i+2} < x_{i+3}$, the proof of Theorem 3.8 shows that there exists a number λ

such that the solution u_i defined by $u_i(x) = u(x) - \lambda w(x)$ has a double zero, say δ_i, in the interval (x_{i+2}, x_{i+3}). We assert that u_i has exactly $i + 3$ zeros on $[\alpha, \delta_i]$ (counting the double zeros at α and δ_i twice each). We shall prove this for odd i and leave the case of even i as an exercise. We may assume without loss of generality that $u(x) > 0$ (as well as $w(x) > 0$) in (x_{i+2}, x_{i+3}). Then $\lambda > 0$ since $u(\delta_i) - \lambda w(\delta_i) = 0$ and both $u(\delta_i)$ and $w(\delta_i)$ are positive. We assert that $u_i(x)$ has two zeros in each of the $(i - 1)/2$ subintervals of (x_3, x_{i+2}) in which $u(x)$ is positive. Since $u_i(x)$ must change sign an even number of times in such a subinterval I by the positivity of $u(x)$ and $\lambda w(x)$, it is sufficient to prove the impossibility of the inequality $\lambda w(x) > u(x)$ throughout I. Let μ be a number (shown to exist in the proof of Theorem 3.8) such that $z(x) \equiv u(x) - \mu w(x)$ has a double zero, say β, in I; it is necessary that $\mu < \lambda$, for $\mu \geq \lambda$ would imply that $\mu w(x) \geq \lambda w(x) > u(x)$ throughout I. It follows that $z(x)$ has a zero γ in (x_{i+2}, x_{i+3}) since

$$z(x_{i+2}) = -\mu w(x_{i+2}) < 0,$$

and

$$z(\delta_i) = u(\delta_i) - \mu w(\delta_i) > u(\delta_i) - \lambda w(\delta_i) = 0.$$

Thus $z(\alpha) = z(\beta) = z'(\beta) = z(\gamma) = 0$, which contradicts Lemma 3.4. We have then proved that $u_i(x)$ has at least two zeros in each of the $(i - 1)/2$ subintervals of (x_3, x_{i+2}) in which $u(x)$ is positive. Since $u_i(x)$ has double zeros at α and δ_i, it has at least $i + 3$ zeros on $[\alpha, \delta_i]$.

Since $u(x) < 0$ in (α, x_3) $(\alpha = x_1 = x_2)$ for odd i, while $w(x) > 0$, $u_i(x)$ cannot have a zero in (α, x_3). Thus $u_i(x)$ must have an *even* number of zeros in $[\alpha, x_{i+3})$. If $u_i(x)$ had more than $i + 3$ zeros on $[\alpha, \delta_i]$ it would therefore have at least $i + 5$ zeros in $[\alpha, x_{i+3})$, and since u has only $i + 2$ zeros in this interval, Theorem 3.9 would be violated. Hence $u_i(x)$ has exactly $i + 3$ zeros on $[\alpha, \delta_i]$.

For even i, $u(x) > 0$ in (α, x_3), and hence $u_i(x)$ is easily seen to have exactly one zero in (α, x_3). The details of the proof are left as an exercise.

To prove assertion (3) of Theorem 3.11, suppose that v is any solution of (3.2) which is not a constant multiple of u_i, such that $v(\alpha) = 0$. Let β be the largest zero of v on $[\alpha, \delta_i]$. If $\beta = \delta_i$, the zeros of v at α and δ_i must be simple by Theorem 3.7 since u_i and v are linearly independent. Since the zeros of u_i and v are interlaced by Theorem 3.8, v has at most i zeros in (α, δ_i) and hence at most $i + 2$ zeros on $[\alpha, \delta_i]$. If $\beta < \delta_i$ we assert that v still has at most $i + 2$ zeros on this interval. Suppose to the contrary that the $(i + 3)$rd zero of v occurred at $\gamma \leq \beta$. Then by the first part of the theorem there would exist a solution u_i^* with double zeros at α and $\delta_i^* \leq \beta < \delta_i$ and exactly $i + 3$ zeros on $[\alpha, \delta_i^*]$. In the case $i = 1$, this is easily seen to be impossible: in fact, as in the proof of Theorem 3.8, there would exist a solution $w_i(x) = u_i(x) - \lambda u_i^*(x)$ with a double zero in (α, δ_i^*) for some positive λ. Since u_i and u_i^* may be taken nonnegative (they cannot change sign outside $[\alpha, \delta_i^*]$ by Lemma 3.4), $w_i(x)$ would have a simple zero in (δ_i^*, δ_i) as well as the zero at α. Thus $w_i(x)$ would have a double zero between two simple zeros, contradicting Lemma 3.4. The same contradiction is obtained for arbitrary i by a slight extension of the argument. This completes the proof of Theorem 3.11.

Let $u(x)$ be a solution of (3.2) with at least $n + 3$ zeros $x_i = x_i(u)$ $(\alpha = x_1 \le x_2 \le \cdots \le x_{n+3}, n = 1, 2, \ldots)$. As pointed out above, equality can hold at most twice since no solution can have more than two double zeros by Lemma 2.4. The number δ_i found in Theorem 3.11 is called the ith *conjugate point* of α, $i = 1, 2, \ldots, n$: it is the minimum of $x_{i+3}(u)$ as u ranges over all nontrivial solutions of (3.2) for which $u(\alpha) = 0$. As usual, a solution will be called *oscillatory* iff it has an infinite sequence of zeros in $(0, \infty)$, and *nonoscillatory* otherwise. Contrary to the second order case, Eq. (3.2) can have some oscillatory solutions as well as the one (or more) nonoscillatory solution(s) guaranteed by Lemma 3.2: The example $u^{(4)} - u = 0$ considered already shows this to be possible. Accordingly, Eq. (3.2) is termed *oscillatory* if it has at least one oscillatory solution, and nonoscillatory otherwise. The proofs of the following theorems of Leighton and Nehari [117] will be omitted.

Theorem 3.12 *If u is a nontrivial solution of (3.2) such that $u(\alpha) = u'(\alpha) = 0$, then the zeros of u in (α, ∞) are separated by the conjugate points δ_i of α, except in the case that the last zero of u is double (when it coincides with a conjugate point).*

Theorem 3.13 *Equation (3.2) is oscillatory iff every positive α has an infinitude of associated conjugate points δ_i, $i = 1, 2, \ldots$.*

Theorem 3.14 *If Eq. (3.2) is nonoscillatory there exists a positive number α such that no solution of (3.2) has more than three zeros in (α, ∞).*

Theorem 3.15 *If $u(x)$ is a solution of (3.2) which has a double zero at α and is positive for $x > \alpha$, the conjugate points δ_i of α coincide with the zeros of the solution of the second order equation*

$$(av')' + [(au')'/u + 2a(u'/u)']v = 0 \tag{3.4}$$

which satisfies $v(\alpha) = 0$, $v'(\alpha) = 1$.

Theorem 3.16 *Suppose (3.2) has a (nontrivial) nonoscillatory solution u. Then (3.2) is oscillatory iff (3.4) is oscillatory.*

As shown by Lemma 3.2, Eq. (3.2) always has one or more nonoscillatory solutions when $c(x)$ is everywhere positive. However, as shown by the theorems below, the solutions of

$$[a(x)u'']'' + c(x)u = 0, \qquad a(x) > 0, \quad c(x) > 0 \tag{3.5}$$

are either all oscillatory or all nonoscillatory. Thus a change of sign of $c(x)$ causes a profound change in the nature of the solutions.

For any solution $u \in \mathscr{C}^4$ of (3.5) let $\varphi = \varphi_u$ be the function defined by

$$\varphi_u(x) = a(x)u'(x)u''(x) - u(x)[a(x)u''(x)]'. \tag{3.6}$$

It follows that

$$\begin{aligned}
\varphi_u'(x) &= a(x)u''^2(x) - u(x)[a(x)u''(x)]'' \\
&= a(x)u''^2(x) + c(x)u^2(x).
\end{aligned} \tag{3.7}$$

Theorem 3.17   (Leighton and Nehari)   *A nontrivial solution of (3.5) has at most one double zero.*

Proof   Since $a(x) > 0$ and $c(x) > 0$, (3.7) shows that $\varphi_u(x)$ is strictly increasing with increasing x, and hence $\varphi_u(x)$ can have at most one zero. If α and β were two double zeros of a solution u $(\alpha < \beta)$, then $\varphi_u(\alpha) = \varphi_u(\beta) = 0$ by (3.6), which is a contradiction.

Theorem 3.18   (Fite [45], Leighton and Nehari)   *If u and v are linearly independent solutions of (3.5) with double zeros at γ, the zeros of u and v separate each other in both $(0, \gamma)$ and (γ, ∞).*

Proof   If $u(x)$ had two consecutive zeros α, β such that $v(x) \neq 0$ on $[\alpha, \beta]$, then, as in the proof of Theorem 3.8, there would exist a constant λ such that $w(x) \equiv u(x) - \lambda v(x)$ has a double zero at some point of (α, β). Since $w(x)$ also has a double zero at γ, Theorem 3.17 is contradicted. If $u(x)$ and $v(x)$ had a common (necessarily simple) zero δ other than γ, the solution $z(x) \equiv v'(\delta)u(x) - u'(\delta)v(x)$ would have a double zero at δ, again contradicting Theorem 3.17.

The *principal solution* $y(x) = y(x, \alpha)$ of (3.5), relative to the point α, is defined as the (unique) solution of (3.5) which satisfies the initial conditions

$$y(\alpha) = y'(\alpha) = y''(\alpha) = 0, \qquad a(\alpha)y'''(\alpha) = 1.$$

The definition of a conjugate point made earlier for Eq. (3.2), of course, does not make sense for Eq. (3.5) since no nontrivial solution of the latter can have two double zeros. Instead the definition is made as follows in terms of the uniquely determined solution with a triple zero at a given point (i.e., the principal solution): The nth *conjugate point* of α is defined as the nth zero of the principal solution $y(x, \alpha)$ in the (open) interval (α, ∞), $n = 1, 2, \ldots$. The nth conjugate point of α will be denoted by $\delta_n = \delta_n(\alpha)$, as before. The proofs of the theorems below are given in the article of Leighton and Nehari [117] and will be omitted.

Theorem 3.19 (Leighton and Nehari) *Principal solutions are antisymmetric, i.e.,* $y(x, \alpha) = -y(\alpha, x)$ *for all x and α.*

Theorem 3.20 (Leighton and Nehari) *The nth conjugate point of α is a continuous, monotone increasing function of α.*

Theorem 3.21 (Leighton and Nehari) *If u is a solution of (3.5) such that $u(\alpha) = 0$ and $\varphi_u(\alpha) \geq 0$, where $\varphi_u(\alpha)$ is defined by (3.6), then the zeros of u and the principal solution relative to α are interlaced in (α, ∞). If u is a solution of (3.5) such that $u(\alpha) = 0$ and $\varphi_u(\alpha) \leq 0$, the zeros of u and the principal solution relative to α are interlaced in $(0, \alpha)$.*

Theorem 3.22 (Leighton and Nehari) *Let $\beta = \delta_n$ be the nth conjugate point of α. If u is a nontrivial solution of (3.5) such that $u(\alpha) = 0$, the number of zeros of u on $[\alpha, \beta]$ is less than the number of zeros of either of the principal solutions $y(x, \alpha)$, $y(x, \beta)$, unless $u(x)$ is a constant multiple of either $y(x, \alpha)$ or $y(x, \beta)$.*

Theorem 3.23 (Leighton and Nehari) *Let β be the nth conjugate point of α, $\beta < \infty$. If u is a nontrivial solution of (3.5) such that $u(\alpha) = 0$, u has at least n zeros on $[\alpha, \beta]$. If, in addition, $\varphi_u(x)$ does not change sign in this interval then u has at least $n + 1$ zeros in $[\alpha, \beta)$.*

Theorem 3.24 *If u and v are nontrivial solutions of (3.5), the number of zeros of u on any closed interval $[\alpha, \beta]$ cannot differ by more than 4 from the number of zeros of v on $[\alpha, \beta]$. In particular, the solutions of (3.5) are either all oscillatory or all nonoscillatory.*

Theorem 3.25 *If there exists a solution u of (3.5) such that neither $u(x)$ nor $\varphi_u(x)$ has a zero in (α, ∞), then no solution of (3.5) has more than 3 zeros in (α, ∞). In particular, if (3.5) is nonoscillatory, there exists a positive number α such that no solution of (3.5) has more than 3 zeros in (α, ∞).*

Exercises
1. Prove Lemmas 3.3 and 3.5.
2. Complete the proof of Theorem 3.11 in the case that i is odd.

3. Show that all the conjugate points of α for Eq. (3.2) coincide with those points $x_i > \alpha$ at which $Au(x) + Bv(x)$ has a double zero for some constants A and B, where u and v are linearly independent solutions of (3.2) with double zeros at α. Show consequently that the conjugate points are completely characterized by the condition $u(x)v'(x) - v(x)u'(x) = 0$.

4. Apply Exercise 3 to the equation $u^{(4)} = u$ in the case $\alpha = 0$. Show in this case that u and v can be taken as follows:

$$u(x) = \sin x - \sinh x; \qquad v(x) = \cos x - \cosh x.$$

Hence the conjugate points of 0 can be determined numerically from the equation $\cosh x = \sec x$.

5. Show how the conjugate points in Exercise 4 are related to the eigenvalues λ of the problem

$$u^{(4)} = \lambda u, \qquad 0 \le x \le 1$$
$$u(0) = u'(0) = u(1) = u'(1).$$

6. Consider the equation $u^{(4)} - u = 0$ as an example of (3.5). Discuss the principal solution relative to 0 and the associated conjugate points.

3. Comparison Theorems for (3.2) and (3.3)

The conclusion of the Sturm comparison theorem 1.1 relative to the fourth order differential equations (3.2), (3.3) is false since these equations have solutions with zeros at three arbitrary points. In fact, if $u(\alpha) = 0$ and (3.3) majorizes (3.2) in some sense, it cannot be true that no solution of (3.2) has a zero in (α, β) if there exists a solution of (3.3) without zeros in (α, β). Comparison theorems of Sturm's type arise very naturally, however, if the hypotheses $u(\alpha) = u(\beta) = 0$ are replaced by *four* boundary conditions, e.g. those of the eigenvalue problem (3.1). Accordingly, we shall base our study of comparison theorems for (3.2), (3.3) upon eigenvalue problems of the type (3.1).

Theorem 3.26 *The eigenvalues of* (3.1) *are all positive and have multiplicity* 1, *i.e., any two eigenfunctions corresponding to the same eigenvalue are linearly dependent.*

Proof If u is an eigenfunction corresponding to the eigenvalue λ of (3.1), then

$$0 = \varphi_u(\beta) - \varphi_u(\alpha) = \int_\alpha^\beta [a(x)|u''(x)|^2 - \lambda c(x)|u(x)|^2]\, dx,$$

where

$$\varphi_u(x) = a(x)\bar{u}'(x)u''(x) - \bar{u}(x)[a(x)u''(x)]'.$$

Since $a(x) > 0$ and $c(x) > 0$, it follows that every eigenvalue λ of (3.1) is positive.

Let u and v be two eigenfunctions associated with the same eigenvalue λ. If $u''(\alpha) = 0$ as well as $u(\alpha) = u'(\alpha) = u(\beta) = 0$ from (3.1), Lemma 3.2 would be contradicted. Thus $u''(\alpha) \neq 0$ and likewise $v''(\alpha) \neq 0$. The eigenfunction w defined by

$$w(x) = v''(\alpha)u(x) - u''(\alpha)v(x)$$

satisfies $w(\alpha) = w'(\alpha) = w''(\alpha) = w(\beta) = 0$ and hence $w(x) \equiv 0$ by Lemma 3.2, i.e., $u(x)$ and $v(x)$ are linearly dependent.

Theorem 3.27   (Rayleigh–Leighton–Nehari) *An eigenfunction (unique except for a constant factor) corresponding to the nth eigenvalue λ_n of (3.1) has exactly $n - 1$ simple zeros in (α, β).*

Theorem 3.28   (Leighton and Nehari) *If $a(x) \equiv 1$, $c(x) > 0$ in (3.2) and n denotes the number of zeros of a solution u on the interval $[\alpha, \beta]$, then*

$$6(n - 3) < \int_\alpha^\beta (x - \alpha)^3 c(x)\, dx.$$

The proofs of the last two results are somewhat involved and will be omitted [117].

Theorem 3.29   (Leighton and Nehari) *Suppose $a(x) \geq A(x)$ and $c(x) \leq C(x)$ in Eqs. (3.2), (3.3), $0 \leq x < \infty$. If δ_n, $\delta_n{}^*$ denote the nth conjugate points of α for Eqs. (3.2), (3.3), respectively, then $\delta_n{}^* \leq \delta_n$.*

Proof It follows from Theorems 3.11 and 3.27 that the nth eigenvalues λ_n, $\lambda_n{}^*$ of the problems

$$(au'')'' = \lambda cu, \qquad u(\alpha) = u'(\alpha) = u(\delta_n) = u'(\delta_n) = 0, \qquad (3.8)$$

$$(Au'')'' = \lambda^* Cu, \qquad u(\alpha) = u'(\alpha) = u(\delta_n{}^*) = u'(\delta_n{}^*) = 0, \qquad (3.9)$$

respectively, are both equal to 1. The problem (3.8) will now be compared with the auxiliary problem

$$(Au'')'' - \mu Cu = 0, \qquad u(\alpha) = u'(\alpha) = u(\delta_n) = u'(\delta_n) = 0. \qquad (3.10)$$

Courant's minimax principle (Theorem 3.1) shows that the nth eigenvalue μ_n of (3.10) does not exceed the nth eigenvalue λ_n of (3.8), i.e., $\mu_n \leq \lambda_n = 1$, $n = 1, 2, \ldots$, since the Rayleigh quotient is not increased when a and c are replaced by A and C, respectively. It is another consequence of Theorem 3.1 that the nth eigenvalue $\mu_n(\beta)$ of the problem

$$(Au'')'' - \mu(\beta)Cu = 0, \qquad u(\alpha) = u'(\alpha) = u(\beta) = u'(\beta) = 0$$

is a continuous decreasing function of β, $\alpha < \beta \leq \delta_n$. Since $\lim \mu_n(\beta) = +\infty$ $(\beta \to \alpha+)$ and $\mu_n(\delta_n) = \mu_n \leq 1$, there exists a unique number γ in $(\alpha, \alpha_n]$ such that $\mu_n(\gamma) = 1$. However, the nth eigenvalue of (3.9) is $\lambda_n^* = 1$ and hence $\gamma = \delta_n^*$. Since $\gamma \in (\alpha, \delta_n]$ it follows that $\delta_n^* \leq \delta_n$.

Comparison theorems for solutions rather than conjugate points are obtained below by combining Theorem 3.29 with the separation theorems 3.8–3.10.

Theorem 3.30   (Leighton and Nehari) *Suppose that $a(x) \geq A(x)$ and $c(x) \leq C(x)$ in Eqs. (3.2) and (3.3), $0 \leq x < \infty$. Let u and v be nontrivial solutions of (3.2) and (3.3), respectively, such that $u(\alpha) = v(\alpha) = u(\beta) = v(\beta) = 0$, $0 < \alpha < \beta$. If n, m denote the number of zeros of u, v, respectively, on $[\alpha, \beta]$ $(n \geq 4)$, then $m \geq n - 1$.*

Proof   By Theorem 3.11, the $(n - 3)$rd conjugate point δ_{n-3} of α satisfies the inequality $\alpha < \delta_{n-3} \leq \beta$ $(n \geq 4)$, and hence Theorem 3.29 yields $\alpha < \delta_{n-3}^* \leq \delta_{n-3} \leq \beta$. If v_1 denotes a nontrivial solution of (3.3) such that $v_1(\alpha) = v_1'(\alpha) = v_1(\beta) = 0$, and m_1 denotes the number of its zeros on $[\alpha, \beta]$, Theorem 3.12 shows, therefore, that $m_1 \geq n$. We assert that $m \geq m_1 - 1$ and hence $m \geq n - 1$, as required. To prove this, it is sufficient to consider the case that v has a *simple* zero at α, since otherwise v and v_1 would be linearly independent by Theorem 3.7, and $m = m_1$. Also, it is sufficient to consider the case that v_1 has a *simple* zero at β, for otherwise β would be a conjugate point of α, and no solution v could have less than m_1 zeros on $[\alpha, \beta]$ by the extremum property of conjugate points (Theorem 3.11). Since the zeros of v_1 and v in (α, β) separate each other by Theorem 3.8, the proof will be finished if it can be shown that the first zero of v in (α, β) precedes the first zero of v_1 in this interval. Suppose to the contrary that $v_1(x_1) = 0$ but $v(x) > 0$ in $(\alpha, x_1]$. Then $vv_1' - v_1v'$ would have at least one zero x_0 in (α, x_1); for otherwise v_1/v is everywhere increasing or decreasing in (α, x_1), which contradicts the fact that v_1/v has the limit zero at both endpoints α and x_1. Hence the function w defined by $w(x) = v_1(x) - \lambda v(x)$, $\lambda = v_1(x_0)/v(x_0)$, would have a double zero at x_0. Since $w(\alpha) = w(\beta) = 0$ and $\alpha < x_0 < \beta$, this contradicts Lemma 3.4.

We remark that in the special case $a(x) \equiv A(x)$, $c(x) \equiv C(x)$, the conclusion of Theorem 3.30 follows from the separation theorem 3.8.

Theorem 3.30 is an analog of Sturm's comparison theorem 1.1 for the fourth order equations (3.2) and (3.3). In view of the extremum property of conjugate points (Theorem 3.11), Theorem 3.29 states, roughly, that under the hypotheses $a(x) \geq A(x)$, $c(x) \leq C(x)$ the fastest oscillation possible for a solution of (3.3) is at least as fast as the fastest oscillation possible for a solution of (3.2).

In the following comparison theorems, (3.2) will be compared with the *second order* equations

$$[a(x)u']' + b(x)u = 0, \tag{3.11}$$

$$[b(x)v']' + c(x)v = 0. \tag{3.12}$$

Theorem 3.31   (Leighton and Nehari)   *Let a, b, c be positive functions of class $\mathscr{C}^2$, $\mathscr{C}^1$, $\mathscr{C}$, respectively, in $0 \le x < \infty$. Suppose there exists a solution u of (3.11) such that $u(\alpha) = 0$ ($\alpha \ge 0$) and $u(x) \ne 0$ in (α, ∞), and a nontrivial solution v of (3.12) with consecutive zeros α, γ_1, γ_2, ... $(\alpha < \gamma_1 < \gamma_2 < \cdots)$. If δ_n denotes the nth conjugate point of α for Eq. (3.2), then $\delta_n \ge \gamma_n$ ($n = 1, 2, \ldots$).*

Theorem 3.32   (Leighton and Nehari)   *Let a, c be positive functions of class $\mathscr{C}^2[0, \infty)$, $\mathscr{C}[0, \infty)$, respectively, such that*

$$\sigma = \frac{1}{\pi} \int_\alpha^\infty \frac{dx}{a(x)} < \infty.$$

Suppose there exists a nontrivial solution v of the equation

$$[a^{-1}(x)v']' + \sigma^2 c(x)v = 0 \tag{3.13}$$

with consecutive zeros α, γ_1, γ_2, ... $(\alpha < \gamma_1 < \gamma_2 < \cdots)$. If δ_n denotes the nth conjugate point of α for Eq. (3.2), then $\delta_n \ge \gamma_n$ ($n = 1, 2, \ldots$).

Theorem 3.33   *Let c be a positive continuous function in $[0, \infty)$. If there exists a nontrivial solution w of the equation*

$$w'' + [4x^2 c(x) - 2x^{-2}]w = 0 \tag{3.14}$$

with consecutive zeros α, γ_1, γ_2, ... $(0 < \alpha < \gamma_1 < \gamma_2 < \cdots)$, then $\delta_n \ge \gamma_n$ ($n = 1, 2, \ldots$), where δ_n denotes the nth conjugate point of α for the equation $u^{(4)} - c(x)u = 0$.

The proof of Theorem 3.31, depending on Theorems 3.1, 3.11, and 3.27, will be omitted. Theorem 3.32 follows from Theorem 3.31 in the special case

$$b(x) = \sigma^{-2} a^{-1}(x).$$

In fact, (3.12) reduces to (3.13) and (3.11) reduces to

$$[a(x)u']' + \sigma^{-2} a^{-1}(x)u = 0,$$

with the solution

$$u(x) = \sin\left[\frac{1}{\sigma} \int_\alpha^x \frac{dt}{a(t)}\right],$$

satisfying $u(\alpha) = 0$ and $u(x) > 0$ in (α, ∞).

Theorem 3.33 is obtained from Theorem 3.31 in the special case $a(x) = 1$, $b(x) = (2x)^{-2}$; indeed, (3.11) then reduces to the nonoscillatory Euler equation $u'' + (2x)^{-2}u = 0$, and (3.12) reduces to

$$(x^{-2}v')' + 4c(x)v = 0,$$

which is satisfied by $v(x) = xw(x)$ in $(0, \infty)$ iff (3.14) is satisfied by $w(x)$ in $(0, \infty)$.

Theorem 3.34   (Leighton and Nehari)   *Let c be a positive continuous function in $[0, \infty)$, and let $a(x) \equiv 1$ in Eq. (3.2). If u and w are nontrivial solutions of (3.2) and (3.14), respectively, with m and n zeros on $[\alpha, \beta]$, $0 < \alpha < \beta < \infty$, then $m \le n + 3$.*

Proof   If α' denotes the first zero of $u(x)$ in $[\alpha, \beta)$, the conjugate point δ_{m-3} of α' will lie on $[\alpha, \beta]$ by Theorem 3.11. It then follows from Theorem 3.33 that the solution of (3.14) which vanishes at $x = \alpha'$ has at least $m - 2$ zeros on $[\alpha', \delta_{m-3}]$. The Sturm separation theorem 1.8 shows, therefore, that the number of zeros of w on $[\alpha, \beta]$ is not less than $m - 3$.

According to the definition made following Theorem 3.11, the *first conjugate point* $\delta_1 = \delta_1(\alpha)$ of α is the *smallest* number β $(\beta > \alpha)$ for which there exists a nontrivial solution of (3.2) satisfying the boundary conditions

$$u(\alpha) = u'(\alpha) = u(\beta) = u'(\beta) = 0.$$

Likewise Barrett defined the number $\mu_1 = \mu_1(\alpha)$ to be the smallest number β $(\beta > \alpha)$ such that there exists a nontrivial solution of (3.2) satisfying

$$u(\alpha) = u'(\alpha) = u_1(\beta) = u_1'(\beta) = 0,$$

where u_1 is defined by $u_1(x) \equiv a(x)u''(x)$. Also, let $\mu_1^*(\alpha)$ denote the analog of $\mu_1(\alpha)$ for the "reciprocal equation"

$$[u''/c(x)]'' - u/a(x) = 0. \tag{3.2*}$$

The quantities δ_1, μ_1, and μ_1^* are compared in the following theorems of Barrett [9, 10]. The proofs are omitted.

Theorem 3.35   (Barrett)   *If $\delta_1(\alpha)$ exists then so do $\mu_1(\alpha)$ and $\mu_1^*(\alpha)$, and $\alpha < \mu_1(\alpha) < \delta_1(\alpha)$.*

Theorem 3.36   (Barrett)   *If $\mu_1(\alpha)$ does not exist, then there exists a solution $u(x)$ of (3.2) such that $u(\alpha) = u'(\alpha) = 0$, and $u(x) > 0$, $u'(x) > 0$, $u_1(x) > 0$, and $u_1'(x) < 0$ in (α, ∞) (where $u_1 = au''$).*

Theorem 3.37   (Barrett)   *If $\mu_1(\alpha)$ exists and*

$$\int_1^\infty a^{-1}(x) \, dx = \infty,$$

then $\delta_1(\alpha)$ exists.

Theorem 3.38   (Barrett)   *If*

$$\int_1^\infty a^{-1}(x) \, dx = \infty$$

and

$$\int_1^\infty c(x) u_1{}^2(x) \, dx = \infty,$$

where u is the unique solution of (3.2) satisfying the initial conditions

$$u(\alpha) = u'(\alpha) = u_1{}'(\alpha) = 0, \qquad u_1(\alpha) = 1$$

($u_1 = au''$), then $\delta_1(\alpha)$ exists and Eq. (3.2) is oscillatory [i.e., (3.2) has at least one nontrivial oscillatory solution in $(0, \infty)$].

4. Comparison Theorems for Other Fourth Order Equations

As pointed out in Section 2, the sign of $c(x)$ has a crucial bearing on the oscillatory behavior of the solutions of (3.2). We shall begin this section by stating Leighton and Nehari's comparison theorem [117] in the case that $c(x) < 0$ in (3.2), i.e., (3.2) is replaced by (3.5), reproduced here for convenience:

$$[a(x)u'']'' + c(x)u = 0, \qquad a(x) > 0, \quad c(x) > 0. \tag{3.5}$$

Recall that in this case the nth conjugate point, δ_n, of α $(0 \le \alpha < \infty)$ is defined as the nth zero of the solution of (3.5) satisfying the initial conditions

$$y(\alpha) = y'(\alpha) = y''(\alpha) = 0, \qquad a(\alpha)y'''(\alpha) = 1,$$

i.e., δ_n is the nth zero of the principal solution $y(x, \alpha)$.
    Equation (3.5) will be compared with each of the equations

$$[a(x)u'']'' + C(x)u = 0, \tag{3.15}$$

$$[A(x)u'']'' + c(x)u = 0, \tag{3.16}$$

where A and C are continuous functions in $[0, \infty)$ satisfying the inequalities

$$C(x) \ge c(x) > 0, \qquad 0 < A(x) \le a(x), \tag{3.17}$$

for $0 \leq x < \infty$. The analogs of the nth conjugate point δ_n will be denoted by δ_n^*, δ_n' for Eqs. (3.15), (3.16), respectively. The proof of the theorem below, given in Ref. [117], is omitted.

Theorem 3.39   (Leighton and Nehari)   *Under the assumptions* (3.17), *the conjugate points of α for* (3.5), (3.15), *and* (3.16) *are related by the inequalities*

$$\delta_n^* \leq \delta_{2n-1}, \qquad \delta_n' < \delta_{2n} \qquad (n = 1, 2, \ldots).$$

In particular, Eqs. (3.15) *and* (3.16) *are both oscillatory if* (3.5) *is oscillatory.*

As a generalization of Eq. (3.2), Barrett [10] considered the fourth order equation

$$[a(x)u'']'' + [b(x)u']' - c(x)u = 0, \tag{3.18}$$

where a, b, c are functions of class $\mathscr{C}^2$, $\mathscr{C}^1$, $\mathscr{C}$, respectively, and $a(x) > 0$, $b(x) \geq 0$, and $c(x) \geq 0$, $0 \leq x < \infty$.

The *first conjugate point* $\delta_1 = \delta_1(\alpha)$ is defined as the smallest number β ($\beta > \alpha \geq 0$) for which there exists a nontrivial solution of (3.18) satisfying the boundary conditions

$$u(\alpha) = u'(\alpha) = u(\beta) = u'(\beta) = 0.$$

Additional numbers $\beta > \delta_1(\alpha)$ for which there exists such a solution are denoted by $\delta_2(\alpha)$, $\delta_3(\alpha), \ldots (\delta_2(\alpha) < \delta_3(\alpha) < \cdots)$. Likewise, $\mu_1 = \mu_1(\alpha)$ is defined as the smallest number β for which there exists a nontrivial solution of (3.18) satisfying

$$u(\alpha) = u'(\alpha) = u_1(\beta) = u_2(\beta) = 0,$$

where the subscript notation is used as follows:

$$u_1(x) = a(x)u''(x), \qquad u_2(x) = u_1'(x) + b(x)u'(x);$$

and $\mu_n(\alpha)$ is defined as the nth such β ($\alpha < \mu_1(\alpha) < \mu_2(\alpha) < \cdots$). The theorems of Leighton and Nehari in Section 3 dealt with the special case $b(x) \equiv 0$. It is possible under special conditions to remove the term $[b(x)u']'$ from (3.18), that is, reduce (3.18) to the form (3.2) by a change of variable. In such cases, comparison theorems for (3.18) can be deduced from the corresponding theorems of Section 3, that is, from the theorems already known for the case $b(x) \equiv 0$. Leighton and Nehari [117] showed in particular that the change of variable

$$t = \int_\alpha^x s(z)\, dz, \tag{3.19}$$

where $s(x)$ is a solution of the second order equation

$$[a(x)s']' + b(x)s = 0 \tag{3.20}$$

such that $s(x) > 0$ for $x > \alpha$ ($\alpha \geq 0$), transforms (3.18) into the equation

$$D_t^2[as^3 \ D_t^2u] - s^{-1}cu = 0, \qquad t > 0 \quad (D_t = d/dt), \qquad (3.21)$$

where a, c, and s are understood to have been transformed into functions of t by the (monotone) mapping (3.19). For this reduction to be possible it is required, of course, that (3.20) be nonoscillatory. The reduction is always possible if $b(x)$ is everywhere negative since (3.20) is trivially nonoscillatory in this case. The proof of (3.21) is merely an exercise in calculus. We remark that the coefficient of u in (3.21) has the same sign as the coefficient of u in (3.18), and hence, if $c(x)$ has constant sign, the earlier results are applicable to (3.21).

However, as pointed out by Barrett [10], there are advantages in considering (3.18) directly; in particular Barrett does not require (3.20) to be nonoscillatory.

In the special case $c(x) \equiv 0$ in (3.18), $\mu_1(\alpha)$ is related to a corresponding quantity for the second order equation

$$[a(x)u']' + b(x)u = 0 \qquad (3.22)$$

($a(x)$, $b(x)$ the same as in (3.18)); in fact, if $\mu_1^*(\alpha)$ is the smallest β ($\beta > \alpha$) for which there exists a nontrivial solution of (3.22) satisfying the "focal conditions" (compare Chapter 1, Section 6) $u(\alpha) = u'(\beta) = 0$, the following theorem is easily verified.

Theorem 3.40   *If $c(x) \equiv 0$ then $\mu_1(\alpha)$ exists iff $\mu_1^*(\alpha)$ exists, and $\mu_1(\alpha) = \mu_1^*(\alpha)$ if either one exists ($\alpha \geq 0$).*

Barrett [10] obtained the following results by using a vector formulation of (3.18), i.e., by rewriting (3.18) in the usual way [35] as a system of differential equations. Earlier, R. L. Sternberg and H. M. Sternberg [182] had used the same method to obtain special cases of these theorems.

Theorem 3.41   (Barrett)   *If $\delta_1(\alpha)$ exists then $\mu_1(\alpha)$ exists and satisfies $\alpha < \mu_1(\alpha) < \delta_1(\alpha)$.*

Theorem 3.42   (Barrett)   *If either*

$$\int_1^\infty x^2 c(x) \, dx = \infty \qquad or \qquad \int_1^\infty b(x) \, dx = \infty,$$

then $\mu_1(\alpha)$ exists.

Theorem 3.43   (Barrett–Sternberg) *Suppose*

$$\int_1^\infty a^{-1}(x)\,dx = \infty$$

and b(x) and c(x) are not both identically zero for large x. Then $\delta_1(\alpha)$ exists iff $\mu_1(\alpha)$ exists.

Theorem 3.44   (Barrett)   *If both $\mu_1(\alpha)$ and $\mu_2(\alpha)$ exist and*

$$\int_1^\infty x^2 a^{-1}(x)\,dx = \infty,$$

then $\delta_1(\alpha)$ exists.

Theorem 3.45   (Barrett)   *If $\mu_1(\alpha)$, $\mu_2(\alpha)$, and $\mu_3(\alpha)$ all exist, then $\delta_1(\alpha)$ exists.*

Theorem 3.46   (Barrett)   *If $\delta_1(\alpha)$ does not exist and*

$$\int_1^\infty c(x)\,dx = \infty,$$

then $\mu_1(\alpha)$ and $\mu_2(\alpha)$ both exist.

Theorem 3.47   (Barrett)   *If*

$$\int_1^\infty c(x)\,dx = \infty \qquad and \qquad \int_1^\infty x^2 a^{-1}(x)\,dx = \infty$$

then $\delta_1(\alpha)$ exists.

Consider now, in addition to (3.18), a second equation of the same type

$$[A(x)v'']'' + [B(x)v']' - C(x)v = 0, \tag{3.23}$$

where A, B, C satisfy the same conditions as a, b, c, respectively, in $0 \le x < \infty$. Let $\delta_n{}^0$, $\mu_n{}^0$ denote the analogs of δ_n, μ_n respectively, for this equation. Then the following comparison theorems are valid.

Theorem 3.48   (Barrett) *Suppose that the functions a, b, c in (3.18) and A, B, C in (3.23) satisfy the following inequalities throughout $[0, \infty)$:*

$$0 < a(x) \le A(x), \qquad 0 \le B(x) \le b(x), \qquad 0 \le C(x) \le c(x). \tag{3.24}$$

If $\mu_1{}^0(\alpha)$ exists, then $\mu_1(\alpha)$ exists and $\mu_1(\alpha) \le \mu_1{}^0(\alpha)$ $(\alpha \ge 0)$. Furthermore $\mu_1(\alpha) = \mu_1{}^0(\alpha)$ iff

$$a(x) \equiv A(x), \qquad b(x) \equiv B(x), \qquad c(x) \equiv C(x)$$

in the interval $\alpha < x \le \mu_1{}^0(\alpha)$.

Theorem 3.49   (Barrett)   *If $\mu_1^*(\alpha)$ exists for the second order equation (3.22), then $\mu_1(\alpha)$ exists for (3.18) and $\mu_1(\alpha) \leq \mu_1^*(\alpha)$.*

Theorem 3.50   (Barrett)   *If $\delta_1{}^0(\alpha)$ exists and the inequalities (3.24) are satisfied throughout the interval $[\alpha, \delta_1{}^0(\alpha)]$, then $\delta_1(\alpha)$ exists and $\delta_1(\alpha) \leq \delta_1{}^0(\alpha)$.*

Theorem 3.51   (Barrett)   *If the first conjugate point $\delta_1{}^0(\alpha)$ exists for either of the equations*

$$[a(x)u'']'' - c(x)u = 0,$$

or

$$[a(x)u'']'' + [b(x)u']' = 0,$$

then the first conjugate point $\delta_1(\alpha)$ exists also for the complete equation (3.18), and $\delta_1(\alpha) \leq \delta_1{}^0(\alpha)$.

Theorem 3.52   (Barrett)   *If the second order equation (3.22) has a non-trivial solution with at least four zeros in $[\alpha, \infty)$, then $\delta_1(\alpha)$ exists for the fourth order equation (3.18).*

Theorem 3.53   (Barrett)   *If no nontrivial solution of (3.22) has more than one zero in an interval $[\alpha, \beta)$ $(0 \leq \alpha < \beta \leq \infty)$, and if $\delta_1(\alpha)$ does not exist in (α, β), then no nontrivial solution of (3.18) has more than 3 zeros in $[\alpha, \beta)$.*

Theorem 3.54   (Barrett)   *If $\delta_1(\alpha)$ does not exist,*

$$\int_1^\infty a^{-1}(x)\, dx = \infty,$$

and $b(x)$ and $c(x)$ are not both identically zero for large x, then no nontrivial solution of (3.18) has more than 3 zeros in $[\alpha, \infty)$.

In addition to $\delta_n(\alpha)$ and $\mu_n(\alpha)$, Barrett [12] obtained comparison theorems for $v_n(\alpha)$, defined as the nth number β $(0 \leq \alpha < \beta < \infty)$ for which there exists a nontrivial solution of (3.18) satisfying the conditions

$$u(\alpha) = u'(\alpha) = u'(\beta) = u_2(\beta) = 0$$

$$(u_2 = (au'')' + bu') \qquad (\alpha < v_1(\alpha) < v_2(\alpha) < \cdots).$$

Theorem 3.55   (Barrett)   *If $\delta_1(\alpha)$ exists, then $\mu_1(\alpha)$ and $v_1(\alpha)$ exist and satisfy the inequalities*

$$\alpha < \mu_1(\alpha) < v_1(\alpha) < \delta_1(\alpha) \qquad (\alpha \geq 0).$$

Theorem 3.56   (Barrett) *If*

$$\int_1^\infty c(x)\, dx = \infty,$$

then $v_1(\alpha)$ exists $(\alpha \geq 0)$.

Theorem 3.57   (Barrett) *If $\mu_1{}^*(\alpha)$ exists (defined as in Theorem* 3.40) *then $\mu_1(\alpha)$ exists and satisfies the inequalities*

$$\alpha < \mu_1(\alpha) \leq \mu_1{}^*(\alpha).$$

Theorem 3.58   (Barrett) *Let $\delta_1{}^*(\alpha)$ denote the smallest number β $(0 \leq \alpha < \beta)$ for which there exists a nontrivial solution of the second order equation* (3.22) *satisfying $u(\alpha) = u(\beta) = 0$. If $\delta_1{}^*(\alpha)$ exists, then $v_1(\alpha)$ exists and satisfies the inequalities*

$$\alpha < v_1(\alpha) \leq \delta_1{}^*(\alpha),$$

with equality iff $c(x) \equiv 0$ on $[\alpha, \delta_1{}^*(\alpha)]$.

Theorem 3.59   (Barrett) *If $v_1(\alpha)$ and $v_2(\alpha)$ exist, then $\delta_1(\alpha)$ exists and satisfies*

$$\alpha < v_1(\alpha) < \delta_1(\alpha) \leq v_2(\alpha).$$

Theorem 3.60   (Barrett) *If $\delta_1{}^*(\alpha)$ and $\delta_2{}^*(\alpha)$ (the second conjugate point of* (3.22)) *both exist, then $v_2(\alpha)$ exists and satisfies*

$$\alpha < v_2(\alpha) \leq \delta_2{}^*(\alpha).$$

Theorem 3.61   (Barrett) *If* (3.22) *has a nontrivial solution with at least* 3 *zeros in $[\alpha, \infty)$, then $\delta_1(\alpha)$ exists for* (3.18) *and satisfies*

$$\alpha < \delta_1(\alpha) \leq \delta_2{}^*(\alpha).$$

5. Comparison Theorems for Eigenfunctions

The comparison theorems for eigenfunctions obtained in Section 5 of Chapter 1 for second order problems will now be extended to problems of arbitrary even order $2m$, $m = 1, 2, \ldots$. As before, the proofs depend on Courant's minimum principle for the quadratic functional associated with an eigenvalue problem.

Let l and L be the differential operators defined by

$$lu = [1/k(x)]\{[(-1)^m a(x)u^{(m)}]^{(m)} + c(x)u\},$$

$$Lv = [1/k(x)]\{[(-1)^m A(x)v^{(m)}]^{(m)} + C(x)v\},$$

where c, C are real-valued continuous functions on an interval $[x_1, x_2]$, k is a positive continuous function on $[x_1, x_2]$ and a, A are positive functions of class $\mathscr{C}^m[x_1, x_2]$. The domain $\mathfrak{D}$ of these operators is defined to be the set of all real-valued functions of class $\mathscr{C}^{2m}[x_1, x_2]$.

Let p_{ij} and P_{ij} be the linear boundary operators defined by

$$p_{ij}[u] = (-1)^i \gamma_{ij} u^{(j)}(x_i) - (-1)^{m+j}[a(x_i)u^{(m)}(x_i)]^{(m-j-1)},$$

$$P_{ij}[u] = (-1)^i \Gamma_{ij} u^{(j)}(x_i) - (-1)^{m+j}[A(x_i)u^{(m)}(x_i)]^{(m-j-1)},$$

$$u \in \mathfrak{D}, \quad \gamma_{ij} > 0, \quad \Gamma_{ij} > 0; \quad i = 1, 2; \quad j = 0, 1, \ldots, m-1.$$

The operator l is the Euler–Jacobi operator associated with the quadratic functional q defined by

$$q[u] = \int_{x_1}^{x_2} (au^{(m)2} + cu^2)\, dx + \sum_{i=1}^{2} \sum_{j=0}^{m-1} \gamma_{ij}[u^{(j)}(x_i)]^2.$$

The *variation* of $q[u]$ is defined as

$$V[u] = \int_{x_1}^{x_2} [(a - A)u^{(m)2} + (c - C)u^2]\, dx$$

$$+ \sum_{i=1}^{2} \sum_{j=0}^{m-1} (\gamma_{ij} - \Gamma_{ij})[u^{(j)}(x_i)]^2.$$

The next theorem compares the eigenvalue problems

$$lu = \lambda u, \qquad p_{ij}[u] = 0 \qquad (i = 1, 2; j = 0, 1, \ldots, m-1), \qquad (3.25)$$

$$Lv = \lambda v, \qquad P_{ij}[u] = 0 \qquad (i = 1, 2; j = 0, 1, \ldots, m-1). \qquad (3.26)$$

Theorem 3.62 *If* (3.25) *has an eigenvalue* λ *with an associated eigenfunction* u *satisfying* $V[u] > 0$, *then* (3.26) *has at least one eigenvalue less than* λ.

The proof will be omitted since it is a special case of that to be given in Chapter 5 for partial differential equations. In the case $m = 1$, Theorem 3.62 reduces to Theorem 1.23. Applications in this case were given in Section 5 of Chapter 1.

A comparison theorem for fourth order equations will now be obtained as an application of Theorem 3.62. In the case $m = 2$, the differential operators l, L, respectively, reduce to the fourth order operators defined by

$$lu = [1/k(x)]\{[a(x)u'']'' + c(x)u\},$$

$$Lv = [1/k(x)]\{[A(x)v'']'' + C(x)v\},$$

$$a(x) > 0, \qquad A(x) > 0, \qquad k(x) > 0,$$

and the boundary conditions reduce to

$$\gamma_{ij} u^{(j)}(x_i) = (-1)^{i+j}[a(x_i)u''(x_i)]^{(1-j)}, \tag{3.27}$$

$$\Gamma_{ij} v^{(j)}(x_i) = (-1)^{i+j}[A(x_i)v''(x_i)]^{(1-j)}, \tag{3.28}$$

$$i = 1, 2; \quad j = 0, 1.$$

Theorem 3.63   *Suppose there exists a nontrivial solution u of lu = 0 satisfying the boundary conditions (3.27) such that V [u] > 0. If C(x) < 0 in (x_1, x_2), then every solution of Lv = 0 satisfying (3.28) has at least one zero in (x_1, x_2).*

Proof   The differential equations $lu = 0$, $Lv = 0$ are equivalent to

$$hu = -C^{-1}[(au'')'' + (c - C)u] = u,$$

$$Hv = -C^{-1}[(Av'')''] = v,$$

respectively, in which the differential operators h, H so defined are of the same type as the operators l, L, respectively. By hypothesis, the eigenvalue problems

$$hu = \lambda u, \quad u \text{ satisfies (3.27)} \tag{3.29}$$

$$Hv = \mu v, \quad v \text{ satisfies (3.28)} \tag{3.30}$$

have eigenvalues $\lambda = 1$, $\mu = 1$, respectively. These problems are of the type (3.25), (3.26) considered in Theorem 3.62. Since $V [u] > 0$, Theorem 3.62 shows that the *smallest* eigenvalue μ_0 of (3.30) satisfies $\mu_0 < 1$. Now, it is a standard theorem (see, for example, Mikhlin [130]) that the eigenfunctions of H are the eigenfunctions of the linear integral equation, $v(x) = \mu \langle v, G(x, \cdot) \rangle$ whose kernel is Green's function. In this case, Kreith [104] has shown that $G(x, t)$ is nonnegative on $x_1 \le x, t \le x_2$, and hence it follows from Jentzsch's theorem [91] that an eigenfunction v_0 corresponding to μ_0 exists which is positive in (x_1, x_2). Since v_0, v are eigenfunctions of (3.30) corresponding to distinct eigenvalues μ_0, μ, v is orthogonal to v_0 by Theorem 3.1, i.e., $\langle v, v_0 \rangle = 0$. This implies that v has at least one zero in (x_1, x_2).

In the special case that

$$a = A = 1, \quad c \ge C, \quad 0 < \Gamma_{ij} < \gamma_{ij}, \quad i = 1, 2; \quad j = 0, 1,$$

Theorem 3.63 reduces to Kreith's comparison theorem [104].

As an example consider the operators l, L defined by

$$lu = u^{(4)} - p^4 u,$$

$$Lv = v^{(4)} - (p^4 + d - x)v, \quad 0 \le x \le \pi,$$

where p is the smallest positive root of the equation $\cosh p\pi = \sec p\pi$. Clearly

$\frac{3}{2} < p < 2$. It is well known and easy to verify that the function u defined by

$$u(x) = S(x) - [S(\pi)/C(\pi)]C(x),$$

where

$$S(x) = \sin px - \sinh px, \qquad C(x) = \cos px - \cosh px,$$

satisfies

$$lu = 0, \qquad u(0) = u'(0) = u(\pi) = u'(\pi) = 0.$$

In this case,

$$a(x) = A(x) = 1, \qquad c(x) = -p^4, \qquad C(x) = -p^4 - d + x,$$

and the variation reduces to

$$V[u] = \int_0^\pi (d - x)u^2(x)\, dx.$$

Let d be any number in the interval $(0, \pi)$ for which $V[u] > 0$. Then, according to Theorem 3.63, every solution of $Lv = 0$ satisfying the boundary conditions (3.28) has at least one zero in $(0, \pi)$. (This cannot be concluded from Kreith's theorem cited above since the pointwise condition $c(x) \geq C(x)$ in (3.30) is not necessarily fulfilled.)

6. Nonoscillation Theorems

Nonoscillation theorems paralleling those obtained in Chapter 2 for second order equations will now be derived for (3.2):

$$[a(x)u'']'' - c(x)u = 0, \qquad a(x) > 0, \quad c(x) > 0. \tag{3.2}$$

The term *nonoscillatory* (without regard to an interval) was defined in Section 2 prior to Theorem 3.12. Equation (3.2) is said to be *nonoscillatory* in an interval (α, ∞) $(\alpha \geq 0)$ iff no nontrivial solution has more than three zeros in $[\alpha, \infty)$. In view of Theorem 3.11, the equation therefore will be nonoscillatory in (α, ∞) iff the first conjugate point $\delta_1(\alpha)$ does not exist in (α, ∞).

The following theorem of Leighton and Nehari is a principal tool for obtaining nonoscillation criteria for Eq. (3.2); it is an analog of Theorem 2.2 for fourth order equations.

Theorem 3.64   (Leighton and Nehari) *Equation (3.2) is nonoscillatory in (α, ∞) iff the smallest eigenvalue $\lambda = \lambda(\beta)$ of the problem*

$$(au'')'' = \lambda c u, \qquad u(\alpha) = u'(\alpha) = u(\beta) = u'(\beta) = 0 \tag{3.1}$$

satisfies $\lambda(\beta) > 1$ for all $\beta > \alpha$.

Proof If (3.2) is not nonoscillatory in (α, ∞), the first conjugate point $\delta_1(\alpha)$ exists in the interval (α, ∞). In view of Theorems 3.11 and 3.27, $\lambda(\delta_1(\alpha)) = 1$. However, $\lambda(\beta)$ is a monotone decreasing function of β in (α, ∞) as a consequence of Courant's theorem 3.1, and hence $\lambda(\beta) < 1$ for $\beta > \delta_1(\alpha)$. Thus the condition $\lambda(\beta) > 1$ is sufficient for (3.1) to be nonoscillatory in (α, ∞).

To show that $\lambda(\beta) > 1$ is necessary, suppose to the contrary that there exists $\beta_0 > \alpha$ such that $\lambda(\beta_0) \le 1$. As in the proof of Theorem 3.29, $\lambda(\beta)$ is a continuous decreasing function in (α, ∞) such that $\lim \lambda(\beta) = +\infty$ $(\beta \to \alpha+)$, and hence there exists a number β' in (α, β_0) such that $\lambda(\beta') = 1$. By Theorems 3.11 and 3.27 again, β' coincides with the first conjugate point $\delta_1(\alpha)$. The existence of $\delta_1(\alpha)$, however, contradicts the assumption that (3.2) is nonoscillatory.

Howard [84] obtained oscillation criteria for Eq. (3.2), as indicated in the sequel, by applying the following analog of Theorem 3.64 relative to the eigenvalue problem

$$(au'')'' = \mu c u, \qquad u(\alpha) = u'(\alpha) = u_1(\beta) = u_1{}'(\beta) = 0 \qquad (3.31)$$
$$(u_1 = au'').$$

This problem was mentioned earlier, in Section 3, in connection with Barrett's comparison theorems.

Theorem 3.65   (Howard)   *Suppose*

$$\int_\alpha^\infty a^{-1}(x) \, dx = \infty$$

in (3.2). *Then* (3.2) *is nonoscillatory in* (α, ∞) *iff the smallest eigenvalue* $\mu(\beta)$ *of* (3.31) *satisfies* $\mu(\beta) > 1$ *for all* $\beta > \alpha$.

Since it is a well-known consequence of Courant's theorem 3.1, see, for example, [39], that $\lambda(\beta) > \mu(\beta)$, Theorem 3.65 contains a stronger necessary condition than the necessary condition $\lambda(\beta) > 1$ of Theorem 3.64. However, the necessity proof is somewhat involved and will not be included here. To prove the sufficiency, observe that if (3.2) is not nonoscillatory, there exists a number $\beta > \delta_1(\alpha)$ such that $\lambda(\beta) < 1$ according to the proof of the previous theorem; but then $\mu(\beta) < \lambda(\beta) < 1$, as just noted. Therefore the condition $\mu(\beta) > 1$ is sufficient for (3.2) to be nonoscillatory in (α, ∞).

In 1962, Barrett [12] extended Theorem 3.65 to the more general equation (3.18). In this connection, (3.31) is replaced by the eigenvalue problem

$$[a(x)u'']'' + [b(x)u']' = \mu c(x)u,$$
$$u(\alpha) = u'(\alpha) = u_1(\beta) = u_2(\beta) = 0, \qquad (3.31')$$
$$(u_1 = au'', \qquad u_2 = u_1{}' + bu'),$$

where a, b, and c are functions of class $\mathscr{C}^2$, $\mathscr{C}^1$, and $\mathscr{C}$ respectively and $a(x) > 0$, $b(x) \geq 0$, and $c(x) \geq 0$ in $0 \leq x < \infty$. Barrett proved that Theorem 3.65 is still valid: Eq. (3.18) is nonoscillatory in (α, ∞) iff the smallest eigenvalue of (3.31′) satisfies $\mu(\beta) > 1$ for all $\beta > \alpha$.

Theorem 3.66   (Leighton and Nehari)   *Let w be a function with a piecewise continuous second derivative in (α, β) satisfying the boundary conditions $w(\alpha) = w'(\alpha) = w(\beta) = w'(\beta) = 0$ $(0 \leq \alpha < \beta)$. If (3.2) is nonoscillatory in (α, ∞), then*

$$\int_\alpha^\beta c(x)w^2(x)\, dx \leq \int_\alpha^\beta a(x)w''^2(x)\, dx. \tag{3.32}$$

Proof   Since the smallest eigenvalue $\lambda(\beta)$ of (3.1) is the minimum of the Rayleigh quotient

$$\int_\alpha^\beta aw''^2\, dx \bigg/ \int_\alpha^\beta cw^2\, dx$$

among all admissible functions w by Theorem 3.1, it follows from Theorem 3.64 that

$$\int_\alpha^\beta aw''^2\, dx \bigg/ \int_\alpha^\beta cw^2\, dx \geq \lambda(\beta) > 1,$$

as required.

Every function w fulfilling the conditions of Theorem 3.66 will therefore give rise to a necessary condition for nonoscillation, of the form (3.32). The next two theorems contain examples of such necessary conditions.

Theorem 3.67   (Leighton and Nehari)   *If $a(x) \leq m$ and Eq. (3.2) is nonoscillatory in (α, ∞), then*

$$\int_\alpha^\infty x^2 c(x)\, dx < \infty, \tag{3.33}$$

and

$$\int_{x_0}^\infty (x - x_0)^2 c(x)\, dx \leq \frac{4m}{x_0 - \alpha}, \qquad \alpha < x_0. \tag{3.34}$$

Proof   Let β, γ, and h be positive numbers such that

$$\alpha + h < \gamma - h < \gamma + h < 2\gamma + \alpha - h < 2\gamma + \alpha = \beta.$$

Suppose the function w in Theorem 3.66 is defined as follows:

$$w(x) = (x - \alpha)^2, \qquad\qquad x \in [\alpha, \alpha + h]$$

$$w(x) = h(2x - 2\alpha - h), \qquad\qquad x \in [\alpha + h, \gamma - h]$$

$$w(x) = 2h(\gamma - \alpha - h) - (x - \gamma)^2, \qquad x \in [\gamma - h, \gamma + h]$$

$$w(x) = h(4\gamma - 2x - h - 2\alpha), \qquad x \in [\gamma + h, 2\gamma + \alpha - h]$$

$$w(x) = (2\gamma + \alpha - x)^2, \qquad\qquad x \in [2\gamma + \alpha - h, 2\gamma + \alpha].$$

One can verify easily that w and w' are continuous in $(\alpha, 2\gamma + \alpha)$, while w'' is continuous except for four jump discontinuities. Moreover, $w(x)$ has double zeros at α and β and hence it is admissible in (3.32). Thus (3.32) implies that

$$h^2 \int_{\alpha+h}^{\gamma-h} (x - \alpha - \tfrac{1}{2}h)^2 c(x)\, dx$$

$$\leq \tfrac{1}{4} \int_\alpha^\beta w^2(x) c(x)\, dx$$

$$\leq \int_\alpha^{\alpha+h} a(x)\, dx + \int_{\gamma-h}^{\gamma+h} a(x)\, dx + \int_{2\gamma+\alpha-h}^{2\gamma+\alpha} a(x)\, dx$$

$$\leq 4mh.$$

It follows that the integral

$$\int_\alpha^\infty (x - \alpha - \tfrac{1}{2}h)^2 c(x)\, dx$$

exists and satisfies the inequality

$$\int_{\alpha+h}^\infty (x - \alpha - \tfrac{1}{2}h)^2 c(x)\, dx \leq 4mh^{-1}. \qquad (3.35)$$

Thus (3.33) holds, and the substitution $x_0 = \alpha + h$ in (3.35) yields (3.34) since $x - \alpha - \tfrac{1}{2}h > x - x_0$.

Leighton and Nehari also obtained the following extension of (3.33) by selecting a more complicated function w than that used above. The proof is deleted.

Theorem 3.68   (Leighton and Nehari) *Suppose that $a(x)$ is bounded and that there exists a positive number p such that*

$$\int_\alpha^\infty x^{p-4} a(x)\, dx < \infty.$$

If (3.2) is nonoscillatory, then $c(x)$ satisfies the condition

$$\int_\alpha^\infty x^p c(x)\, dx < \infty.$$

In particular, if the equation $u^{(4)} = c(x)u$ is nonoscillatory in (α, ∞), then

$$\int_\alpha^\infty x^q c(x)\, dx < \infty \tag{3.36}$$

for any number q satisfying $q < 3$.

The nonoscillatory equation

$$u^{(4)} - (9/16)x^{-4}u = 0$$

shows that the conclusion (3.36) does not hold for $q = 3$, and accordingly this result is the best possible of its type.

Howard [84] stated the following analog of Theorem 3.66, which is proved from Theorem 3.65 in the same way that Theorem 3.66 was proved from Theorem 3.64.

Theorem 3.69 (Howard) *Let w be a function with a piecewise continuous second derivative in (α, β) such that $w(\alpha) = w'(\alpha) = 0$. If Eq. (3.2) is nonoscillatory in (α, ∞) and*

$$\int_\alpha^\infty a^{-1}(x)\, dx = \infty,$$

then

$$\int_\alpha^\beta c(x)w^2(x)\, dx \le \int_\alpha^\beta a(x)w''^2(x)\, dx.$$

Howard obtained the following nonoscillation theorems by specializing w. The proofs are along the lines of the proof of Theorem 3.67 and are omitted.

Theorem 3.70   (Howard) *If the equation $u^{(4)} = c(x)u$ is nonoscillatory in (α, ∞), then the following three inequalities are valid:*

$$\int_x^\infty (t - x)^2 c(t)\, dt \le (x - \alpha)^{-1};$$

$$\int_x^\infty (t - x)c(t)\, dt \le 3^{-1/2}(12 - 6\sqrt{3})(x - \alpha)^{-2};$$

$$\int_x^\infty c(t)\, dt \le 3(x - \alpha)^{-3} \qquad (\alpha < x < \infty).$$

Theorem 3.71   (Howard)   *If the equation $u^{(4)} = c(x)u$ is nonoscillatory in (α, ∞), if $c'(x)$ exists and is integrable in (α, ∞), and if there exists a constant m such that*

$$0 < c(x) \le m^{4/3}, \qquad c'(x) \le m^4 \left[c(x) \int_\alpha^x c(t)\, dt \right]^{-1},$$

and

$$c'^2(x) \le m^4 c(x) \left[\int_\alpha^x c(t)\, dt \right]^{-2},$$

then there exists a universal constant γ_0 such that the inequality

$$\int_\alpha^\infty c(x)\, dx \le \gamma m$$

holds for $\gamma = \gamma_0$, but not in general for $\gamma = \gamma_0 - \varepsilon$ $(\varepsilon > 0)$. The constant γ_0 satisfies the inequalities

$$0.289 < \gamma_0 < 2.96.$$

Theorem 3.71 is a fourth order analog of Nehari's theorem 2.6.

7. Leighton and Nehari's Sufficient Conditions for Nonoscillatory Equations

The next theorem gives sufficient conditions for Eq. (3.2) to be non-oscillatory. It is a direct analog of Leighton's corollary 2.28 for the second order equation (1.1). The proof is based on the conjugacy theorem 3.13.

Theorem 3.72   (Leighton and Nehari)   *If the two integrals*

$$\int_\alpha^\infty \frac{dx}{a(x)}, \qquad \int_\alpha^\infty x^2 c(x)\, dx \qquad (\alpha > 0)$$

both exist and are finite, then Eq. (3.2) is nonoscillatory.

Proof Suppose to the contrary that (3.2) is oscillatory. Then, by Theorem 3.13, α has an infinite sequence of conjugate points $\delta_i(\alpha) \uparrow \infty$ $(i = 1, 2, \ldots)$. Accordingly there exists a nontrivial solution $u(x)$ of (3.2) such that

$$u(\alpha) = u'(\alpha) = u(\beta) = u'(\beta) = 0 \qquad (\beta = \delta_1(\alpha)). \tag{3.37}$$

Multiplying (3.2) by u, integrating from α to β, using partial integration twice on the first term, and applying the conditions (3.37), we obtain

$$\int_\alpha^\beta c(x)u^2(x)\, dx = \int_\alpha^\beta a(x)u''^2(x)\, dx. \tag{3.38}$$

However

$$u(x) = \int_\alpha^x (x - t)u''(t)\, dt,$$

and hence Schwarz's inequality yields

$$u^2(x) \le \left[\int_\alpha^x \frac{(x - t)^2}{a(t)}\, dt \right]\left[\int_\alpha^x a(t)u''^2(t)\, dt \right]$$

$$\le \left[\int_\alpha^x \frac{(x - t)^2}{a(t)}\, dt \right]\left[\int_\alpha^\beta a(t)u''^2(t)\, dt \right]$$

for $\alpha \le x \le \beta$, since $a(t) > 0$. Multiplying both sides by $c(x)$, integrating from α to β, and using (3.38), we obtain the inequality

$$1 \le \int_\alpha^\beta c(x)\left[\int_\alpha^x \frac{(x - t)^2}{a(t)}\, dt \right] dx.$$

Since

$$\int_\alpha^x \frac{(x - t)^2}{a(t)}\, dt \le (x - \alpha)^2 \int_\alpha^x \frac{dt}{a(t)} \le (x - \alpha)^2 \int_\alpha^\beta \frac{dt}{a(t)},$$

it follows that

$$1 \le \left[\int_\alpha^\beta (x - \alpha)^2 c(x)\, dx \right]\left[\int_\alpha^\beta \frac{dx}{a(x)} \right].$$

By hypothesis, the second factor on the right is a bounded function of β,

$$\int_\alpha^\beta \frac{dx}{a(x)} < \int_\alpha^\infty \frac{dx}{a(x)} = M < \infty,$$

and hence

$$1 \le M \int_\alpha^\beta (x - \alpha)^2 c(x)\, dx \le M \int_\alpha^\beta x^2 c(x)\, dx. \tag{3.39}$$

Repetition of the procedure just used on the intervals $[\delta_i(\alpha),\ \delta_{i+1}(\alpha)]$ ($i = 1, 2, \ldots$) yields the inequalities

$$1 \le M \int_{\delta_i(\alpha)}^{\delta_{i+1}(\alpha)} x^2 c(x)\, dx. \tag{3.40}$$

If we identify $\delta_0(\alpha)$ with α and $\delta_1(\alpha)$ with β, the case $i = 0$ in (3.40) corresponds to (3.39). Adding the inequalities, we obtain

$$n \le M \sum_{i=0}^{n-1} \int_{\delta_i(\alpha)}^{\delta_{i+1}(\alpha)} x^2 c(x)\, dx = M \int_\alpha^{\delta_n(\alpha)} x^2 c(x)\, dx.$$

Since $\delta_n(\alpha) \to \infty$ as $n \to \infty$, it follows that the integral

$$\int_\alpha^\infty x^2 c(x)\, dx$$

cannot be finite. The contradiction establishes Theorem 3.64.

By a modification of the above procedure, Leighton and Nehari obtained the following more general result.

Theorem 3.73   (Leighton and Nehari)   *Suppose $c(x)$ has the property that the integral*

$$f(x) = \int_x^\infty t^2 c(t)\, dt$$

is finite, $x \geq \alpha \geq 0$. Then, if

$$\int_\alpha^\infty \frac{f(x)}{a(x)}\, dx < \infty,$$

Eq. (3.2) *is nonoscillatory.*

8. Comparison Theorems for Nonoscillation

If Eq. (3.3) is known to be nonoscillatory (it might, for example, be a nonoscillatory Euler equation), the problem is to find conditions on the coefficients in (3.2) to ensure that (3.2) also is nonoscillatory. Leighton and Nehari [117] obtained such comparison theorems as direct consequences of Theorems 3.11, 3.29, and 3.31.

Theorem 3.74   (Leighton and Nehari)   *Suppose that $a(x) \geq A(x)$ and $c(x) \leq C(x)$ in Eqs. (3.2), (3.3) $(0 \leq x < \infty)$. If (3.3) is nonoscillatory in (α, ∞) then the same is true of (3.2) $(\alpha \geq 0)$.*

Proof   Since (3.3) is defined to be nonoscillatory in (α, ∞) iff no solution has more than three zeros in $[\alpha, \infty)$, the equation is nonoscillatory in (α, ∞) iff the first conjugate point $\delta_1^*(\alpha)$ does not exist, according to Theorem 3.11. If it were not true that (3.2) is nonoscillatory, then $\delta_1(\alpha)$ would exist; but then $\delta_1^*(\alpha)$ would exist and satisfy $\delta_1^*(\alpha) \leq \delta_1(\alpha)$ by Theorem 3.29. This contradiction establishes Theorem 3.74.

The same argument establishes the following result.

Theorem 3.74′ *Suppose there exists a number* α *such that* $a(x) \geq A(x)$ *and* $c(x) \leq C(x)$ *when* $x \geq \alpha$. *Then* (3.2) *is nonoscillatory whenever* (3.3) *is nonoscillatory.*

Theorem 3.75   (Leighton and Nehari) *Let* p *denote an arbitrary real number. Then Eq.* (3.2) *is oscillatory if*

$$\limsup_{x \to \infty} x^{-2-p} a(x) < 1, \tag{3.41}$$

and

$$\liminf_{x \to \infty} x^{2-p} c(x) > (1 - p^2)^2/16; \tag{3.42}$$

and (3.2) *is nonoscillatory if*

$$\liminf_{x \to \infty} x^{-2-p} a(x) > 1 \tag{3.43}$$

and

$$\limsup_{x \to \infty} x^{2-p} c(x) < (1 - p^2)^2/16. \tag{3.44}$$

In particular, the equation $u^{(4)} = c(x)u$, $c(x) > 0$, *is oscillatory or nonoscillatory according as*

$$\liminf_{x \to \infty} x^4 c(x) > 9/16 \quad or \quad \limsup_{x \to \infty} x^4 c(x) < 9/16.$$

Proof Theorem 3.74′ will be applied in the special case that (3.3) is the Euler equation

$$(x^{p+2} v'')'' - \gamma^2 x^{p-2} v = 0 \qquad (\gamma = \text{constant}). \tag{3.45}$$

This equation has the solutions

$$v(x) = x^{(2q+1-p)/2},$$

where q is any root of the equation

$$q^2 = \frac{1+p^2}{4} \pm \left(\frac{p^2}{4} + \gamma^2\right)^{1/2}. \tag{3.46}$$

In fact, the substitution $v = x^m$ into (3.45) leads to the condition

$$m(m-1)(m+p)(m+p-1) = \gamma^2.$$

If $m = (2q+1-p)/2$, this quartic equation reduces to the following quadratic equation in q^2:

$$16q^4 - 8(p^2 + 1)q^2 + (p^2 - 1)^2 - 16\gamma^2 = 0,$$

whose roots are given by (3.46).

Equation (3.45) is oscillatory (i.e., has at least one oscillatory solution) iff $q^2 < 0$ for some q. It then follows from (3.46) that (3.45) is nonoscillatory iff $\gamma^2 \leq (1 - p^2)^2/16$. We now apply Theorem 3.74' in the case that (3.3) has the form (3.45), i.e.,

$$A(x) = x^{p+2}, \qquad C(x) = \gamma^2 x^{p-2}.$$

Suppose (3.43) and (3.44) hold, and $\gamma^2 = (1 - p^2)^2/16$. Then

$$a(x)/A(x) = x^{-2-p}a(x) \geq 1$$

and

$$c(x)/C(x) = 16(1 - p^2)^{-2}x^{2-p}c(x) \leq 1$$

for sufficiently large x. Since Eq. (3.45) is nonoscillatory for $\gamma^2 = (1 - p^2)^2/16$, Theorem 3.74' shows that Eq. (3.2) is nonoscillatory.

The proof that (3.41) and (3.42) are sufficient for (3.2) to be oscillatory is virtually the same and will be omitted.

In the special case $a(x) \equiv 1$, let $p = -2$ so that $A(x) = x^{p+2} \equiv 1$ in the comparison equation (3.45). Since the hypothesis $a(x) \geq A(x)$ of Theorem 3.74' is satisfied trivially, the conditions (3.41) and (3.43) are not needed in this case. Hence the equation is oscillatory if $\liminf x^4 c(x) > 9/16$ and nonoscillatory if $\limsup x^4 c(x) < 9/16$ $(x \to \infty)$.

The following comparison theorems follow from Theorem 3.31. The details of the proofs are deleted.

Theorem 3.76   (Leighton and Nehari)   *Let a, b, c be positive functions of class $\mathscr{C}^2$, $\mathscr{C}^1$, $\mathscr{C}$, respectively, in $0 \leq x < \infty$. If the two second order equations (3.11) and (3.12) are nonoscillatory in (α, ∞), then also (3.2) is nonoscillatory in (α, ∞) $(\alpha \geq 0)$. If the interval $0 \leq x < \infty$ is replaced by $0 < x < \infty$, the same statement is true provided $\alpha > 0$.*

Theorem 3.77   (Leighton and Nehari)   *If the equation*

$$u'' + [4x^2 c(x) - 2x^{-2}]u = 0$$

$(c(x) > 0)$ is nonoscillatory in (α, ∞), the same is true of $u^{(4)} = c(x)u$ $(\alpha > 0)$.

Theorem 3.78   (Leighton and Nehari)   *The equation $u^{(4)} = c(x)u$ is non-oscillatory if*

$$\limsup_{x \to \infty} x \int_x^\infty t^2 c(t)\, dt < 9/16.$$

The constant 9/16 is the best possible since the Euler equation

$$u^{(4)} - (\varepsilon + 9/16)x^{-4}u = 0$$

is oscillatory for positive ε (by (3.46) with $p = -2$, $\gamma^2 = \varepsilon + 9/16$) and

$$\lim_{x \to \infty} x \int_x^\infty (\varepsilon + 9/16)t^{-2} \, dt = \varepsilon + 9/16.$$

The following theorems apply to the equation

$$[a(x)u'']'' + c(x)u = 0, \qquad a(x) > 0, \quad c(x) > 0 \tag{3.5}$$

and its special case

$$u^{(4)} + c(x)u = 0. \tag{3.47}$$

Theorem 3.79   (Leighton and Nehari)   *If there exists a real number p such that*

$$\limsup_{x \to \infty} x^{-2-p}a(x) < 1 \qquad and \qquad \liminf_{x \to \infty} x^{2-p}c(x) > p^2/4,$$

then Eq. (3.5) is oscillatory. If

$$\liminf_{x \to \infty} x^{-2-p}a(x) > 1 \qquad and \qquad \limsup_{x \to \infty} x^{2-p}c(x) < p^2/4,$$

then (3.5) is nonoscillatory. In particular, (3.47) is oscillatory or nonoscillatory according as

$$\liminf x^4 c(x) > 1 \qquad or \qquad \limsup x^4 c(x) < 1 \qquad (x \to \infty).$$

Theorem 3.80   (Leighton and Nehari)   *Equation (3.47) has a solution $u(x)$ such that* $\lim x^{-3}|u(x)| = c$ *($0 < c < \infty$) as $x \to \infty$ iff*

$$\int_\alpha^\infty x^3 c(x) \, dx < \infty \qquad (0 < \alpha < \infty).$$

Theorem 3.81   (Fite, Leighton and Nehari)   *Equation (3.47) is oscillatory if*

$$\int_\alpha^\infty x^2 c(x) \, dx = \infty \qquad (0 < \alpha < \infty)$$

and in particular if $c(x)$ is not summable in (α, ∞).

9. Howard's Comparison Theorems for Eigenvalue Problems

Howard [84] extended Nehari's theorem 2.10 to fourth order equations in three separate ways and used his results together with Theorem 3.65 to obtain oscillation criteria for the equation $u^{(4)} = c(x)u$, $c(x) > 0$. He compared the eigenvalue problem (3.31) with a second problem of the same type

$$(av'')'' = \nu C v, \qquad v(\alpha) = v'(\alpha) = v_1(\beta) = v_1'(\beta) = 0 \tag{3.48}$$

in which the continuous function C is generally distinct from the positive continuous function c in (3.31).

Theorem 3.82   (Howard) *Suppose that*

$$\int_x^\beta c(t)f(t)\, dt \le \int_x^\beta C(t)f(t)\, dt \qquad (\alpha \le x \le \beta),$$

where f is a positive nonincreasing function of class $\mathscr{C}^1[\alpha, \beta]$. If μ_0, ν_0 denote the smallest eigenvalues of (3.31), (3.48), *respectively, then $\mu_0 \ge \nu_0$.*

Proof An easy extension of the procedure used in the proof of Nehari's theorem 2.10 leads to the inequalities

$$0 < \int_\alpha^\beta c(t)u^2(t)\, dt \le \int_\alpha^\beta C(t)u^2(t)\, dt$$

where u is an eigenfunction of (3.31). Consequently $\mu_0 \ge \nu_0$ by use of the Rayleigh quotient characterization of eigenvalues (Theorem 3.1).

The following similar result is proved by the same technique.

Theorem 3.83   (Howard) *Suppose that*

$$\int_x^\beta (t - \alpha)^p c(t)\, dt \le \int_x^\beta (t - \alpha)^p C(t)\, dt$$

for $\alpha \le x \le \beta$, where p is any number satisfying $p \le 2$. If μ_0, ν_0 denote the smallest eigenvalues of (3.31), (3.48), *respectively, then $\mu_0 \ge \nu_0$.*

In Howard's third theorem, the system (3.31) is compared with

$$(Av'')'' = \nu c v, \qquad v(\alpha) = v'(\alpha) = v_I(\beta) = v_I{'}(\beta) = 0, \qquad (3.49)$$

where A (as well as a) is a positive function of class $\mathscr{C}^2[\alpha, \beta]$, and the subscript I is used as follows:

$$v_I(x) = A(x)v''(x).$$

Theorem 3.84   (Howard) *Suppose that*

$$\int_\alpha^x A(t)f(t)\, dt \le \int_\alpha^x a(t)f(t)\, dt, \qquad \alpha \le x \le \beta, \qquad (3.50)$$

where f is a positive function of class $\mathscr{C}^1[\alpha, \beta]$ such that $a^2(x)f(x)$ is nondecreasing on $[\alpha, \beta]$. If μ_0, ν_0 denote the smallest eigenvalues of (3.31), (3.49), *respectively, then $\mu_0 \ge \nu_0$.*

The proof is along the lines of the proof of Theorem 3.82 and will be omitted.

We note in passing that a special case of (3.50), in which $f(t)$ is identically equal to 1, is

$$\int_{\alpha}^{x} A(t)\, dt \le \int_{\alpha}^{x} a(t)\, dt, \tag{3.51}$$

which in turn is implied by the pointwise inequality $A(x) \le a(x)$ on $\alpha \le x \le \beta$. A natural conjecture would be that the inequality $\mu_0 \ge \nu_0$ reduces to an equality iff (3.51) reduces to an equality, and similar conjectures can be made with respect to Theorems 3.82 and 3.83.

A question which seems to remain open is to find comparison theorems like Theorems 3.82–3.84 in the case that *both* a and c in (3.31) are allowed to vary. Indeed, no such result is available even in the second order case.

As an application of Theorem 3.82, Howard [84] obtained the following oscillation and nonoscillation criteria.

Theorem 3.85   (Howard)   *Let f be a positive nonincreasing function of class $\mathscr{C}^1$ in $[\alpha, \infty)$ ($\alpha \ge 0$) such that*

$$\int_{\alpha}^{\infty} x^{-4} f(x)\, dx < \infty.$$

Then sufficient conditions for the equation $u^{(4)} = c(x)u$ ($c(x) > 0$) to be non-oscillatory or oscillatory are, respectively,

$$\limsup_{x \to \infty} \left(\int_{x}^{\infty} c(t) f(t)\, dt \right) \left(\int_{x}^{\infty} t^{-4} f(t)\, dt \right)^{-1} < 9/16, \tag{3.52}$$

$$\liminf_{x \to \infty} \left(\int_{x}^{\infty} c(t) f(t)\, dt \right) \left(\int_{x}^{\infty} t^{-4} f(t)\, dt \right)^{-1} > 9/16. \tag{3.53}$$

Proof   We shall prove that (3.52) is sufficient for the equation to be non-oscillatory and omit the (similar) proof of the other statement. The proof is based on Theorems 3.65 and 3.82, with the Euler equation (3.45) used as a comparison equation when $p = -2$ and $\gamma^2 = 9/16$. In this case (3.45) reduces to the nonoscillatory equation

$$v^{(4)} - (9/16) x^{-4} v = 0, \tag{3.54}$$

in which $C(x) = (9/16) x^{-4}$. The eigenvalue problems (3.31) and (3.48), with this choice of $C(x)$, will be compared by means of Theorem 3.82. If (3.52) holds, then

$$\int_{x}^{\infty} c(t) f(t)\, dt \bigg/ \int_{x}^{\infty} t^{-4} f(t)\, dt < 9/16$$

for sufficiently large x, which implies the hypothesis of Theorem 3.82 for sufficiently large α and β, and therefore the conclusion $\mu_0(\beta) \geq v_0(\beta)$ of that theorem is valid. However $v_0(\beta) > 1$ by Theorem 3.65 since (3.54) is non-oscillatory, and hence $\mu_0(\beta) > 1$. Again by Theorem 3.65 (the sufficiency this time) Eq. (3.2) is nonoscillatory (when $a(x) \equiv 1$), i.e., $u^{(4)} = c(x)u$ is nonoscillatory.

Theorem 3.85 is a partial generalization of Theorem 3.75 (when $a(x) \equiv 1$ in (3.2)). Indeed, if $f(t) = t^2$ in (3.52) and (3.53), those conditions reduce to, respectively,

$$\limsup_{x \to \infty} x \int_x^\infty t^2 c(t)\, dt < 9/16, \qquad \liminf_{x \to \infty} x \int_x^\infty t^2 c(t)\, dt > 9/16.$$

Hence Theorem 3.85 implies the last statement of Theorem 3.75.

Similarly Howard obtained the following oscillation and nonoscillation criteria by combining Theorems 3.65 and 3.83.

Theorem 3.86   (Howard)   *Sufficient conditions for the equation $u^{(4)} = c(x)u$ $(c(x) > 0)$ to be nonoscillatory or oscillatory are, respectively,*

$$\limsup_{x \to \infty} \left(\int_x^\infty (t - \alpha)^p c(t)\, dt \right) \left(\int_x^\infty t^{-4}(t - \alpha)^p\, dt \right)^{-1} < 9/16,$$

$$\liminf_{x \to \infty} \left(\int_x^\infty (t - \alpha)^p c(t)\, dt \right) \left(\int_x^\infty t^{-4}(t - \alpha)^p\, dt \right)^{-1} > 9/16,$$

where p is a number satisfying $p \leq 2$.

Combination of Theorems 3.65 and 3.84 yields Howard's last theorem in this connection:

Theorem 3.87   (Howard)   *Suppose that*

$$\int_\alpha^\infty \frac{dx}{a(x)} = \infty$$

and

$$\limsup_{x \to \infty} \left(\int_\alpha^x a(t)f(t)\, dt \right) \left(\int_\alpha^x A(t)f(t)\, dt \right)^{-1} < 1,$$

where f is a positive function of class $\mathscr{C}^1[\alpha, \infty)$ $(\alpha \geq 0)$ such that $A^2(x)f(x)$ is nondecreasing in $[\alpha, \infty)$. Then the equation $(au'')'' = cu$ is oscillatory if $(Av'')'' = cv$ is oscillatory.

Chapter 4

Third Order Ordinary Equations, nth Order Ordinary Equations and Systems

1. Introduction

Although the theory of oscillatory behavior of solutions of third order differential equations has been developed mostly during the last decade, especially by Greguš [53–57], Hanan [61], Lazer [111], Ráb [159–162], Švec [187–189], and Villari [203, 204], certain results have been known for a long time. In particular, Birkhoff [21] pioneered the study of separation and comparison theorems for equations of order exceeding two with his paper on third order equations in 1911. Ten years later Reynolds [173] extended some of Birkhoff's results to equations of arbitrary order n (see Section 5). The work of Birkhoff and Reynolds, however, was quite special in nature and did not deal at all with oscillation criteria. Actually Birkhoff devoted considerable attention to the third order self-adjoint case, which contrary to the second and fourth order cases, is little more than a curiosity (see Section 2). Other early results somewhat connected with comparison and oscillation theorems were obtained by Cimmino [33] in 1930, Mammana [128] in 1931, Sansone [175] in 1948, with a complete bibliography to that date, and Zlamal [222] in 1951.

Separation and comparison theorems for third order equations together with the associated theory of conjugate points, largely due to Hanan [61], are given in Sections 2 and 3. The oscillation criteria of Greguš, Hanan, Lazer, Švec, and Villari are contained in Section 4. The proofs are usually omitted since they are similar to those given in Chapter 3.

Differential equations of arbitrary order n are considered in Sections 5 and 6, beginning with Reynold's classical results. A summary of the contributions of the Soviet mathematicians Azbelev and Caljuk [6], Čičkin [30–32], Kiguradze [94], Komlenko [96], Kondrat'ev [99–102], and Levin [119, 120] is

149

included in Section 6. However, no theory of self-adjoint equations of even order has been developed yet to parallel Leighton and Nehari's work on second and fourth order equations; such results can be expected before long since one of the basic tools, Courant's minimax principle, is known to remain valid for eigenvalue problems analogous to (3.1) for even order self-adjoint equations.

Sternberg [183] and Reid [169, 172] studied systems consisting of n second order equations and m $(0 \leq m < n)$ first order equations, and obtained generalizations of Hille's theorems 2.1 and 2.22, Nehari's theorem 2.2, and Wintner's theorems 2.12 and 2.15; these results are described without proof in Section 7. Earlier, Whyburn [210] had considered a special system of two second order equations which are together equivalent to the general self-adjoint fourth order equation, and obtained various oscillation criteria for the system, of type similar to some of the more recent results. Whyburn was the first to obtain separation and oscillation theorems for systems of differential equations. His results are partially contained in Section 8.

2. Separation Theorems for Third Order Equations

In 1961 Hanan [61] developed a theory of conjugate points for the third order equation

$$u''' + a(x)u'' + b(x)u' + c(x)u = 0 \tag{4.1}$$

paralleling the theory of Leighton and Nehari [117] for the fourth order equation (3.2), as described in Chapter 3, Section 2. It is assumed throughout that a, b, and c are real-valued continuous functions in $(0, \infty)$. In all discussions of the *adjoint equation*

$$u''' - [a(x)u]'' + [b(x)u]' - c(x)u = 0,$$

it is assumed in addition that $a \in \mathscr{C}^2(0, \infty)$ and $b \in \mathscr{C}^1(0, \infty)$. In the study of second order and fourth order equations in the preceding chapters, the self-adjoint form of an equation (that which coincides with its adjoint) had special significance. However, the self-adjoint form of the third order equation is

$$u''' + b(x)u' + \tfrac{1}{2}b'(x)u = 0, \tag{4.2}$$

and the general solution is known to be $u = k_1 y^2 + k_2 yz + k_3 z^2$, where y and z are linearly independent solutions of the second order equation $y'' + \tfrac{1}{4}b(x)y = 0$, and k_1, k_2, k_3 are constants. The self-adjoint third order equation, therefore, has no special role in the theory.

As usual, a solution of (4.1) is called *oscillatory* iff it has an infinite number of zeros in $(0, \infty)$, and *nonoscillatory* otherwise. Equation (4.1) is said to be *oscillatory* iff it has at least one (nontrivial) oscillatory solution, and *nonoscillatory* iff all of its solutions are nonoscillatory. Also, (4.1) is called *nonoscillatory in* $[\alpha, \infty)$ iff it has no (nontrivial) solution with more than *two* zeros in $[\alpha, \infty)$. Evidently, there always exists a solution with zeros at two arbitrary points.

Let $u(x)$ be a solution of (4.1) with at least $n + 2$ zeros $\alpha_1, \alpha_2, \ldots, \alpha_{n+2}$ $(n \geq 1)$ in $[\alpha, \infty)$ $(0 < \alpha = \alpha_1 \leq \alpha_2 \leq \cdots \leq \alpha_{n+2})$. The nth *conjugate point* of α, denoted by $\delta_n(\alpha)$, is the smallest possible value of α_{n+2} as u ranges over all nontrivial solutions of (4.1) for which $u(\alpha) = 0$. If there exists at least one nontrivial solution of (4.1) which vanishes at α and has at least $n + 2$ zeros in $[\alpha, \infty)$, the existence of $\delta_n(\alpha)$ is established by the following compactness argument. Let u and v be two linearly independent solutions of (4.1) which vanish at α. Then every solution vanishing at α has the form $y(x) = Au(x) + Bv(x)$, where A and B are constants, and $A^2 + B^2 = 1$ without loss of generality since multiplication by a constant does not affect the zeros. In the case that there exists only a finite number of these solutions with $n + 2$ zeros in $[\alpha, \infty)$, $\delta_n(\alpha)$ is simply the minimum of α_{n+2} among these solutions. Otherwise the set of solutions $y(x)$ is a locally uniformly bounded equicontinuous family of functions, and hence there exists a subsequence which converges to a solution $y_0(x)$ of (4.1). Let β denote the infimum of the α_{n+2} among the solutions $y(x)$. Since any limit point of the zeros of the $y_i(x)$ belonging to the convergent subsequence is a zero of $y_0(x)$, it follows that $y_0(\beta) = 0$. If $\beta = \alpha$, then $y_0(x)$ would have at least a triple zero at α, which implies that $y_0(x) \equiv 0$. Since $A^2 + B^2 = 1$, this is a contradiction, and hence $\beta > \alpha$. The same type of argument could have been used to prove the existence of $\delta_n(\alpha)$ in the fourth order case instead of the direct construction used in the proof of Theorem 3.11.

Definition   *Equation* (4.1) *is said to be of class* I (*class* II) *iff every solution* $u(x)$ *for which* $u(\alpha) = u'(\alpha) = 0$, $u''(\alpha) > 0$ $(0 < \alpha < \infty)$ *has the property that* $u(x) > 0$ *in* $(0, \alpha)$ [*in* (α, ∞)].

Hanan [61] obtained the following analogs of Leighton and Nehari's theorem 3.11 for third order equations of class I and class II, respectively. The proofs are deleted.

Theorem 4.1   (Hanan)   *Suppose that Eq.* (4.1) *is of class* I *and has at least one nontrivial solution with a zero at* α $(\alpha > 0)$ *and at least* $n + 2$ $(n \geq 1)$ *zeros in* $[\alpha, \infty)$. *Then there exists a solution* $u(x, \alpha)$ *of* (4.1) *with the following properties:* (1) $u(x, \alpha)$ *has a double zero at* $x = \alpha$; (2) $u(x, \alpha)$ *has n additional zeros which coincide with the conjugate points* $\delta_1(\alpha), \delta_2(\alpha), \ldots, \delta_n(\alpha)$. *In particular, any nontrivial solution vanishing at* α *has less than* $i + 2$ *zeros on* $[\alpha, \delta_i(\alpha)]$, $i = 1, 2, \ldots, n$, *unless it is a constant multiple of* $u(x, \alpha)$.

If the solution $u(x, \alpha)$ in Theorem 4.1 is normalized by the condition $u''(\alpha, \alpha) = 1$, it is called the *principal solution* of (4.1). Thus the conjugate points of (4.1) coincide with the zeros of the principal solution.

Theorem 4.2   (Hanan)   *Suppose that* (4.1) *is of class* II *and has at least one nontrivial solution with a zero at α ($\alpha > 0$) and at least $n + 2$ ($n \geq 1$) zeros in* $[\alpha, \infty)$. *Then there exist n points $\delta_i(\alpha)$ ($\delta_1 < \delta_2 < \cdots < \delta_n$) and n solutions $u_i(x)$, unique except for multiplicative constants, with the following properties:*
   (1)   *$u_i(x)$ has a simple zero at α and a double zero at $\delta_i(\alpha)$ ($i = 1, 2, \ldots, n$);*
   (2)   *$u_i(x)$ has exactly $i + 2$ zeros on the interval $[\alpha, \delta_i(\alpha)]$, counted according to their multiplicities;*
   (3)   *any other nontrivial solution which vanishes at α has less than $i + 2$ zeros on $[\alpha, \delta_i(\alpha)]$.*

The next two theorems concern the adjoint equation of (4.1):

$$u''' - [a(x)u]'' + [b(x)u]' - c(x)u = 0,$$

where the additional assumptions $a \in \mathscr{C}^2(0, \infty)$, $b \in \mathscr{C}^1(0, \infty)$ are made. The proofs are given in Hanan [61].

Theorem 4.3   (Hanan)   *Equation* (4.1) *is of class* I *iff its adjoint is of class* II.

Theorem 4.4   (Hanan)   *If* (4.1) *is of class* I *then its conjugate points are identical with the conjugate points of its adjoint.*

Theorem 4.5   (Hanan)   *If* (4.1) *is of class* I *(or class* II*) it is oscillatory iff its adjoint is oscillatory.*

In the next theorem, (4.1) is compared with the second order equation

$$u'' + b(x)u = 0. \tag{4.3}$$

Theorem 4.6   (Hanan)   *Suppose $a(x) \equiv 0$ in* (4.1). *If* (4.3) *is nonoscillatory in $(0, \infty)$ and if $c(x) \geq 0$ [$c(x) \leq 0$] then Eq.* (4.1) *is of class* I *(class* II*).*

Sansone [175] first proved the following uniqueness theorem in the case that $a(x) \equiv 0$, $b \in \mathscr{C}^1(0, \infty)$, and $2c(x) - b'(x)$ has constant sign. Hanan [61] extended the theorem to arbitrary third order equations (4.1) which are either of class I or of class II. Mammana [128] showed, in fact, that (4.1) is of class I (class II) if $a(x) \equiv 0$ and $2c(x) - b'(x) > 0$ [$2c(x) - b'(x) < 0$]. The proof is as follows: Let u be a nontrivial solution of (4.1) such that $u(\beta) = u'(\beta) = 0$. If

(4.1) is not of class I, there exists a number $\alpha < \beta$ such that $u(\alpha) = 0$. Multiplication of (4.1) by u and integration from α to β yields

$$\left[uu'' - \tfrac{1}{2}u'^2 + \tfrac{1}{2}bu^2 \right]_\alpha^\beta = \tfrac{1}{2}\int_\alpha^\beta (b' - 2c)u^2 \, dx,$$

or

$$u'^2(\alpha) = -\int_\alpha^\beta (2c - b')u^2 \, dx < 0.$$

The contradiction shows that (4.1) is of class I if $a(x) \equiv 0$ and $2c(x) - b'(x) > 0$. The proof of the analogous statement for class II is almost the same.

Uniqueness Theorem 4.7   (Sansone–Hanan)   *If u and v are linearly independent solutions of a third order linear differential equation of class I or of class II, then u and v cannot have two common zeros.*

Proof   Suppose to the contrary that $u(\alpha) = u(\beta) = v(\alpha) = v(\beta) = 0$. If $\alpha = \beta$, then the function w defined by

$$w(x) = v''(\alpha)u(x) - u''(\alpha)v(x)$$

would be a solution of (4.1) satisfying $w(\alpha) = w'(\alpha) = w''(\alpha) = 0$, and hence $w(x) \equiv 0$ by the uniqueness theorem for the solution of an initial value problem [35]. Suppose then that $\alpha < \beta$. By the definition of class I it follows that $u'(\beta) \neq 0$ and $v'(\beta) \neq 0$. Therefore

$$z(x) = v'(\beta)u(x) - u'(\beta)v(x)$$

is a nontrivial solution of (4.1) satisfying the conditions $z(\alpha) = z(\beta) = z'(\beta) = 0$, which is impossible for class I equations. The proof for class II equations is analogous.

The example $y''' + y' = 0$ shows that Theorem 4.7 is not true for arbitrary third order equations; in fact, this equation has two solutions $u(x) = 1 - \cos x$, $v(x) = \sin x$ with common zeros $2n\pi$ for $n = 1, 2, \ldots$.

The following separation theorem is analogous to Theorem 3.8 for fourth order equations.

Separation Theorem 4.8   (Hanan)   *Let u and v be linearly independent solutions of a third order linear differential equation of class I (class II). If $u(\alpha) = v(\alpha) = 0$, then the zeros of u and v separate each other in (α, ∞) [in $(0, \alpha)$].*

The proof of this and the theorems below are given in [61].

Theorem 4.9   (Hanan)   *If* (4.1) *is of class* I *and if u is a nontrivial solution of* (4.1) *such that* $u(\alpha) = 0$, *then the conjugate points* $\delta_i(\alpha)$ $(i = 1, 2, \ldots)$ *and the zeros of u are interlaced.*

Theorem 4.10   (Švec–Hanan)   *If* (4.1) *is oscillatory and of class* I, *then every solution of* (4.1) *with a zero is oscillatory. In particular, on account of Theorem 4.1, if* (4.1) *is of class* I *then* (4.1) *is oscillatory iff it has an infinite number of conjugate points* $\delta_i(\alpha)$ $(0 < \alpha < \infty)$.

Theorem 4.11   (Hanan)   *If* (4.1) *is of class* I *or class* II, *then between two consecutive zeros of any solution of* (4.1) *there are at most two zeros of any other (nontrivial) solution.*

This result was obtained by Kondrat'ev [99] in 1958 in the special case $a(x) \equiv b(x) \equiv 0$ in (4.1).

Theorem 4.12   (Hanan)   *If* (4.1) *is of class* II *and u and v are linearly independent solutions of* (4.1) *such that* $u(\alpha) = v(\beta) = 0$ $(\alpha < \beta)$, *then the number of zeros of u and v in* $(0, \alpha)$ *differ by at most two.*

Theorem 4.13   (Hanan)   *If* (4.1) *is of class* II *and if u is a solution of* (4.1) *which vanishes at* α *and has at least* $n + 2$ *zeros in* $[\alpha, \infty)$, *then the conjugate points* $\delta_i(\alpha)$ $(i = 1, 2, \ldots n)$ *separate the zeros of u.*

Theorem 4.14   (Hanan)   *If* (4.1) *is of class* II *then* (4.1) *is oscillatory iff there exists an infinite number of conjugate points* $\delta_n(\alpha)$ *for every* $\alpha > 0$.

Birkhoff [21] obtained the following separation theorem in 1911 for the self-adjoint equation:

$$u''' + b(x)u' + \tfrac{1}{2}b'(x)u = 0 \qquad (b \in \mathscr{C}^1), \qquad (4.2)$$

which is neither of class I nor class II in general, as shown by the example $b(x) \equiv 1$ considered above. This theorem was the first separation theorem found for equations of order exceeding two. However, as remarked at the beginning of this section, Eq. (4.2) can be reduced to a second order equation.

Theorem 4.15   (Birkhoff)   *If u and v are linearly independent solutions of* (4.2) *with at least one zero, then the zeros of u and v separate each other singly or in pairs. Also, there always exists a solution of* (4.2) *with no zeros.*

In 1966 Lazer [111] proved the following separation theorems for the equation:

$$u''' + b(x)u' + c(x)u = 0 \tag{4.4}$$

where b and c are continuous and have constant sign in $(0, \infty)$. This equation is the same as (4.1) in the special case $a(x) \equiv 0$. However, (4.4) is not much less general than (4.1) since the second derivative term in (4.1) can always be removed by the transformation

$$u(x) = v(x) \exp\left(-\tfrac{1}{3}\int_\alpha^x a(t)\, dt\right)$$

in (4.1).

Theorem 4.16   (Lazer)   *If* $b(x) \le 0$, $c(x) \le 0$, $b \in \mathscr{C}^1$, *and* $2c(x) \le b'(x)$, *then the zeros of any two linearly independent solutions of* (4.4) *separate each other.*

Theorem 4.17   (Lazer)   *If* $b(x) \le 0$, $c(x) < 0$, $c \in \mathscr{C}^2$, *and*

$$2b(x)/c(x) + [1/c(x)]'' \ge 0,$$

then the zeros of any two linearly independent oscillatory solutions of (4.4) *separate each other.*

Exercises
1. Prove that the self-adjoint equation (4.2) has the general solution stated in the text.
2. Prove Theorem 4.15 with the aid of Exercise 1.
3. Show that the transformation

$$u(x) = v(x) \exp\left(-\tfrac{1}{3}\int_\alpha^x a(t)\, dt\right)$$

   removes the second derivative term from Eq. (4.1). Use this transformation to obtain analogs of Theorems 4.16 and 4.17 for the general equation (4.1).
4. Show that the conjugate points $\delta_n(0)$ $(n = 1, 2, \ldots)$ for the class I equation $u''' + u = 0$ are given by the roots of the transcendental equation

$$e^{-3x/2} = -2 \sin\left(\frac{\sqrt{3}}{2}x - \frac{\pi}{6}\right).$$

   In particular show that $\delta_1(0) < 10\pi/3\sqrt{3}$.
5. Show that the adjoint of the differential equation in Exercise 4 is $u''' - u = 0$. Characterize the conjugate points for this equation by using Theorem 4.4 and Exercise 4.

6. Prove that Eq. (4.4) is of class II if $2c(x) < b'(x)$ in $(0, \infty)$ by an argument analogous to that given in the text for class I equations.
7. Prove the uniqueness theorem 4.7 for class II equations.
8. Check reference [61] for the proofs of Theorems 4.8–4.14.

3. Comparison Theorems for Third Order Equations

In addition to (4.1) consider a second equation of the same type:

$$u''' + a(x)u'' + b(x)u' + C(x)u = 0. \tag{4.5}$$

Hanan [61] obtained the following comparison theorems for (4.1) and (4.5) under the assumption

$$c(x) \geq C(x), \qquad 0 < x < \infty. \tag{4.6}$$

Theorem 4.18   (Hanan)   *If Eq. (4.5) is of class* I *and (4.6) holds, then Eq. (4.1) also is of class* I. *Furthermore, the conjugate points* $\delta_n(\alpha)$, $\delta_n{}^*(\alpha)$ *of (4.1), (4.5), respectively, are related by the inequality*

$$\delta_n(\alpha) \leq \delta^*_{2n-1}(\alpha) \qquad (n = 1, 2, \ldots ; \alpha > 0).$$

In particular, (4.1) is oscillatory if (4.5) is oscillatory.

Theorem 4.18 is a third order analog of Leighton and Nehari's theorem 3.39 for fourth order equations.

Although Theorem 4.18 was not obtained until 1961, Birkhoff [21] using different terminology proved in 1911 that $\delta_1(\alpha) \leq \delta_1{}^*(\alpha)$ in the special case $a(x) \equiv 0$. Birkhoff's result was the first comparison theorem discovered for differential equations of order exceeding two. Birkhoff also proved that $\delta_1(\alpha) \leq \delta_1{}^*(\alpha)$, where $\delta_1(\alpha)$, $\delta_1{}^*(\alpha)$ are the first conjugate points of the self-adjoint equations

$$u''' + b(x)u' + \tfrac{1}{2}b'(x)u = 0, \qquad b \in \mathscr{C}^1, \tag{4.2}$$

$$u''' + B(x)u' + \tfrac{1}{2}B'(x)u = 0, \qquad B \in \mathscr{C}^1, \tag{4.2a}$$

respectively, under the assumption

$$b(x) \geq B(x), \qquad 0 < x < \infty.$$

The proof depends on the fact (mentioned near the beginning of Section 2) that there exists a nontrivial solution y of the associated second order equation

$$y'' + \tfrac{1}{4}B(x)y = 0$$

with consecutive zeros at α, $\delta_1{}^*(\alpha)$. Then for $b(x) \geq B(x)$, every solution z of

$$z'' + \tfrac{1}{4}b(x)z = 0$$

has a zero in $(\alpha, \delta_1{}^*(\alpha))$ unless z is a constant multiple of y by the comparison theorem 1.6, whence $\delta_1(\alpha) \leq \delta_1{}^*(\alpha)$. The details are left as an exercise [21, p. 122].

Theorem 4.19   (Hanan)   *If* (4.1) *and* (4.5) *are of class* II *and* (4.6) *holds, then* (4.5) *is oscillatory if* (4.1) *is oscillatory.*

In the special case that $a(x) \equiv 0$, $b \in \mathscr{C}^1$, and $2c(x) > b'(x)$ in Eq. (4.1) Mammana [128] has shown that (4.1) is of class I: the proof is given below Theorem 4.6. Using this fact, Hanan [61] obtained the following comparison theorem for the equations

$$u''' + b(x)u' + c(x)u = 0 \tag{4.4}$$

$$u''' + B(x)u' + C(x)u = 0, \tag{4.7}$$

under the assumptions

$$b(x) \geq B(x) \geq 0, \qquad c(x) \geq C(x) \qquad (0 < x < \infty) \tag{4.8}$$

and

$$2c(x) > b'(x), \qquad 2C(x) > B'(x) \qquad (0 < x < \infty). \tag{4.9}$$

Theorem 4.20   (Hanan)   *If the inequalities* (4.8) *and* (4.9) *hold, then the* nth *conjugate points* $\delta_n(\alpha)$, $\delta_n{}^*(\alpha)$ *of* (4.4), (4.7), *respectively, are related by the inequality*

$$\delta_n(\alpha) \leq \delta_{kn-1}^*(\alpha)$$

for some integer $k \geq 2$. *In particular,* (4.4) *is oscillatory if* (4.7) *is oscillatory and the inequalities* (4.8) *and* (4.9) *hold for sufficiently large* x.

The next comparison theorem deals with the case that (4.8) and (4.9) are replaced by the inequalities

$$b(x) \geq B(x) \geq 0, \qquad b'(x) - c(x) \geq B'(x) - C(x), \tag{4.10}$$

$$2c(x) < b'(x), \qquad 2C(x) < B'(x) \qquad (0 < x < \infty). \tag{4.11}$$

Theorem 4.21   (Hanan)   *Suppose the coefficients in* (4.4) *and* (4.7) *satisfy the inequalities* (4.10) *and* (4.11). *Then* (4.4) *is oscillatory if* (4.7) *is oscillatory.*

In the following five theorems, Eq. (4.4) is compared with the second order equation

$$u'' + b(x)u = 0, \qquad b \in \mathscr{C}^1(0, \infty) \tag{4.12}$$

under the assumption that the latter is nonoscillatory. Various sufficient conditions on $b(x)$ for (4.12) to be nonoscillatory were given in Chapter 2, e.g., Hille's condition (Theorem 2.41)

$$\limsup_{x \to \infty} x^2 b(x) < \tfrac{1}{4}.$$

Theorem 4.22   (Hanan) *Suppose* (4.12) *is nonoscillatory and* $c(x)$ *is of constant sign in* $(0, \infty)$. *If* $u(x)$ *is any solution of* (4.4) *such that* $u'(x)$ *is oscillatory, then* $u(x)$ *is likewise oscillatory.*

Theorem 4.23   (Hanan) *Suppose* (4.12) *is nonoscillatory and* $c(x)$ *is positive in* $(0, \infty)$. *If* (4.4) *is oscillatory then every nontrivial nonoscillatory solution u does not vanish in* $(0, \infty)$ *and* $|u|$ *is monotonically decreasing.*

Theorem 4.24   (Hanan) *If* (4.12) *is nonoscillatory and either of the inequalities*

$$b'(x) \geq c(x) \geq 0 \qquad or \qquad b'(x) \leq c(x) \leq 0$$

is satisfied in $(0, \infty)$, *then* (4.4) *is nonoscillatory.*

Theorem 4.25   (Hanan) *If* (4.12) *is nonoscillatory,* $b(x) > 0$, $c(x) > 0$, *and* $c(x) > b'(x)$ *in* (α, ∞) $(\alpha > 0)$, *and if*

$$\int_\alpha^\infty x[c(x) - b'(x)]\, dx = \infty,$$

then Eq. (4.4) *is oscillatory.*

Theorem 4.26   (Hanan) *Suppose* (4.12) *is nonoscillatory,* $b(x) > 0$, *and* $c(x) < 0$ *in* (α, ∞) $(\alpha > 0)$. *Then* Eq. (4.4) *is oscillatory if*

$$\int_\alpha^\infty x[-c(x)]\, dx = \infty$$

and nonoscillatory if

$$\int_\alpha^\infty x^2[-c(x)]\, dx < \infty.$$

Lazer [111] used the second order equation

$$u'' + [b(x) + mxc(x)]u = 0 \tag{4.13}$$

as a comparison equation for (4.4), where m is a constant.

Theorem 4.27   (Lazer)   *Suppose $b(x) \geq 0$, $c(x) \geq 0$, $b \in \mathscr{C}^1$, and $2c(x) \geq b'(x)$. If there exists a number $m < \frac{1}{2}$ such that (4.13) is oscillatory, then (4.4) also is oscillatory.*

The following nonoscillation criterion involves the second order comparison equation

$$u'' + \left[b(x) + \tfrac{3}{2} \int_x^\infty c(t)\, dt \right] u = 0, \tag{4.14}$$

Theorem 4.28   (Lazer)   *Suppose $b(x) \geq 0$, $c(x) \geq 0$, $2c(x) \geq b'(x)$ with strict inequality holding everywhere except at isolated points, $b(\infty) = 0$, and*

$$\int_\alpha^\infty c(x)\, dx < \infty \qquad (\alpha > 0).$$

Then (4.4) is nonoscillatory if (4.14) is nonoscillatory, and in particular if

$$\limsup_{x \to \infty} x^2 \left[b(x) + \tfrac{3}{2} \int_x^\infty c(t)\, dt \right] < \tfrac{1}{4}.$$

Exercises
1. Give the details of the proof of Birkhoff's theorem: $\delta_1(\alpha) \leq \delta_1{}^*(\alpha)$ if $b(x) \geq B(x)$ where $\delta_1(\alpha)$, $\delta_1{}^*(\alpha)$ are the first conjugate points of the self-adjoint equations (4.2), (4.2a), respectively.
2. Show by Birkhoff's theorem that the equation $u''' - xu' - u/2 = 0$ is nonoscillatory.
3. Use Theorem 4.18 and Exercise 4 of Section 2 to show that the conjugate points $\delta_n(0)$ $(n = 1, 2, \ldots)$ of the equation

$$u''' + (1 + x)u = 0$$

satisfy the inequality $\delta_n(0) \leq d_n$, where d_n is the nth root of the transcendental equation

$$e^{-3x/2} = -2 \sin\left(\frac{\sqrt{3}}{2} x - \frac{\pi}{6} \right)$$

$(d_1 < d_2 < \cdots)$, and in particular $\delta_1(0) < 10\pi/3\sqrt{3}$.
4. Show that the differential equation in Exercise 3 is oscillatory by two methods: (1) Application of the conclusion of Exercise 3; (2) Application of Theorem 4.27.
5. Prove using Theorem 4.28 that the equation $u''' + \gamma(1 + x^3)^{-1}u = 0$ is nonoscillatory if $\gamma < \frac{1}{3}$.

6. Prove the following comparison theorem: If the second order equation $u'' + C(x)u = 0$ is nonoscillatory and if

$$\left| \int_x^\infty b(x)\, dx \right| \le 4 \int_x^\infty C(x)\, dx$$

for $x \ge \alpha > 0$, then the third order self-adjoint equation (4.2) is nonoscillatory. This result is due to Taam [198, p. 497]. *Outline of proof:* If y and z are linearly independent solutions of $y'' + \frac{1}{4}b(x)y = 0$, then y^2, yz, and z^2 are three linearly independent solutions of (4.2) (compare Exercise 1 of Section 2) and y and z are nonoscillatory by Theorem 2.12.

4. Oscillation Criteria for Third Order Equations

Oscillation and nonoscillation theorems analogous to those given for second and fourth order equations in Chapters 2 and 3 were obtained for third order equations by Zlamal [222] in 1951, Ráb [159–162] from 1955–1960, Švec [187] in 1957, Greguš [54–57] from 1958–1961, Villari [203, 204] in 1958 and 1960, Hanan [61] in 1961, and Lazer [111] in 1966. Hanan and Lazer give complete self-contained proofs of most of these theorems, and provide a rather complete bibliography of the work on third order equations, beginning with Birkhoff's 1911 paper [16].

The third order equation under consideration is (4.4), i.e., (4.1) with $a(x) \equiv 0$, and it is assumed as before that b and c are real-valued continuous functions in $(0, \infty)$. The problem is to find conditions on the coefficients b and c so that the equation is oscillatory (or nonoscillatory). No comparison equation is involved in these theorems although, as in the second and fourth order cases, comparison theorems are used in the proofs.

Oscillation criteria will be given of both the Kneser–Hille limit type [Chapter 2, Section 8] and the Hille–Wintner–Leighton–Nehari integral type [Chapter 2, Sections 1, 2, 6]. The results are given with particular reference to the three cases:

(1) $b(x) \le 0,\quad c(x) > 0$
(2) $b(x) \le 0,\quad c(x) \le 0$
(3) $b(x) \ge 0,\quad c(x) \ge 0.$

It turns out, under suitable hypotheses, that Eq. (4.4) has oscillatory properties that correspond to the following easily verified properties in the case that b and c are nonzero constants.

Theorem 4.29   (Case of constant coefficients)
(1)   *If $b < 0$ and $c > 0$, Eq. (4.4) is oscillatory iff*

$$c - (2/3\sqrt{3})(-b)^{3/2} > 0.$$

When this condition is satisfied, all solutions of (4.4) *are oscillatory except constant multiples of one solution* u_1; $u_1(x)$ *does not vanish in* $(0, \infty)$ *and tends monotonically to zero along with all of its derivatives as* $x \to \infty$.

(2) *If* $b < 0$ *and* $c < 0$, (4.4) *is oscillatory iff*

$$c + (2/3\sqrt{3})(-b)^{3/2} < 0.$$

When this condition is fulfilled, (4.4) *has two linearly independent oscillatory solutions.*

(3) *If* $b > 0$ *and* $c > 0$, *all solutions of* (4.4) *are oscillatory except constant multiples of one solution* u_1; $u_1(x)$ *does not vanish in* $(0, \infty)$ *and tends monotonically to zero along with all of its derivatives as* $x \to \infty$.

Hanan derived the following oscillation criteria of the Kneser–Hille type by appealing to the comparison theorem 4.20.

Theorem 4.30   (Hanan)   *Equation* (4.4) *is oscillatory if* $b \in \mathscr{C}^1$, $2c(x) > b'(x)$ $(0 < x < \infty)$, *and*

$$\liminf_{x \to \infty} x^2 b(x) > p, \qquad \liminf_{x \to \infty} x^3 c(x) > -p$$

for some number $p > 1$.

Proof   Choose the comparison equation (4.7) in Theorem 4.20 to be the Euler equation

$$u''' + qx^{-2}u' + rx^{-3}u = 0 \qquad (q, r \text{ constants}) \tag{4.15}$$

with solutions $u = x^m$, where m is a root of the cubic polynomial equation

$$f(m) \equiv m^3 - 3m^2 + (2 + q)m + r = 0. \tag{4.16}$$

A local maximum or minimum point on the graph of f can occur only if $m = 1 \mp [(1 - q)/3]^{1/2}$. Thus (4.16) has only real roots if $q > 1$, and consequently (4.15) is oscillatory if $q > 1$ for all real r.

Since the comparison equation (4.7) coincides with (4.15), $B(x) = qx^{-2}$ and $C(x) = rx^{-3}$. By hypothesis there exists a number $q > p$ such that $x^2 b(x) > q$ for sufficiently large x. With the choice $r = -p$, the following inequalities are satisfied:

$$b(x) - B(x) > 0, \qquad c(x) - C(x) > 0,$$

and

$$2C(x) - B'(x) = 2(r + q)x^{-3} > 2(-p + p)x^{-3} = 0$$

for sufficiently large x. Since (4.15), (i.e., (4.7)) is oscillatory for $q > 1$ and all real r, and $2c(x) > b'(x)$ by hypothesis, Theorem 4.20 shows that Eq. (4.4) is oscillatory.

Theorem 4.31   (Hanan)   *Suppose $b \in \mathscr{C}^1$ and $2c(x) > b'(x)$ $(0 < x < \infty)$. Then Eq. (4.4) is oscillatory if there exists a number p satisfying $0 < p < 1$ such that*

$$\liminf_{x \to \infty} x^2 b(x) > p, \qquad \liminf_{x \to \infty} x^3 c(x) > 2 \left(\frac{1 - p}{3} \right)^{3/2} - p$$

and nonoscillatory if there exists a number p $(0 < p < 1)$ such that

$$\limsup_{x \to \infty} x^2 b(x) < p, \qquad \limsup_{x \to \infty} x^3 c(x) < 2 \left(\frac{1 - p}{3} \right)^{3/2} - p.$$

Proof   An easy calculation shows that the relative maximum and minimum points on the graph of the polynomial (4.16) are $(m_+, f(m_+))$ and $(m_-, f(m_-))$, respectively, where

$$m_\pm = 1 \mp [(1 - q)/3]^{1/2}, \qquad f(m_\pm) = q + r \pm 2[(1 - q)/3]^{3/2}$$

in the case $q < 1$. If $q + r > 0$, it follows that (4.15) is oscillatory iff

$$q + r > 2[(1 - q)/3]^{3/2}, \tag{4.17}$$

and if $q + r < 0$, (4.15) is oscillatory iff

$$q + r > -2[(1 - q)/3]^{3/2}.$$

By hypothesis there exists a number q satisfying $0 < p < q < 1$ such that $x^2 b(x) > q$ for sufficiently large x. With the choice

$$r = -p + 2[(1 - p)/3]^{3/2},$$

the following inequalities are satisfied:

$$b(x) - B(x) > 0, \qquad c(x) - C(x) > 0,$$

$$2C(x) - B'(x) = 2(r + q)x^{-3} > 2[(1 - p)/3]^{3/2} x^{-3} > 0$$

$(x \geq x_0, \ 0 < p < 1)$. Since $q + r$ is positive and satisfies (4.17), Eq. (4.15) (i.e., (4.7)) is oscillatory, and hence (4.4) also is oscillatory by Theorem 4.20. The proof of the nonoscillation criterion is similar.

The next theorem concerns the special case

$$u''' + c(x)u = 0, \qquad c(x) > 0 \tag{4.18}$$

of Eq. (4.4), when $b(x) \equiv 0$. As remarked before (in the discussion after Theorem 4.6), Eq. (4.18) is of class I if $c(x) > 0$. Theorem 4.5 shows, therefore, that (4.18) is oscillatory iff its adjoint

$$u''' - c(x)u = 0$$

is oscillatory. Choosing the comparison equation (4.7) to be the Euler equation

$$u''' + rx^{-3}u = 0 \qquad (r = \text{constant}), \qquad (4.19)$$

we obtain the following oscillation criteria by applying Theorem 4.20. The proof is very similar to that of Theorem 4.30 and is deleted.

Theorem 4.32   (Hanan)   *If $c(x)$ has constant sign, then Eq. (4.18) is oscillatory if*

$$\liminf_{x \to \infty} x^3 |c(x)| > 2/3\sqrt{3},$$

and nonoscillatory if

$$\limsup_{x \to \infty} x^3 |c(x)| < 2/3\sqrt{3}.$$

The proofs of the following additional oscillation theorems will not be given here. They can be found in the references cited, especially Lazer [111].

Theorem 4.33   (Kondrat'ev [99]–Lazer [111])   *Equation (4.4) is oscillatory if $b(x) \leq 0$, $c(x) > 0$ $(0 < x < \infty)$, and if there is a number $\alpha > 0$ such that*

$$\int_\alpha^\infty [c(x) - (2/3\sqrt{3})(-b(x))^{3/2}] \, dx = \infty.$$

Kondrat'ev obtained this result in 1958 when $b(x) \equiv 0$. Note the resemblance of Theorem 4.33 to the first statement of Theorem 4.29.

Theorem 4.34   (Greguš [56])   *Suppose $b \in \mathscr{C}^1$, $b(x) \leq 0$, $c(x) > 0$, and $2c(x) \geq b'(x)$ with equality occurring only at isolated points $(0 < x < \infty)$. If Eq. (4.4) has one oscillatory solution, then all solutions of (4.4) are oscillatory except constant multiples of one nonvanishing solution $u_1(x)$; furthermore $u_1(x)$ tends to a finite limit as $x \to \infty$.*

Theorem 4.35   (Lazer [111])   *Suppose $c \in \mathscr{C}^2$, $b(x) \leq 0$, $c(x) > 0$, and*

$$2b(x)/c(x) + [1/c(x)]'' \leq 0 \qquad (0 < x < \infty).$$

Then the conclusion of Theorem 4.34 is valid.

Theorem 4.36   (Švec [187]–Villari [204]) *If $b(x) \equiv 0$, $c(x) > 0$, and (4.4) has one oscillatory solution, then every nonoscillatory solution tends to zero as $x \to \infty$.*

Theorem 4.37   (Lazer [111]) *Suppose $b(x) \leq 0$, $c(x) > 0$ $(0 < x < \infty)$ and*

$$\int_{\alpha}^{\infty} x^2 c(x) \, dx = \infty$$

for some $\alpha > 0$. Then, if (4.4) has one oscillatory solution, every nonoscillatory solution tends to zero as $x \to \infty$.

In the case of constant coefficients b and c, statement (1) of Theorem 4.29 shows that the conclusion of Theorem 4.36 is valid for arbitrary $b < 0$ and $c > 0$. However, it is still an open question whether or not this is true for nonconstant coefficients.

Theorem 4.38   (Lazer) *If $b \in \mathscr{C}^1$, $b(x) \leq 0$, $c(x) < b'(x)$, and*

$$\int_{\alpha}^{\infty} [b'(x) - c(x) - (2/3\sqrt{3})(-b(x))^{3/2}] \, dx = \infty,$$

for some $\alpha > 0$, then (4.4) has two linearly independent oscillatory solutions.

Theorem 4.39   (Zlamal [222]–Lazer [111]) *Suppose that $b \in \mathscr{C}^1$, $b(x) \geq 0$, $c(x) \geq d$ where d is a positive constant, and $c(x) \geq b'(x)$ $(0 < x < \infty)$. If $u(x)$ is any nonoscillatory solution of (4.4), then*

$$u \in \mathscr{L}^2(1, \infty), \qquad \lim_{x \to \infty} u(x) = \lim_{x \to \infty} u'(x) = 0.$$

Moreover, any two nonoscillatory solutions are linearly dependent.

Further results are contained in the papers of Azbelev and Caljuk [6], Červen [28], Greguš [52–57], Kalafati [92], Kondrat'ev [99–101], Ráb [159–162], and Švec [187–189].

Exercises
1. Verify the three statements of Theorem 4.29 (case of constant coefficients).
2. Prove the nonoscillation criterion of Theorem 4.31.
3. Prove Theorem 4.32 by using the Euler equation (4.19) as a comparison equation.
4. Consider the example

$$u''' - (2 - \sin x^2)^{2/3} u' + (k + 4/3\sqrt{3})u = 0 \qquad (k > 0).$$

Show that all the hypotheses of Theorem 4.33 are satisfied and hence this equation is oscillatory. Show also by Theorem 4.35 that every nonoscillatory solution is a constant multiple of one nonvanishing solution. However, Theorem 4.34 is not applicable since

$$2c(x) - b'(x) = (2k + 8/3\sqrt{3}) - (4x/3)\cos x^2(2 - \sin x^2)^{-1/3}$$

has negative values for arbitrarily large x.

5. Separation and Comparison Theorems for nth Order Equations

In 1921 Reynolds [173] obtained separation and comparison theorems for the nth order equation

$$u^{(n)} + \sum_{i=2}^{n} a_i(x)u^{(n-i)} = 0, \qquad \alpha \le x \le \beta, \tag{4.20}$$

where a_i $(i = 2, 3, \ldots, n)$ is a real-valued continuous function of class $\mathscr{C}^{(n-i)}[\alpha, \beta]$. Reynold's treatment was modelled after Birkhoff's study of the third order case [21]. The equation adjoint to (4.20) is

$$z^{(n)} + \sum_{i=2}^{n} (-1)^i [a_i(x)z]^{(n-i)} = 0. \tag{4.21}$$

It is well known from the theory of linear differential equations [35] that this equation is satisfied by z_i, the cofactor of $u_i^{(n-1)}$ in the Wronskian determinant

$$W(x) = W(u_1, u_2, \ldots, u_n; x) = \det(u_i^{(j-1)}(x))$$

$(i, j = 1, 2, \ldots, n)$, where $u_1, u_2, \ldots, u_n$ denote linearly independent solutions of (4.20). Since $W(x)$ is a constant by Abel's formula [90], we can assume without loss of generality that $W(x) \equiv 1$.

Theorem 4.40   (Reynolds)   *Let u and v be two solutions of (4.20) such that $u(x_1) = u(x_2) = 0$, $v(x_1) \ne 0$, $v(x_2) \ne 0$ $(x_1 < x_2)$. Then the number of zeros of v plus the number of zeros of $uv' - vu'$ in the interval (x_1, x_2) is odd.*

Proof   Without loss of generality $u(x) > 0$ in $x_1 < x < x_2$. Then there exist integers j and k such that

$$u(x_1) = u'(x_1) = \cdots = u^{(j-1)}(x_1) = 0, \qquad u^{(j)}(x_1) > 0,$$

$$u(x_2) = u'(x_2) = \cdots = u^{(k-1)}(x_2) = 0, \qquad (-1)^k u^{(k)}(x_2) > 0,$$

where $j < n$ and $k < n$ since $W(x) \neq 0$. Define $f = v(uv' - vu')$. Successive differentiation yields

$$f^{(m)}(x_1) = 0, \qquad m < j - 1$$

$$f^{(m)}(x_2) = 0, \qquad m < k - 1$$

$$f^{(j-1)}(x_1) = -v^2(x_1)u^{(j)}(x_1) < 0,$$

$$(-1)^k f^{(k-1)}(x_2) = -(-1)^k v^2(x_2)u^{(k)}(x_2) < 0,$$

or

$$(-1)^{k-1} f^{(k-1)}(x_2) > 0.$$

Hence $f(x)$ has an odd number of zeros between x_1 and x_2, which is equivalent to the conclusion of Theorem 4.40.

Theorem 4.40 is a general separation theorem. For second order equations it implies Sturm's separation theorem 1.8 that the zeros of linearly independent solutions are interlaced, since $uv' - vu' \neq 0$ in the case $n = 2$. For third order equations, Theorem 4.40 reduces to the following theorem of Birkhoff [21].

Theorem 4.41   (Birkhoff)   *Suppose $n = 3$ in Eq. (4.20). Let u_1, u_2, u_3 be linearly independent solutions of (4.20) with Wronskian $W(x) = 1$ and let z_1, z_2, z_3 be the solutions of the adjoint equation defined above, that is,*

$$z_1 = u_2 u_3' - u_3 u_2', \qquad z_2 = u_3 u_1' - u_1 u_3', \qquad z_3 = u_1 u_2' - u_2 u_1'.$$

Between any two consecutive zeros of u_i (or z_i) the number of zeros of u_j plus the number of zeros of z_k is odd, where (i, j, k) is any permutation of $(1, 2, 3)$.

Birkhoff obtained the same result with the slight additional generality that a second derivative term is allowed to occur in the differential equation (4.20) (when $n = 3$); however, this term can always be removed by an elementary transformation (Exercise 3 of Section 2). Reynolds obtained an analog of Theorem 4.41 in the fourth order case [173, p. 227] when the differential equation is self-adjoint, i.e., when (4.20) coincides with (4.21), but this will not be given here due to its complicated nature.

For u_i, z_i as above, $i = 1, 2, \ldots, n$, define

$$\varphi(x, t) = \sum_{i=1}^{n} z_i(t)u_i(x), \qquad \alpha \leq x, t \leq \beta.$$

It can be proved by direct substitution that any function v satisfying the linear integral equation

$$v(x) = u(x) - \int_{\alpha}^{x} \varphi(x, t)R(t)v(t)\, dt,$$

for a continuous function R, is a solution of the linear system

$$v^{(n)} + \sum_{i=2}^{n} a_i(x)v^{(n-i)} + R(x)v = 0$$

$$v^{(k)}(\alpha) = u^{(k)}(\alpha), \qquad k = 0, 1, \ldots, n-1. \tag{4.22}$$

Reynolds used this fact to compare Eqs. (4.20) and (4.22).

Definitions   *An interval $[\alpha, \beta]$ is said to be regular of the first kind for Eq. (4.20) whenever $\varphi(x, t) \geq 0$ (n odd) and whenever $\varphi(x, t) > 0$ (n even) for $\alpha \leq t < x \leq \beta$. The interval is said to be regular of the second kind whenever $\varphi(x, t) \geq 0$ (n odd) and whenever $\varphi(x, t) < 0$ (n even) for $\alpha \leq x < t \leq \beta$.*

The proofs of the following comparison theorems will be deleted.

Theorem 4.42   (Birkhoff–Reynolds)   *A regular interval of the first (second) kind for an equation (4.20) of odd order is also a regular interval of the same kind for Eq. (4.22), provided $R(x) \leq 0$ ($R(x) \geq 0$) throughout the interval.*

Theorem 4.43   (Reynolds)   *A regular interval of either kind for Eq. (4.20) of even order is also a regular interval of the same kind for Eq. (4.22), provided $R(x) \leq 0$ throughout the interval.*

Theorem 4.44   (Reynolds)   *Let $[\alpha, \beta]$ be a regular interval of the first (second) kind for an equation (4.22) of odd order, throughout which $R(x) < 0$ ($R(x) > 0$) except for at most a finite number of zeros. If u and v are nontrivial solutions of (4.20) and (4.22), respectively, such that*

$$u^{(k)}(\gamma) = v^{(k)}(\gamma), \qquad \alpha \leq \gamma \leq \beta, \quad k = 0, 1, \ldots, n-1,$$

then between γ and the smallest (largest) zero of $v(x)$ ($u(x)$) which is larger (smaller) than γ, there exists at least one zero of $u(x)$ ($v(x)$) of odd order.

An interesting separation theorem was obtained by Kondrat'ev [102] in 1961 in the case of the equation $u^{(n)} + c(x)u = 0$, for $n \geq 5$. This result states that, *given a positive integer m, there exists a positive continuous function c such that between two consecutive zeros of any nontrivial solution of the equation, there are m zeros of another solution.* This result is false if $n \leq 4$ [101]. Other related results are described in the next section.

We remark that many of the preceding results can be extended to nth order linear differential inequalities: some such theorems were stated as exercises in Sections 1 and 3 of Chapter 1. Extensive treatments of the theory of differential inequalities are contained in the references [13, 179, 197] already cited.

Caligo [26], Bellman [15], and others obtained the following generalization of Hukuhara's theorem [85] (stated at the end of Section 9, Chapter 2 in the case of the second order equation (2.1)): *Let f_i be a measurable function in $[0, \infty)$ such that*

$$\int_0^\infty |f_i(x)|\, dx < +\infty \qquad (i = 1, 2, \ldots, n).$$

If every solution of the differential equation

$$u^{(n)} + \rho_1 u^{(n-1)} + \cdots + \rho_n u = 0$$

is bounded in $[0, \infty)$ for some real numbers ρ_i $(i = 1, 2, \ldots, n)$, then every solution of the equation

$$v^{(n)} + [\rho_1 + f_1(x)]v^{(n-1)} + \cdots + [\rho_n + f_n(x)]v = 0$$

also is bounded in $[0, \infty)$. Analogs of this theorem for systems of first order equations have been obtained by the above authors, Levinson [123], and Weyl [209]. Although such results are comparison theorems under the general interpretation stated in the Preface, they belong in the realm of stability theory and as such have been treated very thoroughly in Cesari's well-known monograph [29] and elsewhere.

6. General Oscillation Theorems

Between 1955 and 1965 Glazman [50, 51] Levin [119, 120], Kiguradze [94], Komlenko [96], Kondrat'ev [100–102], and others [1, 2, 32, 42, 60, 86, 132] obtained various oscillation criteria for the general nth order equation

$$Lu \equiv u^{(n)} + \sum_{i=1}^{n} a_i(x)u^{(n-i)} = 0, \qquad \alpha \leq x \leq \beta \qquad (4.23)$$

with continuous coefficients a_i on $[\alpha, \beta]$, $i = 1, 2, \ldots, n$. This equation is slightly more general than (4.20) since the $(n-1)$st derivative term appears and a_i is not required to be in the differentiability class $\mathscr{C}^{n-1}$.

If no nontrivial solution of (4.23) has more than $n-1$ zeros on $[\alpha, \beta]$, then $[\alpha, \beta]$ is called an *interval of nonoscillation* of (4.23); otherwise $[\alpha, \beta]$ is called an *interval of oscillation* of (4.23). If α is the left hand endpoint of some interval of oscillation, we define the (first) *conjugate point* $\delta(\alpha)$ as the infimum of all numbers γ $(\gamma > \alpha)$ for which $[\alpha, \gamma]$ is an interval of oscillation of (4.23). Evidently $\delta(\alpha) > \alpha$ and $[\alpha, \delta(\alpha)]$ is an interval of oscillation of (4.23). In the cases $n = 3$, 4, conjugate points already have been considered in detail (Sections 1, 2 of this Chapter, Sections 1, 2 of Chapter 3, respectively).

Theorem 4.45   (Levin [119]) *If the point* α *has a conjugate, then there exists a nontrivial solution of Eq.* (4.23) *which is positive in* $(\alpha, \delta(\alpha))$, *has a zero of order not less than* k *at* α, *and has a zero of order not less than* $n - k$ *at* $\delta(\alpha)$ *for some* k $(1 \leq k \leq n - 1)$.

The proof depends on properties of Green's function for de La Vallée Poussin's multiple point boundary problem [40] obtained by Čičkin [32] and earlier for $n = 3$ by Azbelev [5].

An interval $[\alpha, \beta]$ is said to be an interval of $(k, n - k)$ oscillation for (4.23) if $\beta \geq \delta(\alpha)$ and there exists a solution of (4.23) which is positive in $(\alpha, \delta(\alpha))$ and has zeros of order not less than $k, n - k$ at $\alpha, \delta(\alpha)$, respectively. The interval is said to be of *even* or *odd oscillation type* according as the integer $n - k$ is even or odd. According to Theorem 4.45, for each interval of oscillation there exist one or more of the $n - 1$ possible types of oscillation $(n - 1, 1)$, $(n-2, 2), \ldots, (1, n - 1)$. It is an easily established fact that each interval of $(k, n - k)$ oscillation for (4.23) is an interval of $(n - k, k)$ oscillation for the adjoint equation

$$z^{(n)} + \sum_{i=1}^{n} (-1)^i [a_i(x)z]^{(n-i)} = 0$$

where now $a_i \in \mathscr{C}^{n-i}$, $i = 1, 2, \ldots, n$. In particular, if (4.23) is self-adjoint, each interval of $(k, n - k)$ oscillation is also an interval of $(n - k, k)$ oscillation.

In addition to (4.23), consider a second differential equation of the same type:

$$v^{(n)} + \sum_{i=1}^{n} a_i(x)v^{(n-i)} + R(x)v = 0 \tag{4.24}$$

which differs from (4.23) only by the perturbation $R(x)v$, where R is supposed to be a continuous function on the interval under consideration. The following comparison theorem of Sturm's type was obtained by Levin [119] on the basis of Theorem 4.45. For $n = 2$ the first assertion of the theorem is equivalent to Sturm's theorem 1.1.

Theorem 4.46   (Levin) *If* $R(x) \geq 0$ *on* $[\alpha, \beta]$, *every interval of odd oscillation type for* (4.23) *is also an interval of odd oscillation type for* (4.24), *and every interval of even oscillation type for* (4.24) *is also an interval of even oscillation type for* (4.23).

In addition to (4.23), (4.24), consider a third differential equation

$$v^{(n)} + \sum_{i=1}^{n} a_i(x)v^{(n-i)} + S(x)v = 0 \tag{4.25}$$

of the same type, where S is continuous on the interval under consideration.

Theorem 4.47   (Kondrat'ev–Levin)   *If $S(x) \geq R(x) \geq 0$ on $[\alpha, \beta]$, every interval of nonoscillation for both (4.23) and (4.25) is an interval of nonoscillation for (4.24).*

Proof The assumption that (4.24) has odd oscillation on the interval contradicts the first assertion of Theorem 4.46 when applied to (4.24) and (4.25), while the assumption that (4.24) has even oscillation contradicts the second assertion when applied to (4.23) and (4.24).

In the special case of the equation $u^{(n)} + c(x)u = 0$, an analog of Theorem 4.47 was obtained by Kondrat'ev [102].

Theorem 4.48   (Levin)   *If $c(x) \geq 0$ the intervals of oscillation for the equation $u^{(n)} + c(x)u = 0$ are all of odd type, and if $c(x) \leq 0$ they are all of even type.*

Proof To prove the first statement, suppose to the contrary that the equation had an interval of even oscillation type. Since $c(x) \geq 0$, the second assertion of Theorem 4.46 would show that the equation $u^{(n)} = 0$ also has an interval of even oscillation type, which contradicts the fact that a nontrivial polynomial of degree $n - 1$ cannot have n zeros. The second statement is proved similarly from the first assertion of Theorem 4.46.

Theorem 4.48 shows, in particular, that for $n = 2, 3, 4, 5,$ and 6 the possible oscillation types $(k, n - k)$ $(1 \leq k \leq n - 1)$ for the equation $u^{(n)} + c(x)u = 0$

TABLE II

n	Oscillation types possible	
	$c(x) \geq 0$	$c(x) \leq 0$
2	(1, 1)	None
3	(2, 1)	(1, 2)
4	(3, 1) = (1, 3)	(2, 2)
5	(4, 1), (2, 3)	(3, 2), (1, 4)
6	(5, 1) = (1, 5), (3, 3)	(4, 2) = (2, 4)

are as given in Table II. Note that the oscillation type (if it exists) is uniquely determined by the sign of $c(x)$ in several cases. Results of the above type were obtained in the third order case by Azbelev and Caljuk [6].

Theorem 4.49   (Levin)   *If each of the integrals*

$$\int_\alpha^\beta c^+(x)\,dx, \qquad \int_\alpha^\beta c^-(x)\,dx$$

is bounded above by $32(\beta - \alpha)^{-2}$ $(\beta > \alpha)$, where $c^+(x) = \max[0, c(x)]$ and $c^-(x) = \max[0, -c(x)]$, then the third order equation $u''' + c(x)u = 0$ is nonoscillatory on $[\alpha, \beta]$. The constant 32 is the best possible.

Theorem 4.50   (Levin)   If

$$\int_\alpha^\beta c^+(x)\, dx \le 384(\beta - \alpha)^{-3}, \qquad \int_\alpha^\beta c^-(x)\, dx \le 192(\beta - \alpha)^{-3}$$

$$(\beta > \alpha),$$

the equation $u^{(4)} + c(x)u = 0$ is nonoscillatory on $[\alpha, \beta]$. The constants are the best possible.

Corollary   If $c(x) \ge 0$ on $[\alpha, \beta]$ and

$$\int_\alpha^\beta c(x)\, dx \le 384(\beta - \alpha)^{-3} \qquad (\beta > \alpha)$$

then the equation $u^{(4)} + c(x)u = 0$ is nonoscillatory on $[\alpha, \beta]$.

Let L be a differential operator of order n of the type (4.23). Levin [120] introduced the class T_{ik} of operators L for which the equation $Lu = 0$ has no nontrivial solution with a zero of order $\ge i$ at α and a zero of order $\ge k$ at β $(i + k \ge n)$, that is, no nontrivial solution u such that

$$u(\alpha) = u'(\alpha) = \cdots = u^{(i-1)}(\alpha) = u(\beta) = u'(\beta) = \cdots = u^{(k-1)}(\beta) = 0.$$

The generalized first conjugate point $\rho_k(\alpha)$ is defined as the infimum of all numbers γ $(\gamma > \alpha)$ for which $Lu = 0$ has a nontrivial solution with a zero of order $\ge n - k$ at α and a zero of order $\ge k$ at γ. If no such γ exists, $\rho_k(\alpha)$ is defined to be $+\infty$. The operator L^* adjoint to L is defined by the equation

$$L^*u = (-1)^n u^{(n)} + \sum_{i=1}^n (-1)^{n-i}[a_i(x)u]^{(n-i)}$$

as usual [35], and L is said to be *self-adjoint* iff $L = L^*$. It is easy to see that the following three statements are equivalent:
(1) $\rho_k(\alpha) = +\infty$;
(2) $L \in T_{n-k,k}$;
(3) $L^* \in T_{k, n-k}$ $(k = 1, 2, \ldots, n-1)$.

For $n = 2m$ $(m = 1, 2, \ldots)$, let M be the differential operator defined by the equation

$$Mu = \sum_{i=1}^m (-1)^{i+1}[b_i(x)u^{(m-i)}]^{(m-i)}, \tag{4.26}$$

where b_i denotes a nonnegative function of class $\mathscr{C}^{(m-i)}$ on $[\alpha, \beta]$. Levin obtained the following comparison theorem for the operators L and $L - M$.

Theorem 4.51　　　(Levin)　*Let L be a self-adjoint operator of the form (4.23) of even order $n = 2m$, and let M be the operator (4.26). If $L \in T_{m, m}$ then $L - M \in T_{m, m}$. In particular $D^n - M \in T_{m, m}$ where D denotes the operator d/dx.*

Levin [120] applied Theorem 4.51 to obtain the following nonoscillation theorem relative to the fourth order equations:

$$lu \equiv u^{(4)} + [b(x)u']' + c(x)u = 0,$$

$$Lu \equiv u^{(4)} + [B(x)u']' + C(x)u = 0,$$

where c, C are continuous and b, B are of class $\mathscr{C}^1$ on $[\alpha, \beta]$.

Theorem 4.52　　　(Čičkin [31]–Levin)　*The equation $lu = 0$ is nonoscillatory on $[\alpha, \beta]$ iff there exist functions B, C such that $B \in \mathscr{C}^1$, $C \in \mathscr{C}$, $B(x) \geq b(x)$, $C(x) \leq c(x)$, and $L \in T_{22}$ on $[\alpha, \beta]$, and a nontrivial nonnegative function v satisfying $v(\alpha) = v'(\alpha) = 0$ and $lv \leq 0$ on $[\alpha, \beta]$.*

Theorem 4.53　　　(Levin)　*If $n = 2m - 1$ ($m = 2, 3, \ldots$) then $D^n + M \in T_{m, m-1}$ and $D^n - M \in T_{m-1, m}$, where $D = d/dx$ and M is given by (4.26).*

Theorem 4.54　　　(Levin)　$D^{2m} - (-1)^m c(x) \in T_{m, m}$ *if c is continuous on $[\alpha, \beta]$ and*

$$\int_\alpha^\beta c^+(x)\, dx \leq 4^{2m-1}(2m - 1)[(m - 1)!]^2(\beta - \alpha)^{1-2m},$$

$$\beta > \alpha, \quad m = 1, 2, \ldots.$$

Theorem 4.55　　　(Levin)　*If each of the numbers i_1, $i_2 - i_1$, $\ldots$, $i_{n-1} - i_{n-2}$ is either zero or one, and if $c_i(x) \geq 0$ on $[\alpha, \beta]$ ($i = 0, 1, \ldots, n - 2$), then $L \in T_{n-1, 1}$ where L is defined by*

$$Lu = u^{(n)} - \sum_{k=1}^{n-1} [c_k(x)u^{(i_k)}]^{(k-i_k)} - c_0(x)u.$$

Examples of operators L for which this theorem is applicable are as follows:

(1)　$Lu = u^{(n)} + c_{n-1}u^{(n-1)} - c_{n-2}u^{(n-2)} - \cdots - c_0 u,$
　　　$c_i(x) \geq 0$　　　$(i = 0, 1, \ldots, n - 2);$
(2)　$Lu = u''' + (bu')' - cu$　　　$(c \geq 0);$
(3)　$Lu = u''' - (bu)' - cu$　　　$(b \geq 0;\ c \geq 0);$
(4)　$Lu = u^{(4)} - (bu')' - cu$　　　$(b \geq 0;\ c \geq 0).$

Levin also obtained the following monotonicity theorems for the function $\rho_k(\alpha)$ defined above.

Theorem 4.56   (Levin)   *If L is a self-adjoint operator of order $n = 2m$ of the form (4.23), then either $\rho_m(x)$ is strictly increasing on $[\alpha, \beta]$ or $\rho_m(x) = \infty$ for some x in $[\alpha, \beta)$.*

Theorem 4.57   (Levin)   *For some integer $k \geq 1$, suppose that the operator L defined by (4.23) has the properties*
   (1) $L \in T_{n-k+1,k} \cap T_{n-k,k+1}$;
   (2) $L^* \in T_{k+1,n-k}$.
Then either $\rho_k(x)$ is strictly increasing on $[\alpha, \beta]$ or $\rho_m(x) = \infty$ for some x in $[\alpha, \beta)$.

Theorem 4.58   (Levin)   *Suppose that $\rho_k(\alpha) = \beta < \infty$ for some α and some integer $k \geq 2$, and that*

$$\beta < \min[\rho_1(\alpha), \ldots, \rho_{k-1}(\alpha)].$$

Then a nontrivial solution of $Lu = 0$ with a zero of order $\geq n - k$ at α and a zero of order $\geq k$ at β is unique except for a constant factor and has no zeros in (α, β).

In 1962 Kiguradze [94] obtained the theorem below for the differential equation

$$u^{(n)} + c(x)u = 0, \qquad n \geq 2, \tag{4.27}$$

where c is continuous on $[0, \infty)$, as a special instance of his study of a class of nonlinear equations. The special case $Q(x) = x$ of the theorem had been found earlier by Kondrat'ev [102]. For even n and $Q(x) = x^{n-1}$, part (2) is an old result of Fite [45].

Theorem 4.59   (Fite–Kondrat'ev–Kiguradze)   *Let Q be an absolutely continuous function in $(0, \infty)$ with the properties $Q(x) > 0$, $Q'(x) \geq 0$ (where it exists), and*

$$\int^{\infty} [xQ(x)]^{-1} \, dx < \infty.$$

Then
   (1)   *If*

$$\int^{\infty} x^{n-1} |c(x)| \, dx < \infty,$$

   Eq. (4.27) is nonoscillatory;
   (2)   *If*

$$\int^{\infty} x^{n-1} c(x) Q^{-1}(x) \, dx = \infty \qquad and \qquad c(x) \geq 0,$$

   then Eq. (4.27) has an oscillatory solution and every nonoscillatory solution tends monotonically to zero as $x \to \infty$;

(3) *If*

$$\int^{\infty} x^{n-1} |c(x)| Q^{-1}(x) \, dx = \infty \qquad and \qquad c(x) \leq 0,$$

there exists a fundamental set of $[3 + (-1)^n]/2$ nonoscillatory solutions and $n - [3 + (-1)^n]/2$ oscillatory solutions, $n \geq 3$.

In the special case $n = 4$ and $Q(x) = x$, assertion (1) reduces to Theorem 3.81. Theorem 4.59 also partially contains some of the other oscillation criteria of Chapter 3 and Section 4 of this chapter.

Glazman [50, p. 96] obtained the following modification of the nonoscillation criterion (1) of Theorem 4.59: *For even $n = 2m$, Eq. (4.27) is nonoscillatory if*

$$\limsup_{x \to \infty} x^{2m-1} \int_x^{\infty} |c^-(t)| \, dt < \alpha_m^2/(2m - 1),$$

where $\alpha_m = 2^{-m}(2m - 1)!!$ and $c^-(t)$ is defined in Theorem 4.49. This is an extension of Hille's Theorem 2.1 (when $n = 2$) and Howard's Theorem 3.86 (when $n = 4$). Glazman also proved [50, p. 96] that (4.27) is nonoscillatory if the inequality $c(x) \geq (-1)^{m+1} \alpha_m^2 x^{-2m}$ ($n = 2m$) holds for all $x \geq x_0$ for some x_0. This extends Kneser's classical theorem on second order equations (Chapter 2, Section 1), and also can be compared with Theorem 3.75 in the case $n = 4$.

Glazman gave the following conditions, any one of which is sufficient for (4.27) to be oscillatory (when $n = 2m$) [50, 51]:

(1) $(-1)^m \int_0^{\infty} c(x) \, dx = -\infty$ (where no assumption is made on the sign of $c(x)$)

(2) $(-1)^m c(x) \leq 0$ for large x and

$$\limsup_{x \to \infty} x^{2m-1} \int_x^{\infty} |c(t)| \, dt > A_m^2,$$

where

$$A_m^{-1} = \frac{(2m - 1)^{1/2}}{(m - 1)!} \sum_{k=1}^{m} \frac{(-1)^{k-1}}{2m - k} \binom{m - 1}{k - 1}.$$

(3) $f(x) \equiv (-1)^m c(x) + \alpha_m^2 x^{-2m} \leq 0$ and

$$\limsup_{r \to \infty} \log r \int_r^{\infty} x^{2m-1} |f(x)| \, dx = \infty.$$

Additional related results of Glazman are contained in the references cited.

The following related result was found by Anan'eva and Balaganskiĭ [1] under the assumptions that $c(x) > 0$ and

$$\int^{\infty} x^{n-2}c(x)\,dx = \infty,$$

the latter being condition (2) of Theorem 4.59 when $Q(x) = x$: *For even n every nontrivial solution of* (4.27) *is oscillatory, and for odd n every solution which is not oscillatory has the property that* $u^{(k)}(x) \to 0$ *as* $x \to \infty$ $(k = 0, 1, \ldots, n - 1)$. Anan'eva and Balaganskiĭ give an example to show that this theorem is false under the weaker assumption

$$\int^{\infty} x^{n-1}c(x)\,dx = \infty.$$

A classical result of Kneser [95] gives the same conclusions under the stronger assumption $\lim c(x) > 0$ $(x \to \infty)$.

Komlenko [96] in 1965 gave estimates for the length of the interval $(0, R)$ in which the solution $u(x)$ of the initial value problem

$$u^{(n)} + c(x)u = 0$$

$$u^{(k)}(0) = 0 \quad (k = 0, 1, \ldots, n - 2), \quad u^{(n-1)}(0) = 1 \tag{4.28}$$

has no zeros, where c is assumed only to be real-valued and summable on each finite interval. As pointed out by Komlenko, a number of problems can be reduced to such an estimate: for example, the question of sign invariance of Green's function for various boundary problems associated with Eq. (4.27). Komlenko appeals to the following comparison theorem of Azbelev and Caljuk [6] in obtaining his results.

Theorem 4.60   (Azbelev and Caljuk)   *Let $u(x)$ be the solution of* (4.28) *and let $v(x)$ be the solution of the same initial value problem with $c(x)$ replaced by $c^{+}(x)$ (defined in Theorem 4.49). If $v(x) > 0$ in $(0, R)$, then $v(x) \leq u(x)$ in this interval.*

Let $y_1, y_2, \ldots, y_n$ denote a set of n linearly independent solutions of the differential equation $y^{(n)} + c(x)y = 0$, where c is a real-valued summable function on the interval under consideration. The Wronskian $\det(y_i^{(j-1)}(x))$ $(i, j = 1, 2, \ldots, n)$ of these solutions is a constant by Abel's formula [90, p. 119], and can be taken to be 1 without loss of generality. Then the Cauchy function (that is, the variation of parameters kernel [35, p. 190]) of $y^{(n)} + c(x)y$ is given by

$$G(x, t) = \begin{vmatrix} y_1(t) & y_2(t) & \cdots & y_n(t) \\ \vdots & \vdots & \vdots & \vdots \\ y_1^{(n-2)}(t) & y_2^{(n-2)}(t) & \cdots & y_n^{(n-2)}(t) \\ y_1(x) & y_2(x) & \cdots & y_n(x) \end{vmatrix}.$$

Theorem 4.61   (Komlenko)   *If the inequalities*

$$G(x, t) > 0, \qquad \int_t^x G(x, s)G(s, t)[c(s) - f(s)]^+ \, ds < G(x, t)$$

hold in the triangle $0 < t < x < R$, *then the solution* $u(x)$ *of* (4.28) *has no zeros in* $(0, R)$.

Theorem 4.62   (Komlenko)   *If the inequality* $c(x) \leq (2n - 1)!/(n - 1)! R^n$ *holds almost everywhere on* $[0, R]$, *then the solution of* (4.28) *has no zeros in* $(0, R)$.

Theorem 4.63   (Komlenko)   *Let* $C_2 = 1$, $C_3 = 343/81\sqrt{3}$, $C_4 = 9$. *If* $c(x) \leq C_n(\pi/R)^n$ $(n = 2, 3, 4)$ *almost everywhere on* $[0, R]$, *then the solution of* (4.28) *has no zeros in* $(0, R)$. *If* $|c(x)| \leq C_3(\pi/R)^3$ *almost everywhere on* $[0, R]$, *then every nontrivial solution of Eq.* (4.27) *with* $n = 3$ *has at most two zeros on* $[0, R]$ *(counting a double zero twice)*.

Komlenko applied the above results, in particular, to the second order equation $u'' + c(x)u = 0$ and obtained some nonoscillation and boundedness criteria for the solutions.

Various modifications, connections with other topics, and applications of the theorems in this section are contained in the work of Anan'eva and Balaganskiĭ [1], Aramă [2], Atkinson [4], Azbelev [5], and Azbelev and Caljuk [6], Čičkin [32], El'šin [42], Glazman [51], Halanay and Shandar [60], Hukuhara [86], Hustý [88], Kalafati [92], Kiguradze [94], Kondrat'ev [99–102], Levin [119, 120], Mikusiński [132], Pavlyuk [148], Putnam [157], and Zoobawa [223].

Exercises

1. Complete the table of oscillation types after Theorem 4.48 to $n = 10$.
2. What is the analog of Theorem 4.49 when $n = 2$?
3. Find some connections that Theorem 4.53 has with the results of Section 2 when $n = 3$.
4. Discuss Theorem 4.54 when $m = 2$.
5. Give some examples besides those in the text of operators L to which Theorem 4.55 could be applied.
6. Show that Theorem 4.59 contains some of the oscillation criteria obtained earlier when $n = 2, 3$, and 4.

Research problems

7. The comparison theorems 4.46–4.48 deal only with the case that $a_n(x)$ in (4.23) varies. However, comparison theorems are known (see Chapters 1,

3, and 4, Section 2) for $n = 2$, 3, and 4 when $a_{n-1}(x)$ as well as $a_n(x)$ varies. What are the analogs of these theorems for $n > 4$?

8. Can Theorems 4.49 and 4.50 be extended to $n > 4$?

9. Find Hille–Kneser-type oscillation criteria for arbitrary integers n.

10. An analog of the eigenvalue problem (3.1) can be stated for arbitrary self-adjoint operators of even order $2m$ ($m = 1, 2, \ldots$), with an associated Courant minimax principle (Theorem 3.1). Use this as a starting point for generalizing the results of Chapter 3 to self-adjoint differential equations of order $2m$.

7. Nonoscillation Theorems for Systems of Differential Equations

In 1952 Sternberg [183] extended the results of Hille [81], Leighton [115], and Wintner [215] for second order equations, as described in Chapter 2, to systems composed of n linear second order ordinary equations together with m ($0 \leq m < n$) linear first order ordinary equations.

Systems of this type (when $m = 0$) had been considered earlier by Morse [136], Bliss and Schoenberg [23], and Reid [168] in connection with the calculus of variations. These authors defined conjugate and focal points for systems and obtained some separation, comparison, and oscillation theorems akin to those described above for single equations. Later related results are contained in papers by Barrett [11], Levinson [124], Reid [169–172], Sternberg [183], and Wintner [218].

Using two variational theorems of Reid obtained in connection with Bolza's classical nonparametric problem in the calculus of variations, Sternberg [183] obtained a matrix analog of Hille's necessary and sufficient condition (Theorem 2.22) for a single second order equation to be nonoscillatory: This is Sternberg's theorem 4.66 below. In addition, Sternberg obtained analogs of both the integral type and the limit type oscillation criteria of Hille, Wintner, and Leighton, as described in Chapter 2 (e.g., Theorems 2.1, 2.24, and 2.41).

Notations Capital Roman letters A, B, C, $\ldots$ will be used to denote n-square matrices and capital German letters $\mathfrak{A}$, $\mathfrak{B}$, $\ldots$ to denote $m \times n$ matrices, all of whose elements are real-valued functions on an interval $\alpha \leq x \leq \beta$ ($\alpha < \beta$). Lower case Roman letters u, v, $\ldots$ will denote n-vectors and lower case German letters $\mathfrak{a}$, $\mathfrak{b}$, $\ldots$ will denote m-vectors ($0 \leq m < n$). A matrix or vector is said to be of class $\mathscr{C}^m$ ($m = 0, 1, \ldots$) iff its elements are all of class $\mathscr{C}^m$. A superscript T will denote the transpose of a matrix or vector and a prime will denote the derivative with respect to x. The notation $\lim A(x)$ ($x \to x_0$) refers to the matrix whose elements (if they exist) are the limits of the elements of $A(x)$ as $x \to x_0$.

Sternberg considered the following system of $n + m$ ($0 \leq m < n$) ordinary differential equations

$$L[y, \mathfrak{a}] \equiv [A(x)y' + B(x)y + \mathfrak{A}^T(x)\mathfrak{a}]'$$
$$\qquad - [B^T(x)y' + C(x)y + \mathfrak{B}^T(x)\mathfrak{a}] = 0 \qquad (4.29)$$
$$M[y] \equiv [\mathfrak{A}(x)y' + \mathfrak{B}(x)y] = 0$$

in an interval $[\alpha, \infty)$, where A, B are n-square matrices of class $\mathscr{C}^1$, C is an n-square matrix of class $\mathscr{C}$, $\mathfrak{A}$ is an $m \times n$ matrix of class $\mathscr{C}^1$, $\mathfrak{B}$ is an $m \times n$ matrix of class $\mathscr{C}$, and A, C are symmetric. In the case $m = 0$, (4.29) is a system of n second order equations of the form

$$Ly \equiv [A(x)y' + B(x)y]' - [B^T(x)y' + C(x)y] = 0, \qquad (4.30)$$

and it is assumed that $A(x)$ is positive definite in $[\alpha, \infty)$ (and therefore non-singular). In the case of general m ($0 < m < n$) the positive definiteness of $A(x)$ is replaced by the assumption that $\mathfrak{A}(x)$ has constant rank m and $u^T A(x)u > 0$ for all n-vectors $u \neq 0$ such that $\mathfrak{A}(x)u = 0$.

Sternberg showed that the system (4.29) can be reduced to the canonical form

$$u' = E(x)v, \qquad v' = -F(x)u \qquad (4.31)$$

by a suitable transformation, where $E(x)$ and $F(x)$ are symmetric n-square matrices of class $\mathscr{C}^1[\alpha, \infty)$, $E(x)$ is positive semidefinite and of constant rank $n - m$ in $[\alpha, \infty)$, and u, v are unknown n-vectors. The details of the reduction as well as the proofs of the theorems below will not be given here. (See Sternberg [183] and Reid [169, 172].)

As in the case $n = 1$, $m = 0$ considered in Chapter 2, the system (4.31) is said to be *nonoscillatory in* $[\alpha_0, \infty)$ iff no nontrivial solution u, v of (4.31) exists such that $u(x)$ is equal to the zero vector at two points of $[\alpha_0, \infty)$; it is said to be *nonoscillatory* (without reference to an interval) iff there exists a number α_0 ($\alpha_0 \geq \alpha$) such that it is nonoscillatory in $[\alpha_0, \infty)$. The system (4.29) is defined to be nonoscillatory iff (4.31) is nonoscillatory.

Theorem 4.64   (Reid [168]–Sternberg [183])   *The system* (4.31) *(and hence also* (4.29)*) is nonoscillatory iff there exists an n-square symmetric matrix $W = W(x)$ of class $\mathscr{C}^1$ which satisfies the Riccati-type matrix differential equation*

$$S[W] \equiv W' + WE(x)W + F(x) = 0 \qquad (4.32)$$

for large x.

Theorem 4.65   (Sternberg)   *The system* (4.31) *is nonoscillatory iff there exists an n-square symmetric matrix $W = W(x)$ of class $\mathscr{C}^1$ such that $S[W]$, as defined by* (4.32)*, is negative semidefinite for large x.*

Theorem 4.65 reduces to Wintner's theorem 2.15 in the case of a single second order differential equation. In 1956 Reid [169, p. 745] extended the last two theorems to matrices with complex-valued elements. He obtained necessary and sufficient conditions analogous to those given in Theorems 4.64 and 4.65 for (4.31) to be nonoscillatory specifically in an interval $[\alpha, \infty)$.

Theorem 4.66   (Sternberg)   *Suppose that $B(x) \equiv 0$ in (4.30) (without essential loss of generality, as shown by Sternberg), and that $u^T A(x)u \le (x^p/k)u^T u$ in $[\alpha, \infty)$, $\alpha > 0$, $k > 0$, $0 \le p < 1$, for all n-vectors u. Suppose also that $F(x)$ in the canonical form (4.31) is positive semidefinite in $[\alpha, \infty)$. Then (4.30) is nonoscillatory iff*

$$\int_\alpha^\infty F(x)\, dx$$

exists and an n-square positive semidefinite symmetric matrix $W(x)$ of class $\mathscr{C}^1$ exists which satisfies the matrix integral equation

$$W(x) = \int_x^\infty W(t)E(t)W(t)\, dt + \int_x^\infty F(t)\, dt$$

for large x. Moreover, if (4.30) is nonoscillatory under the hypotheses given, then

$$\limsup_{x \to \infty} [kx^{1-p}/(1-p)]v^T W(x)v \le 1 \qquad\qquad (*)$$

for each such matrix $W(x)$ and each constant vector v satisfying $v^T v = 1$. In particular $\lim x^r W(x) = 0$ $(x \to \infty)$ for every number $r < 1 - p$.

Theorem 4.66 generalizes Hille's theorem 2.22, proved in Chapter 2 for a single second order differential equation. In 1956 Reid [169] extended Theorem 4.66 to systems involving complex-valued functions. Reid also showed that Theorem 4.66 remains true if k/x^p in that theorem is replaced by $\varphi(x)$ and $(*)$ is replaced by

$$\limsup_{x \to \infty} \left(\int_\alpha^x \varphi(t)\, dt \right) v^T W(x)v \le 1,$$

where φ is any positive function in $[\alpha, \infty)$ such that

$$\int_\alpha^\infty \varphi(x)\, dx = \infty.$$

Reid obtained an interesting extension to systems of Leighton and Wintner's sufficient condition for a second order equation to be oscillatory (Theorem 2.24). Actually Reid's theorem generalizes the Leighton–Wintner result slightly even in the case of a single equation. Additional related results of Reid can be found in [168–172]. The details are omitted since these results are not exactly within the scope of this book.

The next result generalizes Hille's theorem 2.1.

Theorem 4.67   (Sternberg)   *Suppose that $B(x) \equiv 0$ in (4.30) and that $A(x)$ and $F(x)$ satisfy the same hypotheses as in Theorem 4.66. Then necessary conditions for (4.30) to be nonoscillatory are that*

$$\int_\alpha^\infty x^r F(x)\, dx$$

exists for each number r satisfying $0 \le r < 1 - p$, and that for each constant n-vector v satisfying $v^T v = 0$ the following inequalities hold:

$$\lim_{x \to \infty} \sup [kx^{1-p}/(1 - p)] v^T \left[\int_x^\infty F(t)\, dt \right] v \le 1,$$

$$\lim_{x \to \infty} \inf [kx^{1-p}/(1 - p)] v^T \left[\int_x^\infty F(t)\, dt \right] v \le \tfrac{1}{4}.$$

Sternberg also gave a partial analog of this result for the system (4.29), i.e., for arbitrary m ($0 \le m < n$). The next result gives a sufficient condition for nonoscillation of (4.29).

Theorem 4.68   (Sternberg)   *Suppose that $B(x) \equiv 0$ and $\mathfrak{B}(x) \equiv 0$ in (4.29) (without essential loss of generality, as shown by Sternberg). Suppose that $u^T A(x)u \ge ku^T u$ in $[\alpha, \infty)$, $\alpha > 0$, $k > 0$, for all n-vectors u satisfying $\mathfrak{A}(x)u = 0$. Then a sufficient condition for (4.29) to be nonoscillatory is that there exists a symmetric constant matrix H such that*

$$\left| v^T \left[\int_\alpha^x tF(t)\, dt - H \right] v \right| < k/2$$

for each constant n-vector v satisfying $v^T v = 1$ and each sufficiently large number x. In particular, (4.29) is nonoscillatory under the hypotheses given in the theorem if

$$\int_\alpha^\infty xF(x)\, dx$$

exists.

The next theorem is a generalization of the Hille–Wintner comparison theorem 2.12 to systems. Consider, in addition to (4.29), a second system

$$L^* y \equiv [A^*(x)y']' - C^*(x)y = 0 \qquad (4.33)$$

(of the form (4.30)) of n second order equations whose coefficients A^*, C^*

satisfy the same conditions as A, C, respectively, in (4.29), with associated canonical form

$$u' = E^*(x)v, \qquad v' = -F^*(x)u. \tag{4.34}$$

Comparison Theorem 4.69   (Sternberg)   *Suppose that $B(x) \equiv 0$, $\mathfrak{B}(x) \equiv 0$ in (4.29) (without essential loss of generality), that $u^T A^*(x)u \leq (1/k^*)u^T u$ in $[\alpha, \infty)$, $\alpha > 0$, $k^* > 0$, for all n-vectors u, and that $v^T A(x)v \geq kv^T v$ in $[\alpha, \infty)$ for some $k > 0$ and all n-vectors v satisfying $\mathfrak{A}(x)v = 0$. Suppose also that*

$$\int_\alpha^\infty F(x)\, dx \qquad and \qquad \int_\alpha^\infty F^*(x)\, dx$$

exist and are finite, and that each of the matrices $F(x)$, $F^*(x)$, and

$$\int_x^\infty [F^*(t) - F(t)]\, dt$$

is positive semidefinite in $\alpha \leq x < \infty$. If

$$\int_\alpha^\infty xF^*(x)\, dx$$

converges and (4.33) is nonoscillatory, then also

$$\int_\alpha^\infty xF(x)\, dx$$

converges and (4.29) is nonoscillatory.

Reid [172] obtained an analog of the Nehari–Leighton–Howard non-oscillation criterion, relative to an eigenvalue problem associated with the system (4.31) (Theorem 2.2 for a second order equation; Theorems 3.64 and 3.65 for a fourth order equation). In order to simplify the statements we shall obtain the results for (4.31) rather than the slightly more general system considered by Reid.

For $\alpha \leq \gamma < \delta < \infty$, consider the eigenvalue problem

$$u' = E(x)v, \qquad v' = -[F(x) + \lambda K(x)]u, \qquad v(\gamma) = u(\delta) = 0, \tag{4.35}$$

where $E(x)$ and $F(x)$ are as in (4.31) and $K(x)$ is a continuous symmetric matrix in $[\alpha, \infty)$ such that the matrix

$$\int_\gamma^\delta y^T(x)K(x)\, dx$$

is positive definite for arbitrary vectors $y \in \mathscr{C}^1$. It is assumed in addition that (4.31) is identically normal in $[\alpha, \infty)$, that is, if u, v is a solution of (4.31) and $u(x) \equiv 0$ on $[\gamma, \delta]$ ($\alpha \leq \gamma < \delta < \infty$), then $v(x) \equiv 0$ on $[\gamma, \delta]$.

In addition to (4.35), Reid considered the eigenvalue problem

$$u' = E(x)v, \qquad v' = -[F(x) + \mu K(x)]u, \qquad u(\gamma) = v(\delta) = 0. \qquad (4.36)$$

Reid [172] showed that (4.35), (4.36) have denumerable sets of eigenvalues λ_j, μ_j, respectively ($j = 1, 2, \ldots$) with the usual properties. The notations $\lambda_j[\gamma, \delta]$, $\mu_j[\gamma, \delta]$ will be used for the jth eigenvalues of (4.35), (4.36), respectively, to indicate the dependence on the interval $[\gamma, \delta]$. The following extends Theorem 3.64 to systems of differential equations.

Theorem 4.70   (Reid) *Suppose for arbitrary γ ($\gamma \geq \alpha$) there exists a number $\delta > \gamma$ such that $\lambda_n[\gamma, \delta] < 0$. Then, for $\alpha_1 \geq \alpha$, (4.31) is nonoscillatory in $[\alpha_1, \infty)$ iff $\mu_1 [\alpha_1, \beta] > 0$ for all $\beta > \alpha_1$.*

On the basis of this result Reid obtained the following oscillation criteria.

Theorem 4.71   (Reid) *Suppose in addition to the assumptions stated in connection with (4.31) and (4.35) that (1) $F(x)$ is positive semidefinite in $[\alpha, \infty)$ and positive definite at some points x_k in $[\alpha, \infty]$ such that $\lim x_k = \infty$ ($k \to \infty$); and (2)*

$$v^T\left[\int_\alpha^x E(t)\, dt\right]v \to \infty \qquad as \quad x \to \infty$$

for all constant nonzero n-vectors v. Then, for $\alpha_1 \geq \alpha$, the system (4.31) is non-oscillatory in $[\alpha_1, \infty)$ iff $\mu_1[\alpha_1, \beta] > 0$ for all $\beta > \alpha_1$.

Theorem 4.72   (Reid) *Suppose in addition to the assumptions stated in connection with (4.31) and (4.35) that $F(x)$ is positive semidefinite in $[\alpha, \infty)$, that*

$$v_0^T\left[\int_\alpha^x F(t)\, dt\right]v_0 \to \infty \qquad as \quad x \to \infty$$

for some constant nonzero vector v_0, and that (2) of Theorem 4.71 holds. Then the system (4.31) is oscillatory in $[\alpha, \infty)$.

We conclude this section with an interesting comparison theorem of Reid, relating the eigenvalues of (4.35), (4.36), and the problem

$$u' = E(x)v, \qquad v' = -[F(x) + \nu K(x)]u, \qquad u(\gamma) = u(\delta) = 0. \qquad (4.37)$$

Theorem 4.73   (Reid) *For arbitrary β, γ, δ satisfying $\alpha \leq \beta < \gamma < \delta$ and arbitrary positive integers i, j, satisfying $i + j > n$,*

$$\nu_{i+j-n}[\beta, \delta] \leq \max(\mu_i[\beta, \gamma], \lambda_j[\gamma, \delta]).$$

This theorem is basic in Reid's proofs of Theorems 4.70–4.72.

Yakubovič [221, 222] obtained general oscillation theorems for canonical "Hamiltonian" systems of the form $dY/dx = JH(x)Y$, where Y is a $2k$-vector $(k = 1, 2, \ldots)$, $H(x)$ is a real symmetric $2k$-square matrix with Lebesgue-integrable elements $[0, \infty)$, and J is the $2k$-square symplectic matrix given by

$$J = \begin{pmatrix} 0 & I_k \\ -I_k & 0 \end{pmatrix},$$

where I_k is the unit k-square matrix. Yakubovič gave some new definitions of nonoscillation for such systems and obtained nonoscillation criteria somewhat different from those described above.

8. Whyburn's Second Order System

Whyburn [210] considered the second order system

$$y'' + p(x)y = q(x)z$$
$$z'' + p(x)z = r(x)y \tag{4.38}$$

where p, q, and r are continuous functions on an interval $[\alpha, \beta]$. If $q \neq 0$ and $p/q \in \mathscr{C}^2[\alpha, \beta]$, then (4.38) is equivalent to the fourth order equation

$$[a(x)u'']' + [b(x)u']' + c(x)u = 0, \tag{3.18}$$

where $a \neq 0$, and a, b'', and c are continuous on $[\alpha, \beta]$. Indeed, the substitutions

$$a = 1/q, \qquad b = 2p/q, \qquad\qquad c = (p/q)'' + p^2/q - r,$$
$$u = y, \qquad z = u''/q + pu/q \tag{4.39}$$

into (3.18) and simplification yields the system (4.38). On the other hand, division of the first equation (4.38) by $q(x)$, calculation of z'' from the resulting equation, substitution into the second equation (4.38), and use of the relations

$$q = 1/a, \qquad p = b/2a, \qquad r = b''/2 + b^2/4a - c$$

(obtained from (4.39)) yields (3.18).

Theorem 4.74   (Whyburn)   *Let y, z be a nontrivial solution of the system (4.38). If $q(x)r(x) < 0$ on $[\alpha, \beta]$, then the zeros of $y(x)$ and $z(x)$ separate each other on this interval with the possible exception of a neighborhood of one point at which $yz' - zy'$ vanishes.*

Theorem 4.75   (Whyburn)   *Suppose $q(x)r(x) < 0$ on $[\alpha, \beta]$. If there exists a nontrivial solution w of $w'' + p(x)w = 0$ with two zeros on $[\alpha, \beta]$, then $y(x)z(x)$ has at least one zero on $[\alpha, \beta]$ for every solution y, z of (4.38).*

Any pair of nontrivial solutions y, z of (4.38) defines an *integral curve* in the yz-plane as x ranges over $[\alpha, \beta]$. In the case that $\beta = \infty$, the system (4.38) is said to be *oscillatory* iff this integral curve circulates the origin an infinite number of times as x ranges over $[\alpha, \infty)$; this means that, for arbitrary $X \geq \alpha$ there exists a $Y > X$ such that the curve spirals about the origin for $X \leq x \leq Y$.

Theorem 4.76   (Whyburn)   *Suppose that* $p(x) \equiv 0$ *and* $q(x)r(x) < 0$ *in* $[\alpha, \infty]$, *and that*

$$\int_\alpha^\infty xq(x)\, dx = \infty, \qquad \int_\alpha^\infty xr(x)\, dx = \infty. \qquad (4.40)$$

Then every nontrivial solution y, z *of* (4.38) *for which*

$$q(\alpha)[y(\alpha)z'(\alpha) - z(\alpha)y'(\alpha)] \leq 0$$

is oscillatory. If (4.40) *is replaced by*

$$\int_\alpha^\infty q(x)\, dx = \infty, \qquad \int_\alpha^\infty r(x)\, dx = \infty,$$

then every solution y, z *of* (4.38) *is either oscillatory or there exists a number* β *in* $[\alpha, \infty)$ *such that* $y^2(x) + z^2(x)$ *tends monotonically to zero in* $[\beta, \infty)$ *as* $x \to \infty$.

Theorem 4.77   (Whyburn)   *Suppose* $p \in \mathscr{C}^1$, $p(x) < 0$, $p'(x) \leq 0$, *and* $q(x)r(x) < 0$ *in* $[\alpha, \infty)$. *If there exists a constant* γ *such that* $|q|(-p)^{-1/2} \geq \gamma$ *and* $|r|(-p)^{-1/2} \geq \gamma$, *then every solution* y, z *of* (4.38) *is oscillatory provided* $q(\alpha)[y(\alpha)z'(\alpha) - z(\alpha)y'(\alpha)] \leq 0$. *If, in addition to the hypotheses above,* $(q + r)^2 \leq 4p^2$ *in* $[\alpha, \infty)$, *then either every solution* y, z *of* (4.38) *is oscillatory or* $y^2(x) + z^2(x)$ *tends monotonically to zero in* $[\beta, \infty)$ *for some* β.

Whyburn obtained many other similar results in the case that $q(x)r(x) > 0$, and also in the case that $[\alpha, \infty)$ is replaced by the entire x-axis. In particular, he obtained analogs of several of the theorems of Birkhoff and Reynolds (Section 5) involving regular intervals and conjugate points (as they are called today).

Barrett [8–12] obtained nonoscillation and disconjugacy theorems for (4.38), especially in the case $p(x) \equiv 0$, i.e., $b(x) \equiv 0$ in (3.18) and $c(x) = -r(x)$. Barrett's comparison theorems for the conjugate points $\delta_1(\alpha)$, $\mu_1(\alpha)$, and $v_1(\alpha)$ and related results are described in Chapter 3, Sections 3 and 4. In [11] Barrett defined the *first systems-conjugate point* $\omega_1(\alpha)$ to be the smallest number $\beta \in (\alpha, \infty)$ for which there exists a nontrivial solution of (4.38) satisfying $y(\alpha) = z(\alpha) = y(\beta) = z(\beta) = 0$. If $\omega_1(\alpha)$ does not exist, Eq. (3.18) is called *systems-disconjugate in* (α, ∞). Barrett [11] proved that the existence of $\delta_1(\alpha)$ implies the existence of $\omega_1(\alpha)$.

Most of Barrett's results as well as the earlier results of Leighton and Nehari [Chapter 3, Sections 1–4, 6–8] required $c(x)$ to have constant sign. However, Barrett obtained the following interesting comparison theorem for arbitrary continuous functions c [11].

Theorem 4.78   (Barrett)   *Suppose that $a(x) > 0$, $b(x) \equiv 0$, and that a and c are continuous in* $[0, \infty)$. *Let $f(x) = [k/a(x) + c(x)/k]/2$. If there exists a positive constant k such that no nontrivial solution z satisfying $z(\alpha) = 0 (\alpha > 0)$ of either of the second order equations $z'' \pm f(x)z = 0$ has a zero in (α, ∞), then $\delta_1(\alpha)$ and $\omega_1(\alpha)$ do not exist for (3.18) (or equivalently, for the system (4.38)). In other words, if both of the second order equations are disconjugate, then the fourth order equation (3.18) is both disconjugate and systems-disconjugate.*

Related theorems can be found in the papers of Barrett already cited.

The Hukuhara–Caligo–Bellman stability criterion stated at the end of Section 5 has the following analog for systems of first order differential equations: *Let $C = (C_{ij})$ be an n-square constant matrix, and let $A = (A_{ij})$ be an n-square matrix whose elements are measurable functions in* $[0, \infty)$ *such that*

$$\int_0^\infty \sum_{i, j = 1}^n |A_{ij}(x)| \, dx < \infty.$$

If every solution of the system $du/dx = Cu$ is bounded in $[0, \infty)$, *then also every solution of $dv/dx = [C + A(x)]v$ is bounded in* $[0, \infty)$. Various formulations of this theorem and related results were proved by Caligo [26], Bellman [15], Levinson [123], and Weyl [209]. An easy proof is given in Cesari's monograph [29]. The reader also is referred to Bellman's book [17] for a detailed treatment of stability theory.

Chapter 5

Partial Differential Equations

1. Introduction

Comparison theorems of Sturm's type will be obtained for the linear elliptic partial differential equations

$$lu \equiv \sum_{i,j=1}^{n} D_i(a_{ij} D_j u) + 2 \sum_{i=1}^{n} b_i D_i u + cu = 0, \tag{5.1}$$

$$Lv \equiv \sum_{i,j=1}^{n} D_i(A_{ij} D_j v) + 2 \sum_{i=1}^{n} B_i D_i v + Cv = 0 \tag{5.2}$$

in bounded or unbounded domains $\mathscr{R}$ in n-dimensional Euclidean space E^n. The boundary $\mathscr{P}$ of $\mathscr{R}$ is supposed to have a piecewise continuous unit normal vector (n_i) at each point. Points of E^n are denoted by $x = (x^1, x^2, \ldots, x^n)$ and differentiation with respect to x^i is denoted by D_i, $i = 1, 2, \ldots, n$. The coefficients a_{ij}, b_i, c, A_{ij}, B_i, and C in (5.1) and (5.2) are assumed to be real and continuous on $\mathscr{R} \cup \mathscr{P}$, and the matrices (a_{ij}) and (A_{ij}) symmetric and positive definite in $\mathscr{R}$ (ellipticity condition). For some results the b_i are required to be differentiable in $\mathscr{R}$ as well. A "solution" of (5.1) [or (5.2)] is supposed to be continuous in $\mathscr{R} \cup \mathscr{P}$ and have uniformly continuous first partial derivatives in $\mathscr{R}$, and all derivatives involved in (5.1) (or 5.2)) are supposed to exist, be continuous, and satisfy the differential equation at every point in $\mathscr{R}$.

In the self-adjoint case $b_i = B_i = 0$, $i = 1, 2, \ldots, n$, the *variation of lu is* defined as

$$V[u] = \int_{\mathscr{R}} \left[\sum_{i,j=1}^{n} (a_{ij} - A_{ij}) D_i u D_j u + (C - c)u^2 \right] dx. \tag{5.3}$$

This definition will be extended to the general elliptic equations (5.1), (5.2) in Section 3. The following analog of Theorem 1.4 will be proved in the next section; it was obtained in 1965 by Clark and the author [34].

186

Theorem 5.1   *Let $\mathcal{R}$ be a bounded domain in E^n whose boundary $\mathcal{P}$ has a piecewise continuous unit normal. Suppose $b_i = B_i = 0$ in (5.1) and (5.2), $i = 1$, 2, ..., n. If there exists a nontrivial solution u of lu = 0 in $\mathcal{R}$ such that u = 0 on $\mathcal{P}$ and $V[u] \geq 0$, then every solution of Lv = 0 vanishes at some point of $\mathcal{R} \cup \mathcal{P}$.*

In the case $n = 1$, because the solutions of second order ordinary linear differential equations have only simple zeros [35, p. 208], it was shown in Section 1 of Chapter 1 that every solution v of $Lv = 0$ must in fact have a zero in $\mathcal{R}$ [which reduces to an open interval (α, β)] unless v is a constant multiple of u. Thus Theorem 5.1 reduces to the general comparison Theorem 1.5 when $n = 1$.

Hartman and Wintner [79] were the first investigators to extend the Sturm–Picone theorem 1.2 to self-adjoint elliptic equations. They obtained a slightly weaker result than the following special case of Theorem 5.1.

Corollary 5.2   *Let $\mathcal{R}$ be a bounded domain in E^n whose boundary $\mathcal{P}$ has a piecewise continuous unit normal. Suppose that Eqs. (5.1) and (5.2) are self-adjoint, i.e., $b_i = B_i = 0$, $i = 1, 2, \ldots, n$, and that $(a_{ij} - A_{ij})$ is positive semidefinite and $C \geq c$ on $\mathcal{R} \cup \mathcal{P}$. If there exists a nontrivial solution u of lu = 0 in $\mathcal{R}$ such that u = 0 on $\mathcal{P}$, then every solution of Lv = 0 vanishes at some point of $\mathcal{R} \cup \mathcal{P}$.*

Hartman and Wintner assumed in addition that L is a "strict Sturmian majorant" of l. This means in addition to the above nonnegative conditions either that $C \neq c$ at some point or (if $C \equiv c$) that $(a_{ij} - A_{ij})$ is positive definite and $c \neq 0$ at some point. It will be shown in the next section that the Hartman–Wintner theorem is true even if (A_{ij}) is only positive *semidefinite*. Also, an example will be given to illustrate that Theorem 5.1 is stronger than the Hartman–Wintner theorem (or Corollary 5.2). It is interesting to note the simplicity of the proof of Theorem 5.1: all that is required is an extension of the identity (1.7) to n dimensions and Green's identity (i.e., the formula for integration by parts).

Comparison theorems are obtained for the general linear elliptic equations (5.1), (5.2) in Section 3, and the results are extended to unbounded domains in Section 4. Some related theorems for complex-valued solutions and subsolutions are contained in Section 5. Lower bounds for eigenvalues and oscillation criteria are obtained in Sections 6 and 7, respectively, as applications of the results of Section 5. The final section deals with comparison theorems for eigenfunctions, in analogy with Section 5 of Chapter 1.

2. Comparison Theorems for Self-Adjoint Equations in Bounded Domains

In the self-adjoint case, $b_i = B_i = 0$, $i = 1, 2, \ldots, n$ in (5.1), (5.2), respectively. The differential operator L defined by (5.2) is then the Euler–Jacobi operator associated with the quadratic functional

$$M[u] = \int_{\mathscr{R}} \left(\sum_{i,j} A_{ij} D_i u D_j u - Cu^2 \right) dx. \tag{5.4}$$

The domain $\mathfrak{D}$ of M is defined to be the set of all real-valued continuous functions on $\mathscr{R} \cup \mathscr{P}$ which vanish on $\mathscr{P}$ and have uniformly continuous first partial derivatives in $\mathscr{R}$.

The following is an n-dimensional version of Lemma 1.3.

Lemma 5.3 *If there exists $u \in \mathfrak{D}$ not identically zero such that $M[u] \le 0$, then every solution v of $Lv = 0$ vanishes at some point of $\mathscr{R} \cup \mathscr{P}$.*

Proof Suppose to the contrary that there exists a solution v of $Lv = 0$ such that $v \ne 0$ on $\mathscr{R} \cup \mathscr{P}$. For $u \in \mathfrak{D}$ define

$$X^i = v D_i(u/v),$$

$$Y^i = v^{-1} \sum_j A_{ij} D_j v, \qquad i = 1, 2, \ldots, n,$$

$$E[u, v] = \sum_{i,j} A_{ij} X^i X^j + \sum_i D_i(u^2 Y^i).$$

The following identity in $\mathscr{R}$ will now be established:

$$E[u, v] = \sum_{i,j} A_{ij} D_i u D_j u - Cu^2 + u^2 v^{-1} Lv. \tag{5.5}$$

The left member of (5.5) is equal to

$$\frac{1}{v^2} \sum_{i,j} A_{ij}(v D_i u - u D_i v)(v D_j u - u D_j v)$$

$$+ \frac{2u}{v} \sum_{i,j} A_{ij} D_i u D_j v + \frac{u^2}{v^2} \sum_{i,j} (v D_i(A_{ij} D_j v) - A_{ij} D_i v D_j v).$$

Since (A_{ij}) is symmetric, this reduces easily to the right member of (5.5). Since $Lv = 0$ in $\mathscr{R}$, it follows from (5.4) and (5.5) that

$$M[u] = \int_{\mathscr{R}} \left[\sum_{i,j} A_{ij} X^i X^j + \sum_i D_i(u^2 Y^i) \right] dx.$$

Since u vanishes on $\mathscr{P}$, the integral of the second sum is zero by Green's formula. Since (A_{ij}) is positive definite, $M[u] \ge 0$, equality holding iff X^i is identically zero for each $i = 1, 2, \ldots, n$, i.e., u is a constant multiple of v. The latter cannot occur, however, since $u = 0$ on $\mathscr{P}$ while $v \ne 0$ on $\mathscr{P}$, and therefore $M[u] > 0$. This contradicts the hypothesis $M[u] \le 0$ and completes the proof of Lemma 5.3.

The analog of (5.4) for the differential operator (5.1) is the quadratic functional

$$m[u] = \int_{\mathscr{R}} \left(\sum_{i,j} a_{ij} D_i u D_j u - cu^2 \right) dx,$$

and the variation (5.3) is given by

$$V[u] = m[u] - M[u] \qquad u \in \mathfrak{D}. \tag{5.6}$$

It is now easy to prove Theorem 5.1. Since $lu = 0$ in $\mathscr{R}$ and $u = 0$ on $\mathscr{P}$, Green's formula

$$m[u] = -\int_{\mathscr{R}} ulu \, dx + \int_{\mathscr{P}} u \sum_{i,j} a_{ij} n_i D_j u \, ds \tag{5.7}$$

yields $m[u] = 0$. The hypothesis $V[u] \geq 0$ is equivalent to $M[u] \leq m[u]$ and hence the condition $M[u] \leq 0$ of Lemma 5.3. is fulfilled Therefore every solution v of $Lv = 0$ vanishes at some point of $\mathscr{R} \cup \mathscr{P}$.

Corollary 5.2 is an obvious special case of Theorem 5.1. In addition, the following result will be obtained under the hypothesis that L is a *strict Sturmian majorant of l*. (Definition below Corollary 5.2).

Corollary 5.4 *The conclusion of Corollary 5.2 remains valid even if (A_{ij}) is only positive semidefinite provided the following hypotheses are added:* (i) L *is a strict Sturmian majorant of l; and* (ii) *every second partial derivative of every coefficient a_{ij} $(i, j = 1, 2, \ldots, n)$ involved in l exists and satisfies a Lipschitz condition throughout R.*

Proof Aronszajn's unique continuation theorem [3] guarantees on account of hypothesis (ii) that a nontrivial solution u of $lu = 0$ cannot vanish identically in any open subset of $\mathscr{R}$. In the case that $C - c > 0$ at some point in $\mathscr{R}$ it follows that the integral $V[u]$ defined by (5.3) is strictly positive. In the case that $C \equiv c$ in $\mathscr{R}$ it follows from (5.3) and the positive definite hypothesis on $(a_{ij} - A_{ij})$ that $V[u] \geq 0$, equality holding only if $D_i u = 0$ for each $i = 1, 2, \ldots, n$ in some open set $\mathscr{S}$ of $\mathscr{R}$, that is $u = $ constant in $\mathscr{S}$. Since $c \neq 0$ at some point $x_0 \in \mathscr{S}$, the assumption that $V[u] = 0$ would then imply that the differential equation (5.1) is not satisfied by u at x_0. Hence $V[u] > 0$ also in the case that $C \equiv c$. Since $lu = 0$ in $\mathscr{R}$ and $u = 0$ on $\mathscr{P}$, (5.7) shows that $m[u] = 0$ and hence (5.6) gives $M[u] = -V[u] < 0$. When the hypothesis $M[u] \leq 0$ of Lemma 5.3 is strengthened to $M[u] < 0$, it is easy to see that the lemma remains true even if (A_{ij}) is only positive *semidefinite*. Hence every solution of $Lv = 0$ vanishes at some point of $\mathscr{R} \cup \mathscr{P}$.

The following example, similar to Leighton's example for $n = 1$ (Section 1 of Chapter 1), illustrates that Theorem 5.1 is more general than the Hartman–Wintner theorem or Corollary 5.2. Let $n = 2$ and let $\mathscr{R}$ be the square $0 < x^1 < \pi$, $0 < x^2 < \pi$. Let $\Delta = D_1{}^2 + D_2{}^2$ be the Laplacian operator and consider the differential equations

$$lu \equiv \Delta u + 2u = 0$$
$$Lv \equiv \Delta v + Cv = 0,$$

where $C(x^1, x^2) = f(x^1)f(x^2) + 2$ with $f \in \mathscr{C}[0, \pi]$. The function u defined by
$$u(x^1, x^2) = \sin x^1 \sin x^2$$
is zero on $\mathscr{P} = \partial \mathscr{R}$ and satisfies $lu = 0$ in $\mathscr{R}$. Since
$$V[u] = \int_0^\pi \int_0^\pi f(x^1)f(x^2) \sin^2 x^1 \sin^2 x^2 \, dx^1 \, dx^2 \geq 0,$$
Theorem 5.1 shows that every solution of $Lv = 0$ must vanish at some point of $\mathscr{R} \cup \mathscr{P}$. This cannot be concluded from Corollary 5.2 unless $f(x)$ has constant sign.

Leighton's theorem 1.9 also can be generalized to n dimensions if the differential equations (5.1), (5.2) have the forms

$$lu \equiv \sum_{i=1}^n D_i(aD_i u) + cu = 0, \tag{5.8}$$

$$Lv \equiv \sum_{i=1}^n D_i(AD_i v) + Cv = 0, \tag{5.9}$$

respectively, where the coefficients are real and continuous on $\mathscr{R} \cup \mathscr{P}$ and $a > 0$, $A > 0$ in $\mathscr{R}$ as in (5.1) and (5.2).

Theorem 5.5   *Let $\mathscr{R}$ be a bounded domain in E^n whose boundary has a piecewise continuous unit normal. If there exists a nontrivial solution of (5.8) in $\mathscr{R}$ such that $u = 0$ on $\mathscr{P}$ and*

$$\int_{\mathscr{R}} \left[\left(C - \frac{A}{a} c \right) u^2 + au \, \nabla u \cdot \nabla \frac{A}{a} \right] dx \geq 0, \tag{5.10}$$

then every solution of $Lv = 0$ vanishes at some point of $\mathscr{R} \cup \mathscr{P}$.

Proof   Since

$$lu = \sum_i (aD_i^2 u + D_i aD_i u) + cu = 0,$$

the integrand on the left of (5.10) is equal to

$$\left(C - \frac{A}{a} c \right) u^2 + u \sum_i D_i u \left(D_i A - \frac{A}{a} D_i a \right)$$

$$= u \left[Cu + \sum_i D_i AD_i u - \frac{A}{a} \left(cu + \sum_i D_i aD_i u \right) \right]$$

$$= u \left[Cu + \sum_i (D_i AD_i u + AD_i^2 u) \right] = uLu.$$

It then follows from (5.10) and Green's formula that

$$0 \leq \int_{\mathscr{R}} uLu \, dx = -M[u] + \int_{\mathscr{P}} Au \sum_i n_i D_i u \, ds.$$

Since $u = 0$ on $\mathscr{P}$, $M[u] \leq 0$ and the conclusion follows from Lemma 5.3.

In 1962 Kuks [108] extended the theorem of Hartman and Wintner (Corollary 5.2) to strongly elliptic linear systems by essentially the same method as that used by Hartman and Wintner. This result can be generalized to the form of Theorem 5.1 by a few formal changes in our proof.

3. Comparison Theorems for General Second Order Elliptic Equations

The results of Section 2 will now be extended to the general second order linear elliptic equations (5.1) and (5.2). The first comparison theorem of this type was obtained in 1959 by Protter [153] in the case $n = 2$. Protter used the Sturm-type hypotheses that the coefficients in (5.2) majorize those in (5.1) pointwise throughout $\mathscr{R}$, as in Corollary 5.2. The main comparison theorem below is obtained under a Leighton-type hypothesis similar to the hypothesis $V[u] \geq 0$ of Theorem 5.1. Pointwise inequalities which ensure the conclusion of the theorem follow as a special case for arbitrary dimensions n.

Let $Q[z]$ be the quadratic form in $n + 1$ variables $z_1, z_2, \ldots, z_{n+1}$ defined by

$$Q[z] = \sum_{i,\,j=1}^{n} A_{ij} z_i z_j - 2z_{n+1} \sum_{i=1}^{n} B_i z_i + Gz_{n+1}^2, \tag{5.11}$$

where the continuous function G is to be determined so that this form is positive semidefinite. The matrix Q associated with $Q[z]$ has the block form

$$Q = \begin{pmatrix} A & -B \\ -B^T & G \end{pmatrix}, \qquad A = (A_{ij}),$$

where B^T is the n-vector $(B_1, B_2, \ldots, B_n)$. Let $B_i{}^*$ denote the cofactor of $-B_i$ in Q. Since A is positive definite, a necessary and sufficient condition for Q to be positive semidefinite is $\det Q \geq 0$, or

$$G \det(A_{ij}) \geq \sum_{i=1}^{n} B_i B_i{}^*. \tag{5.12}$$

The proof is a slight modification of the well-known proof for positive definite matrices (Gantmacher [48]).

Let M be the quadratic functional defined by

$$M[u] = \int_{\mathscr{R}} F[u]\, dx, \tag{5.13}$$

where

$$F[u] = \sum_{i,\,j} A_{ij} D_i u D_j u - 2u \sum_i B_i D_i u + (G - C)u^2,$$

whose domain $\mathfrak{D}$ was defined below (5.4). The following is an extension of Lemma 5.3 to the general elliptic equation (5.2).

Lemma 5.6   *Suppose G satisfies (5.12) in $\mathscr{R}$. If there exists $u \in \mathfrak{D}$ not identically zero such that $M[u] < 0$, then every solution v of $Lv = 0$ vanishes at some point of $\mathscr{R} \cup \mathscr{P}$.*

Proof   Suppose to the contrary that there exists a solution $v \neq 0$ on $\mathscr{R} \cup \mathscr{P}$. For $u \in \mathfrak{D}$ define X^i, Y^i $(i = 1, 2, \ldots, n)$ as in Lemma 5.3. The following identity in $\mathscr{R}$ will now be established:

$$\sum_{i,j} A_{ij} X^i X^j - 2u \sum_i B_i X^i + Gu^2 + \sum_i D_i(u^2 Y^i) = F[u] + \frac{u^2}{v} Lv. \quad (5.14)$$

The left member of (5.14) is equal to

$$\frac{1}{v^2} \sum_{i,j} A_{ij}(vD_iu - uD_iv)(vD_ju - uD_jv)$$

$$- \frac{2u}{v} \sum_i B_i(vD_iu - uD_iv) + Gu^2$$

$$+ \frac{2u}{v} \sum_{i,j} A_{ij} D_i u D_j v + \frac{u^2}{v^2} \sum_{i,j} (vD_i(A_{ij}D_jv) - A_{ij}D_i vD_jv),$$

which reduces to the right member of (5.14) since (A_{ij}) is symmetric. Since $Lv = 0$ in $\mathscr{R}$,

$$M[u] = \int_{\mathscr{R}} \left[\sum_{i,j} A_{ij} X^i X^j - 2u \sum_i B_i X^i + Gu^2 \right] dx + \int_{\mathscr{R}} \sum_i D_i(u^2 Y^i)\, dx.$$

The integrand in the first term on the right side is a positive semidefinite form by the hypothesis (5.12). Since $u = 0$ on $\mathscr{P}$, the second integral is zero by Green's formula. The contradiction $M[u] \geq 0$ then establishes Lemma 5.6.

In addition to (5.13) consider the quadratic functional defined by

$$m[u] = \int_{\mathscr{R}} \left[\sum_{i,j} a_{ij} D_i u D_j u - 2u \sum_i b_i D_i u - c^2 \right] dx \quad (5.15)$$

with domain $\mathfrak{D}$. The variation $V[u]$ is defined by $V[u] = m[u] - M[u]$, that is,

$$V[u] = \int_{\mathscr{R}} \left[\sum_{i,j} (a_{ij} - A_{ij})D_i u D_j u - 2u \sum_i (b_i - B_i)D_i u \right. \quad (5.16)$$

$$+ (C - c - G)u^2 \right] dx, \quad u \in \mathfrak{D}.$$

Theorem 5.7   *Suppose G satisfies (5.12) in a bounded domain $\mathscr{R}$ in E^n whose boundary $\mathscr{P}$ has a piecewise continuous unit normal. If there exists a nontrivial solution u of $lu = 0$ such that $u = 0$ on $\mathscr{P}$ and $V[u] > 0$, then every solution of $Lv = 0$ vanishes at some point of $\mathscr{R} \cup \mathscr{P}$. The same conclusion holds under the weaker hypothesis $V[u] \geq 0$ provided the weak inequality (5.12) is replaced by a strict inequality at some point in $\mathscr{R}$.*

Proof For lu, $m[u]$ defined by (5.1), (5.15), respectively, Green's formula (5.7) remains valid, and hence the hypotheses $lu = 0$ in $\mathscr{R}$ and $u = 0$ on $\mathscr{P}$ imply that $m[u] = 0$. Thus

$$M[u] = m[u] - V[u] = -V[u] < 0$$

and the first statement of the theorem follows from Lemma 5.6.

To prove the second statement we need only note that Lemma 5.6 remains valid under the weakened hypothesis $M[u] \leq 0$ (instead of $M[u] < 0$) since Q is positive definite at some point in $\mathscr{R}$ at which strict inequality holds in (5.12).

In the case that equality holds in (5.12) everywhere in $\mathscr{R}$, that is

$$G \equiv -\sum_{i=1}^{n} B_i B_i^* / \det(A_{ij}),$$

we define

$$\delta = \sum_{i=1}^{n} D_i(b_i - B_i) + C - c - G, \qquad (5.17)$$

under the additional assumptions that $b_i \in \mathscr{C}^1(\mathscr{R})$, $B_i \in \mathscr{C}^1(\mathscr{R})$ $(i = 1, 2, \ldots, n)$. It follows from (5.16) by partial integration that

$$V[u] = \int_{\mathscr{R}} \left[\sum_{i,j} (a_{ij} - A_{ij}) D_i u D_j u + \delta u^2 \right] dx. \qquad (5.18)$$

L is called a *strict Sturmian majorant* of l when the following conditions hold:

(1) $(a_{ij} - A_{ij})$ is positive semidefinite and $\delta \geq 0$ in $\mathscr{R}$; and

(2) either $\delta > 0$ at some point of $\mathscr{R}$ or $(a_{ij} - A_{ij})$ is positive definite and $c \neq 0$ at some point.

A function defined in $\mathscr{R}$ is said to be of class $\mathscr{C}^{2,1}(\mathscr{R})$ when all of its second partial derivatives exist and are Lipschitzian in $\mathscr{R}$.

Theorem 5.8 *Suppose that L is a strict Sturmian majorant of l in a bounded domain $\mathscr{R}$ whose boundary $\mathscr{P}$ has a piecewise continuous unit normal, and that all the coefficients a_{ij} involved in ℓ are of class $\mathscr{C}^{2,1}(\mathscr{R})$. If there exists a nontrivial solution u of lu = 0 such that u = 0 on $\mathscr{P}$, then every solution of Lv = 0 vanishes at some point of $\mathscr{R} \cup \mathscr{P}$.*

It follows as in the proof of Corollary 5.4 that $V[u] > 0$ and hence the conclusion of Theorem 5.8 is a consequence of Theorem 5.7.

In the case $n = 2$ considered by Protter [153], the condition $\delta \geq 0$ of Theorem 5.8 reduces to

$$(A_{11}A_{22} - A_{12}^2)\left(\sum_{i=1}^{2} D_i(b_i - B_i) + C - c \right) \geq A_{11}B_2^2 - 2A_{12}B_1B_2$$
$$+ A_{22}B_1^2, \qquad (5.19)$$

which is considerably simpler than the condition given by Protter. In the special case $B_1 = B_2 = 0$, it reduces to Protter's condition

$$\sum_{i=1}^{2} D_i b_i + C - c \geq 0.$$

It also coincides with Protter's condition in the case that $A_{12} = a_{12} = 0$, $A_{11} = a_{11}$, and $A_{22} = a_{22}$.

The following example in the case $n = 2$ illustrates that Theorem 5.7 is more general than Theorem 5.8, i.e., $V[u] > 0$ is a weaker hypothesis than the pointwise condition (5.19). (Condition (1) of the strict Sturmian hypothesis is trivially satisfied in this example.)

Let $\mathscr{R}$ be the square $0 < x^1 < \pi$, $0 < x^2 < \pi$, and consider the elliptic equations

$$lu \equiv D_1{}^2 u + D_2{}^2 u + 2u = 0,$$

$$Lv \equiv D_1{}^2 v + D_2{}^2 v + D_1 v + Cv = 0,$$

where $C(x^1, x^2) = f(x^1)f(x^2) + 9/4$, and $f \in \mathscr{C}[0, \pi]$ is not identically zero. Since $u = \sin x^1 \sin x^2$ is zero on $\mathscr{P}$ and satisfies $lu = 0$ in $\mathscr{R}$, and since (5.18) reduces to

$$V[u] = \int_0^\pi \int_0^\pi f(x^1)f(x^2) \sin^2 x^1 \sin^2 x^2 \, dx^1 \, dx^2 > 0,$$

it follows from Theorem 5.7 that every solution of $Lv = 0$ vanishes at some point of $\mathscr{R} \cup \mathscr{P}$. This cannot be concluded from (5.19) or from Protter's result [153] unless f has constant sign in $\mathscr{R}$.

In the case $n = 1$ the results of this section reduce easily to those given in Section 3 of Chapter 1.

Kreith [106, 107] has recently proved that the conclusion of Theorem 5.8 can be strengthened to "every solution of $Lv = 0$ vanishes at some point of $\mathscr{R}$," provided the boundary $\mathscr{P}$ has bounded curvature. This is accomplished by a corresponding strengthening or Lemma 5.6 with the aid of a modification of the Hopf maximum principle [83].

4. Comparison Theorems on Unbounded Domains [192]

The elliptic equations (5.1) and (5.2) will now be considered in an unbounded domain $\mathscr{R}$ of E^n under the assumptions on the coefficients stated in Section 1.

Let $\mathscr{T}_a$ denote the n-disk $\{x \in E^n \colon |x - x_0| < a\}$ and let $\mathscr{S}_a$ denote the bounding $(n-1)$-sphere, where x_0 is a fixed point in E^n. Define

$$\mathscr{R}_a = \mathscr{R} \cap \mathscr{T}_a, \qquad \mathscr{P}_a = \mathscr{P} \cap \mathscr{T}_a, \qquad \mathscr{C}_a = \mathscr{R} \cap \mathscr{S}_a.$$

Clearly there exists a positive number a_0 such that $\mathscr{R}_a$ is a bounded domain with boundary $\mathscr{P}_a \cup \mathscr{C}_a$ for all $a \geq a_0$.

Let M_a be the quadratic functional defined by

$$M_a[u] = \int_{\mathscr{R}_a} F[u] \, dx, \qquad (5.20)$$

where

$$F[u] = \sum_{i,j} A_{ij} D_i u D_j u - 2u \sum_i B_i D_i u + (G - C)u^2 \qquad (5.21)$$

and G is a continuous function in $\mathscr{R}$ satisfying (5.12). Define $M[u] = \lim M_a[u] \ (a \to \infty)$ whenever the limit exists. The domain $\mathfrak{D}_M$ of M is defined to be the set of all real-valued continuous functions u in $\mathscr{R} \cup \mathscr{P}$ such that u has uniformly continuous first partial derivatives in $\mathscr{R}_a$ for all $a \geq a_0$, $M[u]$ exists, and u vanishes on $\mathscr{P}$. Define

$$[u, v]_a = \int_{\mathscr{C}_a} u \sum_{i,j} A_{ij} n_i D_j v \, ds, \qquad (5.22)$$

where (n_i) is the unit normal to $\mathscr{C}_a$, and define

$$[u, v] = \lim_{a \to \infty} [u, v]_a \qquad (5.23)$$

whenever the limit on the right side exists.

Lemma 5.9 *Suppose G satisfies (5.12) in $\mathscr{R}$. If there exists $u \in \mathfrak{D}_M$ not identically zero such that $M[u] < 0$, then every solution v of $Lv = 0$ satisfying $[u^2/v, v] \geq 0$ vanishes at some point of $\mathscr{R} \cup \mathscr{P}$.*

Proof The proof is a modification of that given above for Lemma 5.6. For $u \in \mathfrak{D}_M$ and any solution v of $Lv = 0$ satisfying $v \neq 0$ on $\mathscr{R} \cup \mathscr{P}$, it is a consequence of the identity (5.14) that

$$\int_{\mathscr{R}_a} F[u] \, dx = \int_{\mathscr{R}_a} \left[\sum_{i,j} A_{ij} X^i X^j - 2u \sum_i B_i X^i + Gu^2 \right] dx + \int_{\mathscr{R}_a} \sum_i D_i(u^2 Y^i) \, dx. \qquad (5.24)$$

The first integrand on the right side is a positive semidefinite form by the hypothesis (5.12). Since $u = 0$ on $\mathscr{P}_a$, it follows from Green's formula that

$$\int_{\mathscr{R}_a} \sum_i D_i(u^2 Y^i) \, dx = \int_{\mathscr{P}_a \cup \mathscr{C}_a} \sum_i u^2 n_i Y^i \, ds$$

$$= \int_{\mathscr{C}_a} \frac{u^2}{v} \sum_{i,j} A_{ij} n_i D_j v \, ds,$$

where the definition of Y^i in Lemma 5.3 has been used at the last step. Hence (5.22) and (5.24) yield

$$\int_{\mathscr{R}_a} F[u] \, dx \geq [u^2/v, v]_a.$$

Since $[u^2/v, v] \geq 0$ by hypothesis,

$$M[u] = \lim_{a \to \infty} \int_{\mathscr{R}_a} F[u] \, dx \geq 0.$$

This contradiction establishes Lemma 5.9.

Lemma 5.10   (Self-adjoint case) *Suppose $B_i \equiv 0$ in (5.2) and (5.21), $i = 1, 2, \ldots, n$, and $G \equiv 0$. If there exists $u \in \mathfrak{D}_M$ not identically zero such that $M[u] \leq 0$, then every solution v of $Lv = 0$ satisfying $[u^2/v, v] \geq 0$ vanishes at some point of $\mathscr{R} \cup \mathscr{P}$.*

Proof   In this case the first integrand on the right side of (5.24) is a positive definite form. Hence

$$\int_{\mathscr{R}_a} \sum_{i,j} A_{ij} X^i X^j \, dx \geq 0,$$

equality holding iff X^i is identically zero for each $i = 1, 2, \ldots, n$, i.e., u is a constant multiple of v. The latter cannot occur since $u = 0$ on $\mathscr{P}$ and $v \neq 0$ on $\mathscr{P}$, and therefore (5.24) yields

$$\int_{\mathscr{R}_a} F[u] \, dx > [u^2/v, v]_a.$$

It follows as in the previous lemma that $M[u] > 0$, contrary to the hypothesis $M[u] \leq 0$.

In addition to (5.20) consider the quadratic functional defined by

$$m_a[u] = \int_{\mathscr{R}_a} \left[\sum_{i,j} a_{ij} D_i u D_j u - 2u \sum_i b_i D_i u - cu^2 \right] dx$$

and let $m[u] = \lim m_a[u]$ $(a \to \infty)$ whenever the limit exists. The domain $\mathfrak{D}_m$ of m is defined as the set of all real-valued continuous functions u in $\mathscr{R} \cup \mathscr{P}$ such that u has uniformly continuous first partial derivatives in $\mathscr{R}_a$ for all $a \geq a_0$, $m[u]$ exists, and u vanishes on $\mathscr{P}$. The *variation* $V[u]$ is defined to be $m[u] - M[u]$, that is

$$V[u] = \int_{\mathscr{R}} \left[\sum_{i,j} (a_{ij} - A_{ij}) D_i u D_j u - 2u \sum_i (b_i - B_i) D_i u + (C - c - G) u^2 \right] dx, \tag{5.25}$$

with domain $\mathfrak{D}_V = \mathfrak{D}_m \cap \mathfrak{D}_M$. The analogs of (5.22), (5.23) for the operator l are

$$\{u, v\}_a = \int_{\mathscr{C}_a} u \sum_{i, j} a_{ij} n_i D_j v \, ds$$

$$\{u, v\} = \lim_{a \to \infty} \{u, v\}_a.$$

Theorem 5.11 *Suppose G satisfies (5.12) in $\mathscr{R}$. If there exists a nontrivial solution $u \in \mathfrak{D}_V$ of $lu = 0$ such that $\{u, u\} \leq 0$ and $V[u] > 0$, then every solution v of $Lv = 0$ satisfying $[u^2/v, v] \geq 0$ vanishes at some point of $\mathscr{R} \cup \mathscr{P}$. The same conclusion holds the if conditions $V[u] > 0$, $[u^2/v, v] \geq 0$ are replaced by $V[u] \geq 0$, $[u^2/v, v] > 0$, respectively.*

Proof Since $u = 0$ on $\mathscr{P}_a$, it follows from Green's formula that

$$m_a[u] = -\int_{\mathscr{R}_a} u l u \, dx + \{u, u\}_a.$$

Since $lu = 0$ and $\{u, u\} \leq 0$ we obtain in the limit $a \to \infty$ that $m[u] \leq 0$. The hypothesis $V[u] > 0$ is equivalent to $M[u] < m[u]$. Hence the condition $M[u] < 0$ of Lemma 5.9 is fulfilled and v vanishes at some point of $\mathscr{R} \cup \mathscr{P}$. The second statement of Theorem 5.11 follows upon obvious modifications of the inequalities.

Theorem 5.12   (Self-adjoint case) *Suppose $b_i = B_i \equiv 0$ in (5.1) and (5.2), $i = 1, 2, \ldots, n$, and $G \equiv 0$. If there exists a nontrivial solution $u \in \mathfrak{D}_V$ of $lu = 0$ such that $\{u, u\} \leq 0$ and $V[u] \geq 0$, then every solution v of $Lv = 0$ satisfying $[u^2/v, v] \geq 0$ vanishes at some point of $\mathscr{R} \cup \mathscr{P}$.*

This follows from Lemma 5.10 by a proof similar to that of Theorem 5.11.

In the case that equality occurs in (5.12), we define δ by (5.17) as in the case of bounded domains. It follows from (5.25) by partial integration that

$$V[u] = \int_{\mathscr{R}} \left[\sum_{i, j} (a_{ij} - A_{ij}) D_i u D_j u + \delta u^2 \right] dx + \Omega \tag{5.26}$$

where

$$\Omega = \lim_{a \to \infty} \int_{\mathscr{C}_a} \sum_i (B_i - b_i) u^2 n_i \, ds$$

for $b_i \in \mathscr{C}^1(\mathscr{R})$, $B_i \in \mathscr{C}^1(\mathscr{R})$ $(i = 1, 2, \ldots, n)$.

In the case of unbounded domains, L is called a *strict Sturmian majorant* of l when the following conditions are fulfilled: (1) $(a_{ij} - A_{ij})$ is positive semi-definite and $\delta \geq 0$ in $\mathscr{R}$; (2) $\Omega \geq 0$; and (3) either $\delta > 0$ at some point in $\mathscr{R}$ or $(a_{ij} - A_{ij})$ is positive definite and $c \neq 0$ at some point.

Theorem 5.13 *Suppose that L is a strict Sturmian majorant of l and that all the coefficients a_{ij} involved in l are of class $\mathscr{C}^{2,1}(\mathscr{R})$. If there exists a nontrivial solution $u \in \mathfrak{D}_V$ of $lu = 0$ such that $\{u, u\} \leq 0$, then every solution v of $Lv = 0$ satisfying $[u^2/v, v] \geq 0$ vanishes at some point of $\mathscr{R} \cup \mathscr{P}$.*

Proof $V[u]$ exists since $u \in \mathfrak{D}_V$, and hence each term on the right side of (5.26) exists by the strict Sturmian hypothesis. It follows as in the proof of Corollary 5.4 that $V[u] > 0$ and hence the conclusion of Theorem 5.13 is implied by Theorem 5.11.

Theorem 5.14   (Self-adjoint case) *Suppose $b_i = B_i = 0$ in (5.1) and (5.2), $i = 1, 2, \ldots, n$, $C \geq c$, and $(a_{ij} - A_{ij})$ is positive semidefinite in $\mathscr{R} \cup \mathscr{P}$. If there exists a nontrivial solution $u \in \mathfrak{D}_V$ of $lu = 0$ such that $\{u, u\} \leq 0$, then every solution v of $Lv = 0$ satisfying $[u^2/v, v] \geq 0$ vanishes at some point of $\mathscr{R} \cup \mathscr{P}$.*

This is an immediate consequence of Theorem 5.12. We assert that the same conclusion holds even if (A_{ij}) is only positive *semidefinite*, provided L is a strict Sturmian majorant of l and all the coefficients a_{ij} are of class $\mathscr{C}^{2,1}(\mathscr{R})$. In fact, under these assumptions $V[u] > 0$ as in the proof of Corollary 5.4 (or Theorem 5.13), which implies that $M[u] < 0$ by the proof of Theorem 5.11, and Lemma 5.10 remains valid for positive semidefinite (A_{ij}) provided the hypothesis $M[u] \leq 0$ is strengthened to $M[u] < 0$.

In the case $n = 1$ the theorems of this section reduce to Theorems 1.18–1.21 of Chapter 1.

5. Extension to Complex-Valued Solutions and Subsolutions

The elliptic operators l, L defined by (5.1), (5.2), respectively, will be considered under the assumptions stated in Section 1. The domains $\mathfrak{D}_l$, $\mathfrak{D}_L$ of l, L, respectively, are defined to be the sets of all complex-valued functions $u \in \mathscr{C}^1(\mathscr{R} \cup \mathscr{P})$ such that all derivatives of u involved in lu, Lu, respectively, exist and are continuous at every point in $\mathscr{R}$. An L-subsolution (-supersolution) is a real-valued function $v \in \mathfrak{D}_L$ which satisfies $Lv \leq 0$ $(Lv \geq 0)$ at every point in $\mathscr{R}$.

In the case of complex-valued functions, (5.11) and (5.21) are replaced by

$$Q[z] = \sum_{i,j=1}^{n} A_{ij} z_i \bar{z}_j - 2 \sum_{i=1}^{n} B_i \operatorname{Re}(z_i \bar{z}_{n+1}) + G |z_{n+1}|^2,$$

$$F[u] = \sum_{i,j=1}^{n} A_{ij} D_i u D_j \bar{u} - 2 \operatorname{Re}\left(u \sum_i B_i D_i \bar{u}\right) + (G - C) |u|^2,$$

respectively, where a bar denotes complex conjugation. The quadratic functional $M[u]$ is defined to be $\lim M_a[u]$ $(a \to \infty)$ as before, where

$$M_a[u] = \int_{\mathscr{R}_a} F[u]\, dx,$$

with domain $\mathfrak{D}_M$ consisting of all complex-valued functions $u \in \mathscr{C}^1(\mathscr{R} \cup \mathscr{P})$ such that $M[u]$ exists and u vanishes on $\mathscr{P}$. The following are extensions of the results of Section 4 to subsolutions (or supersolutions), and to complex-valued functions $u \in \mathfrak{D}_M(\mathscr{R})$.

Lemma 5.15 *For every $u \in \mathscr{C}^1(\mathscr{R})$ and every real $v \in \mathfrak{D}_L$ which does not vanish in $\mathscr{R}$, the following identity is valid at every point in $\mathscr{R}$:*

$$\sum_{i,j} A_{ij} X^i \overline{X}^j - 2\,\mathrm{Re}\!\left(u \sum_i B_i \overline{X}^i\right) + G |u|^2$$
$$+ \sum_i D_i(|u|^2 Y^i) = F[u] + |u|^2 v^{-1} L v \qquad (5.27)$$

where

$$X^i = v D_i(u/v), \qquad Y^i = v^{-1} \sum_{j=1}^n A_{ij} D_j v \qquad (i = 1, 2, \ldots, n).$$

The proof is a direct calculation similar to the proof of (5.14).

Theorem 5.16 *Suppose G satisfies (5.12) in $\mathscr{R}$. If there exists $u \in \mathfrak{D}_M$ not identically zero such that $M[u] < 0$, then there does not exist an L-subsolution (-supersolution) v satisfying $[|u|^2/v, v] \geq 0$ which is positive (negative) everywhere in $\mathscr{R} \cup \mathscr{P}$. In particular, every real solution of $Lv = 0$ satisfying $[|u|^2/v, v] \geq 0$ must vanish at some point of $\mathscr{R} \cup \mathscr{P}$. In the self-adjoint case $B_i \equiv 0$ $(i = 1, 2, \ldots, n)$ and $G \equiv 0$, the same conclusions are valid when the hypothesis $M[u] < 0$ is weakened to $M[u] \leq 0$.*

Proof Suppose to the contrary that there exists such a positive L-subsolution. Then integration of (5.27) over $\mathscr{R}_a$ yields

$$\int_{\mathscr{R}_a} F[u]\, dx \geq \int_{\mathscr{R}_a} \sum_i D_i(|u|^2 Y^i)\, dx \qquad (5.28)$$

since the first three terms on the left side of (5.27) constitute a positive semi-definite form by the hypothesis (5.12). Since $u = 0$ on $\mathscr{P}_a$, by the definition $\mathfrak{D}_M$, it follows from Green's formula that the right side of (5.28) is equal to

$$\int_{\mathscr{P}_a \cup \mathscr{C}_a} \sum_i |u|^2 n_i Y^i\, ds = \int_{\mathscr{C}_a} \frac{|u|^2}{v} \sum_{i,j} A_{ij} n_i D_j v\, ds = [|u|^2/v, v]_a.$$

Thus (5.23), (5.28), and the hypothesis $[|u|^2/v, v] \geq 0$ imply that

$$M[u] = \lim_{a \to \infty} \int_{\mathscr{R}_a} F[u] \, dx \geq 0.$$

The contradiction proves that a positive L-subsolution satisfying $[|u|^2/v, v] \geq 0$ cannot exist. The analogous statement for a negative L-supersolution v follows from the fact that $-v$ would then be a positive L-subsolution.

   To prove the second statement of Theorem 5.16, suppose to the contrary that there exists a real solution $v \neq 0$ in $\mathscr{R} \cup \mathscr{P}$. Then v would be either a positive L-subsolution or a negative L-supersolution in $\mathscr{R} \cup \mathscr{P}$.

   The proof in the self-adjoint case is similar to that of Lemma 5.10 and will be omitted.

   We remark that the condition $[|u|^2/v, v] \geq 0$ of Theorem 5.16 is a mild "boundary condition at ∞" generalizing the usual condition $v \neq 0$ on the boundary of bounded domains.

   In addition to $M[u]$ consider the quadratic functional defined by

$$m[u] = \lim_{a \to \infty} m_a[u]$$

where

$$m_a[u] = \int_{\mathscr{R}_a} \left[\sum_{i,j} a_{ij} D_i u D_j \bar{u} - 2 \operatorname{Re}\left(u \sum_i b_i D_i \bar{u} \right) - c \, |u|^2 \right] dx,$$

with domain $\mathfrak{D}_m$ consisting of all complex-valued functions $u \in \mathscr{C}^1(\mathscr{R} \cup \mathscr{P})$ such that $m[u]$ exists and u vanishes on $\mathscr{P}$. The *variation* of the differential operator l (relative to the domain $\mathscr{R}$) is defined as $V[u] = m[u] - M[u]$, that is

$$V[u] = \int_{\mathscr{R}} \left[\sum_{i,j} (a_{ij} - A_{ij}) D_i u D_j \bar{u} - 2 \operatorname{Re}\left(u \sum_i (b_i - B_i) D_i \bar{u} \right) \right.$$
$$\left. + (C - c - G) |u|^2 \right] dx, \tag{5.29}$$

with domain $\mathfrak{D}_V = \mathfrak{D}_m \cap \mathfrak{D}_M$. The analogs of (5.22), (5.23) for the operator l are

$$\{u, v\}_a = \int_{\mathscr{C}_a} \sum_{i,j} a_{ij} n_i \operatorname{Re}(u D_j \bar{v}) \, ds;$$
$$\{u, v\} = \lim_{a \to \infty} \{u, v\}_a .$$

When the dependence on the domain $\mathscr{R}$ is to be emphasized, we shall write $V[u; \mathscr{R}]$ for $V[u]$ and $\{u, v; \mathscr{R}\}$ for $\{u, v\}$.

The following comparison theorems of Sturm's type are easy extensions of those in Section 4 to L-subsolutions (-supersolutions) and to complex-valued solutions of $lu = 0$.

Theorem 5.17 *Suppose G is a continuous function in $\mathcal{R}$ satisfying the inequality (5.12). If there exists a nontrivial solution $u \in \mathfrak{D}_V$ of $lu = 0$ such that $\{u, u\} \leq 0$ and $V[u] > 0$ then there does not exist an L-subsolution (-supersolution) which is positive (negative) everywhere in $\mathcal{R} \cup \mathcal{P}$ and satisfies $[|u|^2/v, v] \geq 0$. In particular, every real solution of $Lv = 0$ satisfying $[|u|^2/v, v] \geq 0$ must vanish at some point of $\mathcal{R} \cup \mathcal{P}$. The same conclusions hold if the hypotheses $V[u] > 0$, $[|u|^2/v, v] \geq 0$ are replaced by $V[u] \geq 0$, $[|u|^2/v, v] > 0$, respectively.*

Theorem 5.18 *With G as in Theorem 5.17, if there exists a positive l-super-solution $u \in \mathfrak{D}_V$ such that $\{u, u\} \leq 0$ and $V[u] > 0$, then the conclusions of Theorem 5.17 are valid.*

Theorem 5.19 (Self-adjoint case) *Suppose $b_i = B_i \equiv 0$ $(i = 1, 2, \ldots, n)$ in (5.1) and (5.2) and $G \equiv 0$. If there exists either (1) a nontrivial complex-valued solution $u \in \mathfrak{D}_V$ of $lu = 0$, or (2) a positive l-supersolution $u \in \mathfrak{D}_V$ such that $\{u, u\} \leq 0$ and $V[u] \geq 0$, then an L-subsolution (-supersolution) v satisfying $[|u|^2/v, v] \geq 0$ cannot be everywhere positive (negative) in $\mathcal{R} \cup \mathcal{P}$. In particular, every real solution of $Lv = 0$ satisfying $[|u|^2/v, v] \geq 0$ must vanish at some point of $\mathcal{R} \cup \mathcal{P}$.*

Proof of Theorem 5.17 Since $u = 0$ on $\mathcal{P}_a$, it follows from Green's formula that

$$m_a[u] = -\int_{\mathcal{R}_a} \text{Re}(ul\bar{u}) \, dx + \{u, u\}_a. \tag{5.30}$$

Since $lu = 0$ and l has real-valued coefficients, also $l\bar{u} = 0$. Since $\{u, u\} \leq 0$, we obtain in the limit $a \to \infty$ that $m[u] \leq 0$. The hypothesis $V[u] > 0$ is equivalent to $M[u] < m[u]$. Hence $M[u] < 0$ and Theorem 5.16 shows that an L-subsolution (-supersolution) cannot be everywhere positive (negative) in $\mathcal{R} \cup \mathcal{P}$ under the hypothesis $[|u|^2/v, v] > 0$. The second statement of Theorem 5.17 also follows from Theorem 5.16. The last statement follows upon obvious modifications of the inequalities.

If u is a positive l-supersolution in $\mathcal{R}$ such that $\{u, u\} \leq 0$, it follows again from (5.30) that $m[u] \leq 0$. The proof of Theorem 5.18 is then completed in the same way as that of Theorem 5.17. The proof of Theorem 5.19 follows similarly from the statement in Theorem 5.16 relative to the self-adjoint case.

It follows from (5.29) by partial integration that

$$V[u] = \int_{\mathscr{R}} \left[\sum_{i,j} (a_{ij} - A_{ij}) D_i u D_j \bar{u} + \delta |u|^2 \right] dx + \Omega,$$

where δ is given by (5.17) and

$$\Omega = \lim_{a \to \infty} \int_{\mathscr{C}_a} \sum_i (B_i - b_i) |u|^2 n_i \, ds,$$

whenever the limit exists. The definition of a strict Sturmian majorant is formally identical with that in Section 4.

Theorem 5.20 *Suppose that L is a strict Sturmian majorant of l and that all the coefficients a_{ij} involved in l are of class $\mathscr{C}^{2,1}(\mathscr{R})$. If there exists a nontrivial solution $u \in \mathfrak{D}_V$ of $lu = 0$ such that $\{u, u\} \leq 0$, then no L-subsolution (-supersolution) v satisfying $[|u|^2/v, v] \geq 0$ can be everywhere positive (negative) in $\mathscr{R} \cup \mathscr{P}$. In particular, every real solution of $Lv = 0$ satisfying $[|u|^2/v, v] \geq 0$ must vanish at some point of $\mathscr{R} \cup \mathscr{P}$.*

Theorem 5.21   (Self-adjoint case) *Suppose $b_i = B_i = 0$ ($i = 1, 2, \ldots, n$) in (5.1) and (5.2), $G = 0$, $C \geq c$, and $(a_{ij} - A_{ij})$ is positive semidefinite in $\mathscr{R} \cup \mathscr{P}$. If there exists either (1) a nontrivial complex-valued solution $u \in \mathfrak{D}_V$ of $lu = 0$, or (2) a positive l-supersolution $u \in \mathfrak{D}_V$, such that $\{u, u\} \leq 0$, then the conclusion of Theorem 5.20 is valid.*

Since the pointwise conditions $G = 0$, $C \geq c$, and $(a_{ij} - A_{ij})$ positive semidefinite obviously imply that $V[u] \geq 0$, Theorem 5.21 is an immediate consequence of Theorem 5.19. The fact that the hypotheses of Theorem 5.20 imply $V[u] > 0$ was demonstrated in Corollary 5.4, and consequently the conclusion of Theorem 5.20 follows from Theorem 5.17.

In the special case of the Schrödinger operator $-l = -\Delta + c(x)$ with $c(x)$ bounded from below in $\mathscr{R}$, the hypothesis $\{u, u\} \leq 0$ of Theorems 5.19 and 5.21 can be replaced by the hypothesis that u and lu are square integrable in $\mathscr{R}$ since these conditions imply that $\{u, u\} = 0$ [50, p. 56]. In the self-adjoint elliptic case, the same statement holds under quite general conditions on the coefficients, e.g., those stated in the next section, as shown by Ikebe and Kato [89]. Also, the conclusion of Theorem 5.21 is valid even if (A_{ij}) is only positive *semidefinite* provided L is a strict Sturmian majorant of l and all the coefficients a_{ij} are of class $\mathscr{C}^{2,1}(\mathscr{R})$.

The theory of partial differential inequalities has been developed by Haar [59], Nagumo [139], Osserman [147], Redheffer [164–167], Schröder [177–178], Szarski [196], Westphal [208], and others. The reader is referred to Szarski's book [197] for a detailed treatment and additional references.

Connections between differential inequalities and maximum principles are contained in the recent book by Protter and Weinberger [156]. As a consequence of maximum principles, Osserman [147] and Redheffer [164–167] derived Phragmén–Lindelöf-type theorems, i.e., theorems stating that u is bounded if u satisfies a differential inequality and a growth condition. Collatz [36, 37] and Schröder [177, 178] have used the theory of monotonic operators both to prove the existence of solutions of differential equations and to estimate the errors in numerical procedures.

6. Lower Bounds for Eigenvalues

Let $\mathfrak{H}$ be the Hilbert space $\mathscr{L}^2(\mathscr{R})$, with inner product

$$\langle u, v \rangle = \int_{\mathscr{R}} u(x)\bar{v}(x)\, dx$$

and norm $\|u\| = \langle u, u \rangle^{1/2}$. Let $\mathfrak{D}$ be the set of all complex-valued functions $u \in \mathfrak{D}_L \cap \mathfrak{H}$ such that u vanishes on $\mathscr{P}$. In this section the elliptic operator (5.2), with domain $\mathfrak{D}$, is assumed to have the self-adjoint form

$$Lv = \sum_{i,j} D_i(A_{ij} D_j v) - Cv,$$

under the conditions described below (5.2). In the case of the Schrödinger operator $-L = -\Delta + C(x)$, it is well known [47; 50, p. 146] that the lower part of the spectrum contains only eigenvalues of finite multiplicity if $C(x)$ is bounded from below. In the self-adjoint elliptic case, an assumption on the coefficients A_{ij} is needed as well.

Let $A^+(x)$ denote the largest eigenvalue of $(A_{ij}(x))$ and define

$$\alpha(r) = \max_{1 \le |x| \le r} A^+(x),$$

$$\alpha_0(r) = \max[\alpha(1), \max_{1 \le |x| \le r} |x|^{-2} A^+(x)],$$

which are nondecreasing functions of r. The following assumptions are special cases of those given by Ikebe and Kato [89].

Assumptions (1) $C(x)$ is bounded from below;

$$(2) \quad \int_1^{\infty} [\alpha(r)\alpha_0(r)]^{-1/2}\, dr = \infty.$$

It follows in particular from (1) and (2) that the conditions $u \in \mathfrak{H}$, $Lu \in \mathfrak{H}$ imply that $[u, u] = 0$ [89].

Our purpose is to obtain a useful lower bound for the eigenvalues (if any) of $-L$. In the case of bounded domains, Protter and Weinberger [155] recently obtained results of this type by using a general form of the maximum principle. It will be shown here in the case of unbounded domains that a lower bound is available as an easy consequence of Lemma 5.15.

Theorem 5.22   *Let λ be the lowest eigenvalue and u be an associated normalized eigenfunction of the problem $-Lu = \lambda u$, $u \in \mathfrak{D}$. If v is any function in $\mathfrak{D}_L$ such that $v(x) > 0$ for $x \in \mathscr{R} \cup \mathscr{P}$ and $[|u|^2/v, v] \geq 0$, then*

$$\lambda \geq \inf_{x \in \mathscr{R}} [-Lv(x)/v(x)]. \tag{5.31}$$

Proof   With $B_i = 0$, $i = 1, 2, \ldots, n$ and $G = 0$, integration of (5.27) over $\mathscr{R}_a$ yields

$$M_a[u] + \int_{\mathscr{R}_a} |u|^2 v^{-1} Lv \, dx \geq \int_{\mathscr{R}_a} \sum_i D_i(|u|^2 Y_i) \, dx \tag{5.32}$$

where the positive definiteness of (A_{ij}) has been taken into account. Since $u = 0$ on $\mathscr{P}_a$, it follows from Green's formula that

$$M_a[u] = -\int_{\mathscr{R}_a} \bar{u} Lu \, dx + [u, u]_a$$

$$= \lambda \int_{\mathscr{R}_a} |u|^2 \, dx + [u, u]_a.$$

However, $\lim[u, u]_a = 0$ $(a \to \infty)$ is a general consequence of $u \in \mathfrak{H}$ and $Lu \in \mathfrak{H}$ under the above assumptions [89], and therefore

$$M[u] = \lim_{a \to \infty} M_a[u] = \lambda \|u\|^2 = \lambda.$$

As in the proof of Theorem 5.16, the right member of (5.32) has the limit $[|u|^2/v, v]$ as $a \to \infty$, which is nonnegative by hypothesis. Thus

$$\lambda + \int_{\mathscr{R}} |u|^2 v^{-1} Lv \, dx \geq 0,$$

which implies (5.31).

In the bounded case, the condition $[|u|^2/v, v] \geq 0$ is vacuous and Theorem 5.22 reduces to a well-known result [154]. However, the proof given here is especially easy. We remark that the extra condition $[|u|^2/v, v] \geq 0$ in the unbounded case is a condition on the asymptotic behavior of v as $|x| \to \infty$; it is roughly equivalent to the usual hypotheses for bounded domains that $u = 0$ on the boundary, $v > 0$ in $\mathscr{R} \cup \mathscr{P}$, and $v \in \mathscr{C}^1(\mathscr{R} \cup \mathscr{P})$. In the case of the Schrödinger operator $-\Delta + C(x)$, it is known [50, p. 179] that $|u(x)| < Ke^{-\mu|x|}$, where K and μ are constants, for every eigenfunction u, and hence various exponential functions can serve as the test functions v. As an easy example, consider the one-dimensional harmonic oscillator problem

$$-\frac{d^2u}{dx^2} + x^2u = \lambda u, \qquad 0 \le x < \infty,$$

$$u(0) = 0.$$

The test function $v = \exp(-x^2/2)$ yields the lower bound 1 whereas the exact lowest eigenvalue is known to be 3.

7. Oscillation Theorems

In [105] Kreith obtained oscillation theorems for self-adjoint elliptic equations of the form $Lv = 0$ in the case that one variable x_n is separable. He considered the case of bounded domains for which part of the boundary is singular. Here we shall obtain oscillation theorems of a general nature on unbounded domains by appealing to the comparison theorems 5.17–5.21.

Let $\mathcal{T}_a{}'$ denote the complement of $\mathcal{T}_a$ in E^n. A function u is said to be *oscillatory in $\mathcal{R}$ at* ∞, or simply *oscillatory in $\mathcal{R}$*, whenever u has a zero in $\mathcal{R} \cap \mathcal{T}_a{}'$ for all $a > 0$.

A domain (not necessarily bounded) $\mathcal{Q} \subset \mathcal{R}$ is called a *nodal domain* of a function u iff $u = 0$ on $\partial\mathcal{Q}$ and† $\{u, u; \mathcal{Q}\} \le 0$. If $\mathcal{Q}$ is bounded, the latter condition is understood to be void, and the definition reduces to the standard definition of a nodal domain. If $-l$ is the Schrödinger operator with potential $c(x)$ bounded from below, sufficient conditions for $\mathcal{Q}$ to be a nodal domain of $u \in \mathfrak{D}_l(\mathcal{Q})$ are $u = 0$ on $\partial\mathcal{Q}$, $u \in \mathfrak{H}$, and $lu \in \mathfrak{H}$ [50, p. 56]. A function u is said to have the *nodal property* in $\mathcal{R}$ whenever u has a nodal domain $\mathcal{Q} \subset \mathcal{R} \cap \mathcal{T}_a{}'$ for all $a > 0$.

The following results are immediate consequences of Theorems 5.17–5.21.

Theorem 5.23 *Suppose G is a continuous function in $\mathcal{R}$ satisfying* (5.12). *Suppose there exists either* (1) *a nontrivial complex-valued solution u of $lu = 0$, or* (2) *a positive l-supersolution u, with the nodal property in $\mathcal{R}$ such that $V[u; \mathcal{Q}] > 0$ for every nodal domain $\mathcal{Q}$. Then every real solution of $Lv = 0$ is oscillatory in $\mathcal{R}$ provided $[|u|^2/v, v; \mathcal{Q}] \ge 0$ for every $\mathcal{Q}$. If the nodal domains*

---

† As noted above, the notations $V[u; \mathcal{Q}]$, $\{u, v; \mathcal{Q}\}$, $[u, v; \mathcal{Q}]$ are used for $V[u]$, $\{u, v\}$, $[u,v]$ when the domain dependence is under consideration.

are all bounded, every solution of $Lv = 0$ is oscillatory in $\mathcal{R}$. In the self-adjoint case $b_i = B_i = 0$ $(i = 1, 2, \ldots, n)$ the same conclusions hold under the weaker condition $V[u; \mathcal{D}] \geq 0$ for every nodal domain $\mathcal{D}$.

Theorem 5.24   *Suppose that L is a strict Sturmian majorant of l and that all the coefficients involved in l are of class $\mathscr{C}^{2,1}(\mathcal{R})$. If there exists a nontrivial complex-valued solution of $lu = 0$ with the nodal property in $\mathcal{R}$, then every real solution of $Lv = 0$ is oscillatory in $\mathcal{R}$ provided $[|u|^2/v, v; \mathcal{D}] \geq 0$ for every nodal domain $\mathcal{D}$. If the nodal domains are all bounded, every solution of $Lv = 0$ is oscillatory in $\mathcal{R}$. In the self-adjoint case $b_i = B_i = 0$ $(i = 1, 2, \ldots, n)$ the same conclusions hold under the weaker hypotheses $G = 0$, $C \geq c$, and $(a_{ij} - A_{ij})$ positive semidefinite in $\mathcal{R} \cup \mathcal{P}$.*

Kreith has shown [105] that equations of the form

$$D_n[a(x_n)D_n u] + \sum_{i,j=1}^{n-1} D_i[a_{ij}(\bar{x})D_j u] + c(x_n)u = 0, \qquad (5.33)$$

$$\bar{x} = (x_1, x_2, \ldots, x_{n-1}),$$

have bounded nodal domains in the form of cylinders, under suitable hypotheses, when $\mathcal{R}$ is a *bounded* domain with an $(n-1)$-dimensional singular boundary. We shall show that the analogous construction for unbounded domains is valid provided $\mathcal{R}$ is *limit cylindrical*, i.e., contains an infinitely long cylinder. Without loss of generality we can assume that $\mathcal{R}$ contains a cylinder of the form

$$\mathcal{G} \times \{x_n : 0 \leq x_n < \infty\}$$

where $\mathcal{G}$ is a bounded $(n-1)$-dimensional domain.

Let μ be the smallest eigenvalue of the boundary problem

$$-\sum_{i,j=1}^{n-1} D_i[a_{ij}(\bar{x})D_j \varphi] = \mu\varphi \quad \text{in} \quad \mathcal{G}$$

$$\varphi = 0 \quad \text{on} \quad \partial\mathcal{G}. \qquad (5.34)$$

Theorem 5.25   *If there exists a positive number b such that*

$$\int_b^\infty \frac{dt}{a(t)} = \infty \quad \text{and} \quad \int_b^\infty [c(t) - \mu]\, dt = \infty, \qquad (5.35)$$

then Eq. (5.33) has a solution u with the nodal property in $\mathcal{R}$. If $V[u; \mathcal{D}] > 0$ for every nodal domain $\mathcal{D}$, every solution of $Lv = 0$ is oscillatory in $\mathcal{R}$. In particular, every solution of the self-adjoint equation $Lv = 0$ is oscillatory provided $C \geq c$ and $(a_{ij} - A_{ij})$ is positive semidefinite in $\mathcal{R} \cup \mathcal{P}$.

Proof The hypotheses (5.35) imply that the ordinary differential equation

$$D_n[a(x_n)D_n w] + [c(x_n) - \mu]w = 0$$

is oscillatory at $x_n = \infty$ on account of Theorem 2.24. Let w be a solution with zeros at $x_n = \delta_1, \delta_2, \ldots, \delta_m, \ldots$, where $\delta_m \uparrow \infty$. If φ is an eigenfunction of (5.34) corresponding to the eigenvalue μ, then the function u defined by $u(x) = w(x_n)\varphi(\bar{x})$ is a solution of (5.33) by direct calculation, with nodal domains in the form of cylinders

$$\mathcal{G}_m = \mathcal{G} \times \{x_n : \delta_m < x_n < \delta_{m+1}\} \qquad (m = 1, 2, \ldots).$$

Thus u has a nodal domain $\mathcal{G}_m \subset \mathcal{R} \cap \mathcal{T}_a'$ for all $a > 0$. In fact, given $a > 0$, choose m large enough so that $\delta_m \geq a$. Then $x \in \mathcal{G}_m$ implies $|x| \geq |x_n| > a$ so $x \in \mathcal{T}_a'$. Hence (5.33) has a solution u with the nodal property. The second statement of Theorem 5.25 follows from Theorem 5.23 and the last statement follows from Theorem 5.24.

Equation (5.2) is said to be nonoscillatory in $\mathcal{R}$ iff it has no oscillatory solutions. Kuks [108] showed in the self-adjoint case $B_i \equiv 0$ in (5.2) $(i = 1, 2, \ldots, n)$ that (5.2) is nonoscillatory iff there exists a positive function $v \in \mathcal{C}^2(\mathcal{R})$ such that $Lv \leq 0$ in $\mathcal{R}$.

Śliwiński [181] considered the equation

$$\Delta^m u - c(r)u = 0$$

in the case $n = 3$, where $r = (x_1^2 + x_2^2 + x_3^2)^{1/2}$ and Δ^m denotes the m-times iterated Laplacian,

$$\Delta = D_1^2 + D_2^2 + D_3^2.$$

Śliwiński proved that this differential equation has an oscillatory solution if $c(r) > 0$ and

$$\int_\alpha^\infty r^{2m-2}c(r)\,dr = \infty \qquad (\alpha \geq 0).$$

The proof is obtained by an application of the result of Anan'eva and Balaganskiĭ cited in Section 6 of Chapter 4.

Glazman [50, p. 158] extended the Hille–Kneser theorem 2.41 to the Schrödinger equation

$$\Delta u + c(x)u = 0, \qquad x \in \mathcal{R}, \quad c \in \mathcal{C}^1(\mathcal{R}) \tag{*}$$

$(\mathcal{R} \subset E^n)$ as follows: *Define*

$$f(r) = \min_{|x|=r} c(x), \qquad F(r) = \max_{|x|=r} c(x)$$

$$\omega_* = \liminf_{r \to \infty} r^2 f(r), \qquad \omega^* = \limsup_{r \to \infty} r^2 F(r).$$

Then there exists a nontrivial solution of (∗) *with the bounded nodal property in*
$\mathcal{R}$ *(all nodal domains bounded) if* $\omega_* > (n-2)^2/4$, *and no such solution exists if*
$\omega^* < (n-2)^2/4$. This reduces to Theorem 2.41 in the case $n = 1$. The proof
is based on Glazman's spectral analysis of the Schrödinger operator [50].

8. Comparison Theorems for Eigenfunctions

The comparison theorems for eigenfunctions obtained in Chapter 1,
Section 5 and Chapter 3, Section 5 will now be extended to n dimensions. As
before the proofs depend on Courant's minimum principle for the quadratic
functional associated with an eigenvalue problem. An analog of Theorem 3.62
will be obtained for self-adjoint elliptic equations of arbitrary even order $2m$
in n dimensions $(m, n = 1, 2, \ldots)$.
Linear self-adjoint elliptic partial differential operators l, L defined by

$$lu = k^{-1}\left[\sum_{i,\,j=1}^{n}(-1)^m D_i^{\,m}(a_{ij}D_j^{\,m}u) + cu\right] \tag{5.36}$$

$$Lu = k^{-1}\left[\sum_{i,\,j=1}^{n}(-1)^m D_i^{\,m}(A_{ij}D_j^{\,m}u) + Cu\right] \tag{5.37}$$

will be considered in a bounded domain $\mathcal{R}$ in E^n. As before, the boundary
$\mathcal{P}$ of $\mathcal{R}$ is supposed to have a piecewise continuous unit normal vector (n_i) at
each point. It is assumed that c and C are real-valued continuous functions on
$\mathcal{R} \cup \mathcal{P}$, k is a positive continuous function on $\mathcal{R} \cup \mathcal{P}$, the a_{ij} and A_{ij} are
real-valued and of class $\mathscr{C}^m(\mathcal{R} \cup \mathcal{P})$, and the matrices (a_{ij}) and (A_{ij}) are
symmetric and positive definite in $\mathcal{R}$ (ellipticity condition). The domain $\mathfrak{D}_0$ of
these operators is defined to be the set of all real-valued functions on $\mathcal{R} \cup \mathcal{P}$
of class $\mathscr{C}^{2m}(\mathcal{R} \cup \mathcal{P})$. If $n = 1$, the operators l and L reduce to the ordinary
differential operators under consideration in Section 5 of Chapter 3. If
$n = m = 1$, they reduce to the operators (1.49), (1.61) of Chapter 1, Section 5.
In the case $m = 1$, the operators l, L reduce to the second order elliptic
operators defined by

$$lu = k^{-1}\left[-\sum_{i,\,j=1}^{n} D_i(a_{ij}D_j u) + cu\right], \tag{5.38}$$

$$Lu = k^{-1}\left[-\sum_{i,\,j=1}^{n} D_i(A_{ij}D_j u) + Cu\right]. \tag{5.39}$$

Let p and P be the linear boundary operators defined by

$$p[u] = \gamma u + \sum_{i,\,j=1}^{n} a_{ij}n_i D_j u, \tag{5.40}$$

$$P[u] = \Gamma u + \sum_{i,\,j=1}^{n} A_{ij}n_i D_j u, \tag{5.41}$$

where γ and Γ are nonnegative continuous functions on $\mathscr{P}$. Consider the quadratic functionals q and Q defined by

$$q[u] = \int_{\mathscr{R}} \left[\sum_{i,j} a_{ij} D_i u D_j u + cu^2 \right] dx + \int_{\mathscr{P}} \gamma u^2 \, ds, \qquad (5.42)$$

$$Q[u] = \int_{\mathscr{R}} \left[\sum_{i,j} A_{ij} D_i u D_j u + Cu^2 \right] dx + \int_{\mathscr{P}} \Gamma u^2 \, ds, \qquad (5.43)$$

associated with the operators l, p and L, P, respectively. The domain $\mathfrak{D}$ of these functionals is defined to be the set of all real-valued continuous functions on $\mathscr{R} \cup \mathscr{P}$ which have uniformly continuous first partial derivatives in $\mathscr{R}$. The inner product of two functions u, v is defined as

$$\langle u, v \rangle = \int_{\mathscr{R}} u(x)v(x)k(x) \, dx$$

and the norm of u as $\|u\| = \langle u, u \rangle^{1/2}$. Courant's variational principle for $Q[u]$ may be stated as follows [39, p. 399].

Minimum Principle   The function $u \in \mathfrak{D}$ which minimizes $Q[u]$ under the condition $\|u\| = 1$ is an eigenfunction corresponding to the smallest eigenvalue λ of the problem

$$Lu = \lambda u, \qquad P[u] = 0 \quad \text{on} \quad \mathscr{P}. \qquad (5.44)$$

The analog of (5.44) for the operators l and p is the eigenvalue problem

$$lu = \lambda u, \qquad p[u] = 0 \quad \text{on} \quad \mathscr{P}. \qquad (5.45)$$

The analog of the variation (5.3) for these problems is $V[u] = q[u] - Q[u]$, or

$$V[u] = \int_{\mathscr{R}} \left[\sum_{i,j} (a_{ij} - A_{ij}) D_i u D_j u + (c - C)u^2 \right] dx + \int_{\mathscr{P}} (\gamma - \Gamma) u^2 \, ds,$$
$$u \in \mathfrak{D}.$$

Theorem 5.26   *If the eigenvalue problem* (5.45) *for l has an eigenvalue λ with an associated eigenfunction u satisfying $V[u] > 0$, then the problem* (5.44) *for L has at least one eigenvalue less than λ.*

Proof   Since u is a solution of (5.45), it follows from Green's formula

$$q[u] = \int_{\mathscr{R}} ulu \, k(x) \, dx + \int_{\mathscr{P}} up[u] \, ds$$

that $q[u] = \lambda \|u\|^2$. The condition $V[u] > 0$ is equivalent to $Q[u] < q[u]$. Hence the minimum of $Q[u]$ among functions $u \in \mathfrak{D}$ with $\|u\| = 1$ is less than λ. The conclusion then follows from Courant's minimum principle.

Theorem 5.27   *If* (5.45) *has a nontrivial solution u such that* $V[u] > 0$, *then every solution of* (5.44) (*with the same* λ *as in* (5.45)) *vanishes at some point in* $\mathcal{R}$.

Proof   According to Theorem 5.26, the smallest eigenvalue λ_0 of (5.44) is less than λ. Since C is continuous and k is positive on $\mathcal{R} \cup \mathcal{P}$, there exists a positive number α such that $C + \alpha k > 0$ on $\mathcal{R} \cup \mathcal{P}$. Green's function $G(x, t)$ for the operator $k(L + \alpha)$ with the boundary condition $P[v] = 0$ on $\mathcal{P}$ (i.e., Robin's function) is therefore nonnegative in $\mathcal{R}$ [41, p. 161]. The eigenfunctions of $L + \alpha$ (which are identical with those of L) are the eigenfunctions of the linear integral equation $v(x) = \lambda \langle v, G(x, \cdot) \rangle$ whose kernel is the above Green's function. It follows from Jentzsch's theorem [91] on integral equations with positive kernels that an eigenfunction v_0 corresponding to λ_0 can be assigned which has nonnegative values everywhere in $\mathcal{R}$. Since v_0, v are eigenfunctions of (5.44) corresponding to distinct eigenvalues λ_0, λ, it follows that v is orthogonal to v_0, i.e., $\langle v, v_0 \rangle = 0$. Hence v must vanish at some point in $\mathcal{R}$.

In the special case $\lambda = 0$, $\gamma = \infty$, it can be shown [191, p. 514] that Theorem 5.27 is virtually the same as Theorem 5.1. ($V[u] \geq 0$ in Theorem 5.1 is replaced by the slightly stronger hypothesis $V[u] > 0$).

Corollary 5.28   *Suppose that* $\gamma \geq \Gamma$ *on* $\mathcal{P}$ *and that* $(a_{ij} - A_{ij})$ *is positive semidefinite and* $c \geq C$ *in* $\mathcal{R}$. *Suppose in addition either that* $c > C$ *at some point or that* $(a_{ij} - A_{ij})$ *is positive definite and* $c \neq 0$ *at some point. If there exists a nontrivial solution u of* (5.45) *such that u does not vanish identically in any open set of* $\mathcal{R}$, *then every solution of* (5.44) *vanishes at some point in* $\mathcal{R}$.

Proof   The assumptions imply that $V[u] > 0$ as in Corollary 5.4 and hence the conclusion follows from Theorem 5.27.

The hypothesis that u does not vanish in any open set of $\mathcal{R}$ can be deleted if $a_{ij} \in \mathscr{C}^{2,1}(\mathcal{R})$, for under this assumption Aronszajn's unique continuation theorem [3] ensures that a nontrivial solution of $lu = \lambda u$ cannot vanish identically in any such open set.

Theorem 5.26 will now be extended to the elliptic operators (5.36), (5.37), of arbitrary even order $2m$. Let γ and γ_{ijh} ($i, j = 1, 2, \ldots, n; h = 1, 2, \ldots, m - 1$) be continuous functions on $\mathcal{P}$ such that $\gamma > 0$ and the matrix (γ_{ijh}) ($i, j = 1, 2, \ldots, n$) is symmetric and positive definite on $\mathcal{P}$ for each h. Let p and p_{ih} be the linear boundary operators defined by

$$p[u] = \gamma u - (-1)^m \sum_{i,j} D_i^{m-1}(a_{ij}D_j^m u)n_i \tag{5.46}$$

$$p_{ih}[u] = \sum_{j=1}^{n} [\gamma_{ijh} D_j^h u n_j - (-1)^{m+h} D_i^{m-h-1}(a_{ij}D_j^m u)], \tag{5.47}$$

$$i = 1, 2, \ldots, n; \quad h = 1, 2, \ldots, m - 1.$$

Let q be the quadratic functional defined by

$$q[u] = \int_{\mathcal{R}} \left[\sum_{i,j=1}^{n} a_{ij} D_i^m u D_j^m u + c u^2 \right] dx + \int_{\mathcal{P}} \gamma u^2 \, ds$$

$$+ \int_{\mathcal{P}} \sum_{i,j=1}^{n} \sum_{h=1}^{m-1} \gamma_{ijh} D_i^h u D_j^h u n_i n_j \, ds. \tag{5.48}$$

Let P, P_{ih}, and $Q[u]$ be the analogs of (5.46), (5.47), (5.48), respectively, for the operator L, where γ, γ_{ijh}, a_{ij}, c are replaced by Γ, Γ_{ijh}, A_{ij}, C, respectively, satisfying the same hypotheses. The analogs of the eigenvalue problems (5.44), (5.45) are

$$Lu = \lambda u, \qquad\qquad P[u] = P_{ih}[u] = 0 \quad \text{on} \quad \mathcal{P}, \tag{5.49}$$

$$lu = \lambda u, \qquad\qquad p[u] = p_{ih}[u] = 0 \quad \text{on} \quad \mathcal{P}, \tag{5.50}$$

$$i = 1, 2, \ldots, n, \qquad h = 1, 2, \ldots, m-1.$$

Courant's minimum principle states that the function $u \in \mathscr{C}^m(\mathcal{R} \cup \mathcal{P})$ which minimizes $q[u]$ (or $Q[u]$) under the condition $\|u\| = 1$ is an eigenfunction corresponding to the smallest eigenvalue of the problem (5.50) (or (5.49)).

Theorem 5.29 *If* (5.50) *has an eigenvalue λ with an associated eigenfunction u satisfying $q[u] > Q[u]$, then* (5.49) *has at least one eigenvalue less than λ.*

The proof follows similarly to that of Theorem 5.26 from the following version of Green's formula:

$$q[u] = \int_{\mathcal{R}} u l u \, k(x) \, dx + \int_{\mathcal{P}} \left\{ u p[u] + \sum_{i,h} D_i^h u \, p_{ih}[u] n_i \right\} ds.$$

The comparison Theorem 3.63 was obtained as a consequence of Theorem 5.29 (i.e., Theorem 5.62, when $n = 1$) in the case $n = 1$, $m = 2$.

Exercises

1. Show that Theorem 1.5 follows from Theorem 5.1.
2. Extend Leighton's specific example in Section 1 of Chapter 1 to 2 and 3 dimensions.
3. Obtain an analog of Theorem 5.5 in the case of nonself-adjoint elliptic equations.
4. Generalize Theorem 5.1 to strongly elliptic systems of partial differential equations [108].
5. Prove that (5.12) is a necessary and sufficient condition for Q to be positive semidefinite.
6. Prove that Lemma 5.6 remains valid under the weaker hypothesis $M[u] \le 0$ if Q is positive definite in $\mathcal{R}$.
7. Check the calculations in the example at the end of Section 3.

8. Give detailed proofs of Theorems 5.12, 5.13, 5.23, and 5.24 and Lemma 5.15.
9. Prove the statement in Theorem 5.16 relative to the self-adjoint case.
10. Prove Śliwiński's theorem stated at the end of Section 7.
11. Give the details of the proof of Theorem 5.29 including the version of Green's formula cited.

Bibliography

1. G. V. Anan'eva and V. I. Balaganskiĭ, Oscillation of the solutions of certain differential equations of high order, *Uspehi Mat. Nauk* **14**, No. 1 (85) (1959), 135–140.
2. O. Aramă, Intervals of non-oscillation of linear differential equations, *Acad. R. P. Romîne Fil. Cluj. Cerc. Stud. Mat.* **13** (1962), 213–239.
3. N. Aronszajn, A unique continuation theorem for solutions of elliptic partial differential equations or inequalities of second order, *J. Math. Pures Appl.* **36** (1957), 235–249.
4. F. V. Atkinson, On second-order nonlinear oscillations, *Pacific J. Math.* **5** (1955), 643–647.
5. N. V. Azbelev, On the question of the estimation of the number of zeros of solutions of the equation $y''' + p(x)y' + q(x)y = 0$, *Nauč. Dokl. Vysš. Školy Fiz.-Mat. Nauki* (1958), Nos. 3, 5.
6. N. V. Azbelev, and Z. B. Caljuk, On the question of the distribution of the zeros of solutions of a third-order linear differential equation, *Mat. Sb.* [*N.S.*] **51** (93), (1960), 475–486.
7. J. H. Barrett, Disconjugacy of second-order linear differential equations with nonnegative coefficients, *Proc. Amer. Math. Soc.* **10** (1959), 552–561.
8. J. H. Barrett, Two-point boundary value problems and comparison theorems for fourth-order self-adjoint differential equations and second-order matrix differential equations. Technical Summary Report No. 150, Mathematics Research Center, U.S. Army, Univ. of Wisconsin, Madison, Wisconsin, 1960.
9. J. H. Barrett, Disconjugacy of a self-adjoint differential equation of the fourth-order, *Pacific J. Math.* **11** (1961), 25–37.
10. J. H. Barrett, Fourth-order boundary value problems and comparison theorems, *Canad. J. Math* **13** (1961), 625–638.
11. J. H. Barrett, Systems-disconjugacy of a fourth-order differential equation, *Proc. Amer. Math. Soc.* **12** (1961), 205–213.
12. J. H. Barrett, Two-point boundary problems for linear self-adjoint differential equations of the fourth-order with middle term, *Duke. Math J.* **29**, (1962), 543–554.
13. E. F. Beckenbach and R. Bellman, " Inequalities." Springer, Berlin and New York, 1965.
14. P. R. Beesack, Nonoscillation and disconjugacy in the complex domain, *Trans. Amer. Math. Soc.* **81** (1956), 211–242.

213

15. R. Bellman, The stability of solutions of linear differential equations, *Duke Math. J.* **10** (1943), 643–647; **11**(1944), 513–516.
16. R. Bellman, The boundedness of solutions of linear differential equations, *Duke. Math. J.* **14** (1947), 83–97.
17. R. Bellman, "Stability Theory of Differential Equations." McGraw-Hill, New York, 1953.
18. R. Bellman, On the nonnegativity of Green's functions, *Boll. Un. Math.* **12** (1957), 411–413.
19. R. Bellman, Oscillatory and unimodal properties of solutions of second-order linear differential equations, *Boll. Un. Mat. Ital.* [3] **19** (1964), 306–310.
20. I. Bihari, A generalization of a lemma of Bellman and its application to uniqueness problems of differential equations, *Acta Math. Hung.* **7** (1956), 81–94.
21. G. D. Birkhoff, On solutions of ordinary linear homogeneous differential equations of the third order, *Ann. of Math.* **12** (1911), 103–127.
22. G. A. Bliss, "Lectures on the Calculus of Variations." Univ. of Chicago Press, Chicago, Illinois, 1946.
23. G. A. Bliss and I. J. Schoenberg, On separation, comparison, and oscillation theorems for self-adjoint systems of linear second-order differential equations, *Amer. J. Math.* **53** (1931), 781–800.
24. O. Bolza, "Vorlesungen über Variationsrechnung," Teubner, Berlin, 1909.
25. R. Caccioppoli, Sopra un criterio di stabilità, *Rend. Accad. Lincei* **11** (1930), 251–254.
26. D. Caligo, Un criterio sufficiente di stabilità per le soluzioni dei sistemi di equazioni integrali lineari e sue applicazioni, *Rend. Accad. Italia* [7] **1** (1940), 497–506.
27. S. A. Čaplygin, "New Methods in the Approximate Integration of Differential Equations" (Russian). Gos. Izdat. Tech.-Teoret. Lit., Moscow, 1950.
28. J. Červen, A sufficient condition for non-oscillation of solutions of a linear third-order differential equation, *Acta. Fac. Nat. Univ. Comenian.* **9** (1964), 63–70.
29. L. Cesari, "Asymptotic Behavior and Stability Problems in Ordinary Differential Equations." Springer, Berlin and New York, 1963.
30. E. S. Čičkin, The non-oscillation problem for linear equations of fourth-order, *Izv. Vysš. Učebn. Zaved. Mat.* No. 3(4) (1958), 248–250.
31. E. S. Čičkin, A non-oscillation theorem for a linear self-adjoint differential equation of fourth-order, *Izv. Vysš Učebn. Zaved. Mat.* No. 4(17) (1960), 206–209.
32. E. S. Čičkin, A theorem on a differential inequality for multi-point boundary-value problems, *Izv. Vysš Učebn. Zaved. Mat.* No. 2(27) (1962), 170–179.
33. G. Cimmino, Autosoluzioni e autovalori nelle equazioni differenziali lineari ordinarie autoaggiunte di ordine superiori, *Math. Z.* **32** (1930), 4–58.
34. C. Clark and C. A. Swanson, Comparison theorems for elliptic differential equations, *Proc. Amer. Math. Soc.* **16** (1965), 886–890.
35. E. A. Coddington and N. Levinson, "Theory of Ordinary Differential Equations," McGraw-Hill, New York, 1955.
36. L. Collatz, Application of the theory of monotonic operators to boundary value problems, *in* "Boundary Problems in Differential Equations," pp. 35–45. Publication No. 2, Mathematics Research Center, U.S. Army, Univ. of Wisconsin, Madison, Wisconsin. Univ. of Wisconsin Press, 1960.
37. L. Collatz, "Funktionalanalysis und Numerische Mathematik." Springer, Berlin and New York, 1964.
38. F. Constantinescu, Some applications of the Sturm theorem relative to a linear homogeneous differential equation of the second order, *Studia Univ. Babes–Bolyai Ser. Math.-Phys.* **7** (1962), 27–32.

39. R. Courant and D. Hilbert, "Methods of Mathematical Physics." Wiley (Interscience), New York, 1953.
40. C. de La Vallée Poussin, Sur l'équation différentielle linéaire du second ordre, *J. Math. Pures Appl.* [9] **8** (1929), 125–144.
41. G. F. D. Duff, "Partial Differential Equations." Univ. of Toronto Press, Toronto, 1956.
42. M. I. El'šin, On a solution of a classical oscillation problem, *Dokl. Akad. Nauk SSSR* **147** (1962), 1013–1016.
43. A. Erdélyi, "Asymptotic Expansions." Dover, New York, 1956.
44. A. Erdélyi *et al.*, "Higher Transcendental Functions," Vols. I and II. McGraw-Hill, New York, 1953.
45. W. B. Fite, Concerning the zeros of the solutions of certain differential equations, *Trans. Amer. Math. Soc.* **19** (1917), 341–352.
46. K. O. Friedrichs, Die Randwert-und Eigenwertprobleme aus der Theorie der elastischen Platten, *Math. Ann.* **98** (1928), 206–247.
47. K. O. Friedrichs, Spektraltheorie halbbeschränkter Operatoren und Anwendung auf die Spektralzerlegung von Differentialoperatoren, *Math. Ann.* **109** (1934), 465–487.
48. F. R. Gantmacher, "The Theory of Matrices," Vol. I. Chelsea, New York, 1959.
49. L. Gårding, On the asymptotic distribution of the eigenvalues and eigenfunctions of elliptic differential operators, *Math. Scand.* **1** (1953), 237–255.
50. I. M. Glazman, "Direct Methods of Qualitative Spectral Analysis of Singular Differential Operators" (Israel Program for Scientific Translations). Davey, New York, 1965.
51. I. M. Glazman, Oscillation theorems for differential equations of high orders and the spectrum of the respective differential operators, *Dokl. Akad. Nauk SSSR* [N.S.] **118** (1958), 423–426.
52. M. Greguš, Über einige neue Eigenschaften der Lösungen der Differentialgleichung $y''' + Qy' + Q'y = 0$, *Publ. Fac. Sci. Univ. Masaryk* (1955), 237–254.
53. M. Greguš, Die Differentialgleichung der dritten Ordnung $y''' + 2Ay' + (A' + b)y = 0$ mit allen oszillatorischen Lösungen, *Acta Fac. Nat. Univ. Comenian. Math.* **1** (1956), 41–47.
54. M. Greguš, Bermerkungen zu den oszillatorischen Eigenschaften der Lösungen der Differentialgleichung dritter Ordnung, *Acta Fac. Nat. Univ. Comenian. Math.* **3** (1958), 23–28.
55. M. Greguš, Oszillatorische Eigenschaften der Lösungen der linearen Differentialgleichung dritter Ordnung $y''' + 2Ay' + (A' + b)y = 0$, wo $A = A(x) \leq 0$ ist, *Czechoslovak Math. J.* **9** (84) (1959), 416–428.
56. M. Greguš, Über einige Eigenschaften der Lösungen der Differentialgleichung $y''' + 2Ay' + (A' + b)y = 0$, $A \leq 0$, *Czechoslovak Math. J.* **11** (86) (1961), 106–114.
57. M. Greguš, Oscillatory properties of solutions of a third order differential equation of the type $y''' + 2A(x)y' + [A'(x) + b(x)]y = 0$, *Acta Fac. Nat. Univ. Comenian. Math.* **6** (1961), 275–300.
58. L. A. Gusarov, On the boundedness of the solutions of a linear equation of the second order, *Dokl. Akad. Nauk. SSSR* [N.S.] **68** (1949), 217–220.
59. A. Haar, *Atti Congr. Internat. Mat.*, *Bologna* **3** (1928), 5–10.
60. A. Halanay and Sh. Shandar, Sturm theorems for self-conjugate systems of higher order differential equations, *Dokl. Akad. Nauk. SSSR* [N.S.] **114** (1957), 506–507.
61. M. Hanan, Oscillation criteria for third-order linear differential equations, *Pacific J. Math.* **11** (1961), 919–944.

62. P. Hartman, Differential equations with non-oscillatory eigenfunctions, *Duke Math. J.* **15** (1948), 697–709.
63. P. Hartman, On the linear logarithmico-exponential differential equation of the second order, *Amer. J. Math.* **70** (1948), 764–779.
64. P. Hartman, The number of L^2-solutions of $x'' + q(t)x = 0$, *Amer. J. Math.* **73** (1951), 635–645.
65. P. Hartman, On linear second-order differential equations with small coefficients, *Amer. J. Math.* **73** (1951), 955–962.
66. P. Hartman, Some examples in the theory of singular boundary value problems, *Amer. J. Math.* **74** (1952), 107–126.
67. P. Hartman, On non-oscillatory linear differential equations of second order, *Amer. J. Math.* **74** (1952), 389–400.
68. P. Hartman, and A. Wintner, The asymptotic arcus variation of solutions of real linear differential equations of second order, *Amer. J. Math.* **70** (1948), 1–10.
69. P. Hartman and A. Wintner, On non-conservative linear oscillations of low frequency, *Amer. J. Math.* **70** (1948), 529–539.
70. P. Hartman and A. Wintner, On the Laplace–Fourier transcendents, *Amer. J. Math.* **71** (1949), 367–372, 206–213.
71. P. Hartman and A. Wintner, Oscillatory and non-oscillatory linear differential equations, *Amer. J. Math.* **71** (1949), 627–649.
72. P. Hartman and A. Wintner, On the classical transcendents of mathematical physics, *Amer. J. Math.* **73** (1951), 381–389.
73. P. Hartman and A. Wintner, On an oscillation criterion of Liapounoff, *Amer. J. Math.* **73** (1951), 885–890.
74. P. Hartman and A. Wintner, On non-oscillatory linear differential equations, *Amer. J. Math.* **75** (1953), 717–730.
75. P. Hartman and A. Wintner, Linear differential and difference equations with monotone solutions, *Amer. J. Math.* **75** (1953), 731–743.
76. P. Hartman and A. Wintner, Linear differential equations with completely monotone solutions, *Amer. J. Math.* **76** (1954), 199–206.
77. P. Hartman and A. Wintner, On non-oscillatory linear differential equations with monotone coefficients, *Amer. J. Math.* **76** (1954), 207–219.
78. P. Hartman and A. Wintner, On the assignment of asymptotic values for the solutions of linear differential equations of second order, *Amer. J. Math.* **77** (1955), 475–483.
79. P. Hartman and A. Wintner, On a comparison theorem for self-adjoint partial differential equations of elliptic type, *Proc. Amer. Math. Soc.* **6** (1955), 862–865.
80. P. Hartman and A. Wintner, On disconjugate differential systems, *Canad. J. Math.* **8** (1956), 72–81
81. E. Hille, Non-oscillation theorems, *Trans. Amer. Math. Soc.* **64** (1948), 234–252.
82. E. Hille, Remarks on a paper by Zeev Nehari, *Bull. Amer. Math. Soc.* **55** (1949), 552–553.
83. E. Hopf, A remark on linear elliptic differential equations of the second order, *Proc. Amer. Math. Soc.* **3** (1952), 791–793.
84. H. Howard, Oscillation criteria for fourth order linear differential equations, *Trans. Amer. Math. Soc.* **96** (1960), 296–311.
85. M. Hukuhara, Sur les points singuliers des équation différentielles linéaires, *J. Fac. Sci. Univ. Hokkaido* (1) Math. **2** (1934–1936), 13–81.
86. M. Hukuhara, On the zeros of solutions of linear ordinary differential equations (Japanese), *Sûgaku* **15** (1963), 108–109.

87. M. Hukuhara and M. Nagumo, On a condition of stability for a differential equation, *Proc. Imp. Akad. Tokyo* **6** (1930), 131–132.

88. Z. Hustý, Oszillatorische Eigenschaften der Lösungen einer homogenen linearen Differentialgleichung vierter Ordnung, *Czechoslovak Math. J.* **8** (83) (1958), 62–75.

89. T. Ikebe and T. Kato, Uniqueness of the self-adjoint extension of singular elliptic differential operators, *Arch. Rational Mech. Anal.* **9** (1962), 77–92.

90. E. L. Ince, "Ordinary Differential Equations." Longmans, London, 1927 (Dover, New York, 1956).

91. R. Jentzsch, Über Integralgleichungen mit positivem Kern, *J. Reine Angew. Math.* **141** (1912), 235–245.

92. P. D. Kalafati, Oscillatory properties of the fundamental functions of third-order boundary value problems, *Dokl. Akad. Nauk SSSR* **143** (1962), 518–521.

93. E. Kamke, Zur Theorie Gewöhnlicher Differentialgleichungen II, *Acta Math.* **58** (1932), 57–85.

94. I. T. Kiguradze, Oscillatory properties of solutions of certain ordinary differential equations, *Soviet Math. Dokl.* **3** (1962), 649–652.

95. A. Kneser, Untersuchungen über die reelen Nullstellen der Integrale linearer Differentialgleichungen, *Math. Ann.* **42** (1893), 409–435; *J. Reine Angew. Math.* **116** (1896), 178–212.

96. Ju. V. Komlenko, Some criteria for nonoscillation and boundedness of solutions of linear differential equations, *Soviet Math. Dokl.* **6** (1965), 1212–1215.

97. V. A. Kondrat'ev, Elementary derivation of a necessary and sufficient condition for non-oscillation of the solutions of a linear differential equation of the second order, *Uspehi Mat. Nauk* [N.S.] **12**, No. 3 (75) (1957), 159–160.

98. V. A. Kondrat'ev, Sufficient conditions for non-oscillatory or oscillatory nature of solutions of the second-order equation $y'' + p(x)y = 0$, *Dokl. Akad. Nauk SSSR* [N.S.] **113** (1957), 742–745.

99. V. A. Kondrat'ev, On the oscillation of solutions of linear differential equations of the third and fourth order, *Dokl. Akad. Nauk SSSR* [N.S.] **118** (1958), 22–24.

100. V. A. Kondrat'ev, The zeros of solutions of the equation $y^{(n)} + p(x)y = 0$, *Dokl. Akad. Nauk SSSR* **120** (1958), 1180–1182.

101. V. A. Kondrat'ev, Oscillation of solutions of linear equations of third and fourth order, *Trudy Moskov. Mat. Obšč.* **8** (1959), 259–281.

102. V. A. Kondrat'ev, Oscillatory properties of solutions of the equation $y^{(n)} + p(x)y = 0$, *Trudy Moskov. Mat. Obšč.* **10** (1961), 419–436.

103. K. Kreith, A new proof of a comparison theorem for elliptic equations, *Proc. Amer. Math. Soc.* **14** (1963), 33–35.

104. K. Kreith, Comparison theorems for constrained rods, *SIAM Rev.* **6** (1964), 31–36.

105. K. Kreith, Oscillation theorems for elliptic equations, *Proc. Amer. Math. Soc.* **15** (1964), 341–344.

106. K. Kreith, A strong comparison theorem for self-adjoint elliptic equations, *Proc. Amer. Math. Soc.* (To be published.)

107. K. Kreith, A remark on a comparison theorem of Swanson, *Proc. Amer. Math. Soc.* (To be published.)

108. L. M. Kuks, Sturm's theorem and oscillation of solutions of strongly elliptic systems, *Soviet Math. Dokl.* **3** (1962), 24–27.

109. C. E. Langenhop, Bounds on the norm of a solution of a general differential equation, *Proc. Amer. Math. Soc.* **11** (1960), 795–799.

110. P. D. Lax, On Cauchy's problem for hyperbolic equations and the differentiability of solutions of elliptic equations, *Comm. Pure Appl. Math.* **8** (1955), 615–633. (This paper contains a large number of references.)

111. A. C. Lazer, The behavior of solutions of the differential equation $y''' + p(x)y' + q(x)y = 0$, *Pacific J. Math.* **17** (1966), 435–466.

112. W. Leighton, Principal quadratic functionals and self-adjoint second-order differential equations, *Proc. Nat. Acad. Sci. U.S.A.* **35** (1949), 190–191, 192–193.

113. W. Leighton, On self-adjoint differential equations of second order, *Proc. Nat. Acad. Sci. U.S.A.* **35** (1949), 656–657.

114. W. Leighton, The detection of the oscillation of solutions of a second order linear differential equation, *Duke Math. J.* **17** (1950), 57–62.

115. W. Leighton, On self-adjoint differential equations of second order, *J. London Math. Soc.* **27** (1952), 37–47.

116. W. Leighton, Comparison theorems for linear differential equations of second order, *Proc. Amer. Math. Soc.* **13** (1962), 603–610.

117. W. Leighton and Z. Nehari, On the oscillation of solutions of self-adjoint linear differential equations of the fourth order, *Trans. Amer. Math. Soc.* **89** (1958), 325–377.

118. A. Ju. Levin, A comparison principle for second-order differential equations, *Soviet Math. Dokl.* **1** (1960), 1313–1316.

119. A. Ju. Levin, Some problems bearing on the oscillation of solutions of linear differential equations, *Soviet Math. Dokl.* **4** (1963), 121–124.

120. A. Ju. Levin, Distribution of the zeros of solutions of a linear differential equation, *Soviet Math. Dokl.* **5** (1964), 818–821.

121. A. Ju. Levin, Integral criteria for the equation $x'' + q(t)x = 0$ to be non-oscillatory, *Uspehi Mat. Nauk* **20** (1965), 244–246.

122. N. Levinson, The growth of the solutions of a differential equation, *Duke Math. J.* **8** (1941), 1–10.

123. N. Levinson, The asymptotic behavior of a system of linear differential equations, *Amer. J. Math.* **68** (1946), 1–6.

124. N. Levinson, A remark about Wintner's comparison theorem, *Duke Math. J.* **25** (1958), 519–520.

125. D. London, On the zeros of the solutions of $w''(z) + p(z)w(z) = 0$, *Pacific J. Math.* **12** (1962), 979–991.

126. L. Lorch and J. D. Newman, A supplement to the Sturm separation theorem, with applications, *Amer. Math. Monthly* **72** (1965), 359–366.

127. L. Lorch and P. Szegö, Higher monotonicity properties of certain Sturm–Liouville functions, *Acta. Math.* **109** (1963), 55–73.

128. G. Mammana, Decomposizione delle espressioni differenziali lineari omogenee in prodotti di fattori simbolici e applicazione rellativa allo studio delle equazioni differenziali lineari, *Math. Z.* **33** (1931), 186–231.

129. J. Mařík and M. Ráb, Asymptotische Eigenschaften von Lösungen der Differentialgleichung $y'' = A(x)y$ im nichtszillatorischen Fall, *Czechoslovak Math. J.* **10** (85) (1960), 501–522.

130. S. G. Mikhlin, "Variational Methods in Mathematical Physics." Macmillan, New York, 1964.

131. S. G. Mikhlin, "The Problem of the Minimum of a Quadratic Functional." Holden-Day, San Francisco, 1965.

132. J. Mikusiński, Sur l'équation $x^{(n)} + A(t)x = 0$, *Ann. Polon. Math.* **1** (1955), 207–221.

133. J. C. P. Miller, On a criterion for oscillatory solutions of a linear differential equation of the second order, *Proc. Cambridge Philos. Soc.* **36** (1940), 283–287.

134. R. A. Moore, The behavior of solutions of a linear differential equation of second order, *Pacific J. Math.* **5** (1955), 125–145.

135. R. A. Moore, The least eigenvalue of Hill's equation, *J. Analyse Math.* **5** (1956–1957), 183–196.

136. M. Morse, A generalization of the Sturm separation and comparison theorems in n-space, *Math. Ann.* **103** (1930), 52–69.

137. M. Morse, "The Calculus of Variations in the Large" (Colloq. Publ., Vol. 18). *Amer. Math. Soc.*, Providence, Rhode Island, 1934.

138. M. Morse and W. Leighton, Singular quadratic functionals, *Trans. Amer. Math. Soc.* **40** (1936), 252–286.

139. M. Nagumo, Über die Ungleichung $\partial u/\partial x > f(x, y, u, \partial u/\partial x)$, *Japan. J. Math.* **15** (1938), 51–56.

140. Z. Nehari, The Schwarzian derivative and schlicht functions, *Bull. Amer. Math. Soc.* **55** (1949), 545–551.

141. Z. Nehari, Some criteria of univalence, *Proc. Amer. Math. Soc.* **5** (1954), 700–704.

142. Z. Nehari, On the zeros of solutions of second-order linear differential equations, *Amer. J. Math.* **76** (1954), 689–697.

143. Z. Nehari, Oscillation criteria for second-order linear differential equations, *Trans. Amer. Math. Soc.* **85** (1957), 428–445.

144. V. V. Nemyckii and V. V. Stepanov, "Qualitative Theory of Differential Equations" (Russian). OGIZ, Moscow, 1947 [English translation, Princeton Univ. Press, Princeton New Jersey, 1960].

145. L. D. Nikolenko, Some criteria for non-oscillation of a fourth-order differential equation, *Dokl. Akad. Nauk SSSR* [*N.S.*] **114** (1957), 483–485.

146. O. K. Omel'čenko, The distribution of zeros of eigenfunctions of a self-adjoint elliptic operator of second-order, *Izv. Vysš. Učebn. Zaved. Mat.* No. 4 (5) (1958) 184–190.

147. R. Osserman, On the inequality $\Delta u \geq f(u)$, *Pacific J. Math.* **7** (1957), 1641–1647.

148. I. A. Pavlyuk, A necessary and sufficient condition for non-oscillation of solutions of a linear differential equation of second order, *Kiiv Derž Univ. Nauk Zap.* **16** (1957) [*Kiev. Gos. Univ. Mat. Sb.* **9** (1957), 111–113.]

149. M. Picone, *Ann. Scuola Norm. Sup. Pisa* **11** (1909), 39.

150. Åke Pleijel, On the eigenvalues and eigenfunctions of elastic plates, *Comm. Pure Appl. Math.* **3** (1950), 1–10.

151. V. V. Pokornyi, On some sufficient conditions for univalence, *Dokl. Akad. Nauk SSSR* [*N.S.*] **79** (1951), 743–746.

152. R. L. Potter, On self-adjoint differential equations of second order, *Pacific J. Math.* **3** (1953), 467–491.

153. M. H. Protter, A comparison theorem for elliptic equations, *Proc. Amer. Math. Soc.* **10** (1959), 296–299.

154. M. H. Protter, Lower bounds for the first eigenvalue of elliptic equations, *Ann. of Math.* **71** (1960), 423–444.

155. M. H. Protter and H. F. Weinberger, On the spectrum of general second order operators, *Bull. Amer. Math. Soc.* **72** (1966), 251–255.

156. M. H. Protter and H. F. Weinberger, "Maximum Principles in Differential Equations." Prentice Hall, Englewood Cliffs, New Jersey, 1967.

157. C. R. Putnam, An oscillation criterion involving a minimum principle, *Duke Math. J.* **16** (1949), 633–636.

158. C. R. Putnam, On the first stability interval of the Hill equation, *Quart. Appl. Math.* **16**, No. 4, (1959), 421–422.

159. M. Ráb, Oszillatorische Eigenschaften der Lösungen linearer Differentialgleichungen 3 Ordnung, *Acta Acad. Sci. Čechoslovenicae Basis Brunensis* **27** (1955), 349–360.

160. M. Ráb, Asymptotische Eigenschaften der Lösungen linearer Differentialgleichung dritter Ordnung, *Publ. Fac. Sci. Univ. Masaryk* (1956), 177–184, 441–454.

161. M. Ráb, Über die Differentialgleichung $y''' + 2A(x)y' + (A'(x) + w(x))y = 0$, *Mat. -Fyz. Časopis. Sloven. Akad. Vied* **8** (1958), 115–122.

162. M. Ráb, Über eine Verallgemeinerung eines Satzes von Sansone über Nichtoszillation der Lösungen der Differentialgleichung $y''' + 2A(x)y' + (A'(x) + w(x))y = 0$, *Mat. -Fyz. Časopis. Sloven. Akad. Vied* **10** (1960), 3–8.

163. M. Ráb, Kriterien für die Oszillation der Lösungen der Differentialgleichung $[p(x)y']'$ $+ q(x)y = 0$, *Časopis. Pěst. Mat.* **84** (1959), 335–370; *erratum* **85** (1960), 91.

164. R. Redheffer, A Sturmian theorem for partial differential equations, *Proc. Amer. Math. Soc.* **8** (1957), 458–462.

165. R. Redheffer, Maximum principles and duality, *Monatsh. Math.* **62** (1958), 56–75.

166. R. Redheffer, On entire solutions of nonlinear differential equations, *Proc. Nat. Acad. Sci. USA* **45** (1959), 1292–1294.

167. R. Redheffer, On the inequality $\Delta u \geq f(u, |\text{grad } u|)$, *J. Math. Anal. Appl.* **1** (1960), 277–299.

168. W. T. Reid, A matrix differential equation of Riccati type, *Amer. J. Math.* **68** (1946), 237–246, 460.

169. W. T. Reid, Oscillation criteria for linear differential systems with complex coefficients, *Pacific J. Math.* **6** (1956), 733–751.

170. W. T. Reid, A comparison theorem for self-adjoint differential equations of second order, *Ann. of Math.* [2]**65** (1957), 197–202.

171. W. T. Reid, Principal solutions of non-oscillatory self-adjoint linear differential equations, *Pacific J. Math.* **8** (1958), 147–169.

172. W. T. Reid, Oscillation criteria for self-adjoint differential systems, *Trans. Amer. Math. Soc.* **101** (1961), 91–106.

173. C. N. Reynolds, Jr., On the zeros of solutions of homogeneous linear differential equations, *Trans. Amer. Math. Soc.* **22** (1921), 220–229.

174. I. A. Rus, On Sturm-type theorems (Romanian), *Studia Univ. Babes-Bolyai Ser. Math.-Phys.* **7** (1962), 33–36.

175. G. Sansone, Studi sulle equazioni differenziali lineari omogenee di terzo ordine nel campo reale, *Univ. Nac. Tucuman Rev.* **A6** (1948), 195–253.

176. L. I. Schiff, "Quantum Mechanics." McGraw-Hill, New York, 1949.

177. J. Schröder, Fehlerabschätzungen bei gewöhnlichen und partiellen Differential-gleichungen, *Arch. Rat. Mech. Anal.* **2** (1958–1959), 367–392.

178. J. Schröder, Monotonie-Eigenschaften bei Differentialgleichungen, *Arch. Rat. Mech. Anal.* **14** (1963), 38–60.

179. J. Schröder, Differential Inequalities and Error Bounds, from "Error in Digital Computation," Vol. 2, pp. 141–179. Publication No. 15, Mathematics Research Center, U.S. Army, Univ. of Wisconsin, Madison, Wisconsin. Wiley, New York, 1965.

180. V. Ja. Skorobogat'ko, Theorems in the qualitative theory of second order partial differential equations, *Ukrain. Mat. Ž.* **8** (1956), 435–440.

181. E. Śliwiński, On some oscillation problems for the equation $\Delta^n u - f(r)u = 0$ in a three-dimensional space, *Prace Mat.* **8** (1963–64), 119–120.

182. H. M. Sternberg and R. L. Sternberg, A two-point boundary problem for ordinary self-adjoint differential equations of fourth order, *Canad. J. Math.* **6** (1954), 416–419.

183. R. L. Sternberg, Variational methods and non-oscillation theorems for systems of differential equations, *Duke Math. J.* **19** (1952), 311–322.

184. C. Sturm, Sur les équations différentielles linéaires du second ordre, *J. Math. Pures Appl.* **1** (1836), 106–186.
185. M. Švec, Über einige neue Eigenschaften der oszillatorischen Lösungen der linearen homogenen Differentialgleichung vierter Ordnung, *Czechoslovak Math. J.* **4** (79) (1954), 75–94.
186. M. Švec, Sur les dispersions de l'équation $y^{iv} + Q(x)y = 0$, *Czechoslovak Math. J.* **5** (80) (1955), 29–60.
187. M. Švec, Sur une propriété des intégrales de l'équation $y^{(n)} + Q(x)y = 0$, $n = 3, 4$, *Czechoslovak Math. J.* **7** (82) (1957), 450–462.
188. M. Švec, Asymptotische Darstellung der Lösungen der Differentialgleichung $y^{(n)} + Q(x)y = 0$, $n = 3, 4$ *Czechoslovak Math. J.* **12** (87) (1962), 572–581.
189. M. Švec, Some remarks on a third order linear differential equation (Russian), *Czechoslovak Math. J.* **15** (90) (1965), 42–49.
190. C. A. Swanson, A comparison theorem for elliptic differential equations, *Proc. Amer. Math. Soc.* **17** (1966), 611–616.
191. C. A. Swanson, A generalization of Sturm's comparison theorem, *J. Math. Anal. Appl.* **15** (1966), 512–519.
192. C. A. Swanson, Comparison theorems for elliptic equations on unbounded domains, *Trans. Amer. Math. Soc.* **126** (1967), 278–285.
193. C. A. Swanson, An identity for elliptic equations with applications, *Trans. Amer. Math. Soc.* (in press).
194. C. A. Swanson and V. B. Headley, An extension of Airy's equation, *SIAM J. Appl. Math.* **15** (1967), 1400–1412.
195. J. Szarski, Sur un système d'inégalitiés différentielles, *Ann. Soc. Polon. Math.* **20** (1947), 126–134.
196. J. Szarski, Sur certains systèmes d'inégalitiés différentielles aux dérivées partielles du premier ordre, *Ann. Soc. Polon. Math.* **21** (1948), 7–26.
197. J. Szarski "Differential Inequalities." Polish Sci. Publ., Warsaw, 1965.
198. C.-T. Taam, Non-oscillatory differential equations, *Duke Math. J.* **19** (1952), 493–497.
199. C.-T. Taam, Non-oscillation and comparison theorems of linear differential equations with complex-valued coefficients, *Portugul. Math.* **12** (1953), 57–72.
200. C.-T. Taam, On the solutions of second order linear differential equations, *Proc. Amer. Math. Soc.* **6** (1953), 876–879.
201. A. G. Teterev, Čaplygin's theorem for elliptic equations, *Soviet Math. Dokl.* **1** (1961), 1174–1176.
202. S. Toni, Su alcune estensioni di un teorema di Sturm, *Math. Notae* **17** (1959), 30–36.
203. G. Villari, Sul carattera oscillatario delle soluzioni delle equazioni differenziali lineari omogonee del terzo ordine, *Boll. Un. Mat. Ital* [3] **13** (1958), 73–78.
204. G. Villari, Contributi allo studio asintotico del l'equazioni $x'''(t) + p(t)x(t) = 0$, *Ann. Math. Pura Appl.* **51** (1960), 301–328.
205. T. Ważewski, Systèmes des équations et des inégalitiés différentielles ordinaires aux deuxièmes membres monotones et leurs applications, *Ann. Soc. Polon. Math.* **23** (1950), 112–166.
206. H. F. Weinberger, A maximum property of Cauchy's problem, *Ann. of Math.* [2] **64** (1956), 505–513.
207. D. V. V. Wend, On the zeros of solutions of some linear complex differential equations, *Pacific J. Math.* **10** (1960), 713–722.
208. H. Westphal, Zur Abschätzung der Lösungen nichtlinearer parabolischer Differentialgleichungen, *Math. Z.* **51** (1949), 690–695.

209. H. Weyl, Comment on the preceding paper of N. Levinson, *Amer. J. Math.* **68** (1946), 7–12.
210. W. M. Whyburn, On self-adjoint ordinary differential equations of the fourth order, *Amer. J. Math.* **52** (1930), 171–196.
211. A. Wintner, On the Laplace–Fourier transcendents occurring in mathematical physics, *Amer. J. Math.* **69** (1947), 87–98.
212. A. Wintner, A norm criterion for non-oscillatory differential equations, *Quart. Appl. Math.* **6** (1948), 183–185.
213. A. Wintner, A criterion of oscillatory stability, *Quart. Appl. Math.* **7** (1949), 115–117.
214. A. Wintner, On free vibrations with amplitudinal limits, *Quart. Appl. Math.* **8** (1950), 102–104.
215. A. Wintner, On the non-existence of conjugate points, *Amer. J. Math.* **73** (1951), 368–380.
216. A. Wintner, On the comparison theorem of Kneser–Hille, *Math Scand.* **5** (1957), 255–260.
217. A. Wintner, Energy dissipation and linear stability, *Quart. Appl. Math.* **15** (1957), 263–268.
218. A. Wintner, A comparison theorem for Sturmian oscillation numbers of linear systems of second order, *Duke Math. J.* **25** (1958), 515–518.
219. A. Wiman, Über die reellen Lösungen der linearen Differentialgleichungen zweiter Ordnung, *Ark. Mat. Astr. Fys.* **12**, No. 14 (1917), 22 pp.
220. V. A. Yakubovič, Oscillatory properties of the solutions of standard linear sets of simultaneous differential equations, *Dokl. Akad. Nauk SSSR* **124** (1959), 533–536.
221. V. A. Yakubovič, Oscillation and non-oscillation conditions for canonical linear sets of simultaneous differential equations, *Dokl. Akad. Nauk SSSR* **124** (1959), 994–997.
222. M. Zlamal, Asymptotic properties of the solutions of third-order linear differential equations, *Publ. Fac. Sci. Univ. Masaryk* (1951–1956).
223. A. F. Zoobawa, Concerning oscillation of the solutions of an equation of the second order, *Vestnik Leningrad. Univ.* **12**, No. 1 (1957), 168–174, 211.

Author Index

Numbers in parentheses are reference numbers and indicate that an author's work is referred to, although his name is not cited in the text. Numbers in italics show the page on which the complete reference is listed.

A

Anan'eva, G. V., 168(1), 174, 175, *213*
Aramă, O., 168(2), 176, *213*
Aronszajn, N., 189, 210, *213*
Atkinson, F. V., 176, *213*
Azbelev, N. V., 149, 164, 169, 170, 175, 176, *213*

B

Balaganskii, V. I., 168(1), 174, 175, *213*
Barrett, J. H., 95, 126, 128, 129, 131, 136, 177, 184, 185, *213*
Beckenbach, E. F., 7, 15, 167(13), *213*
Beesack, P. R., *213*
Bellman, R., 7, 15, 45, 95, 167(13), 168, 185, *213*, *214*
Bihari, I., 7, *214*
Birkhoff, G. D., 149, 154, 156, 157(21), 160, 165, *214*
Bliss, G. A., 177, *214*
Bolza, O., 3(24), *214*

C

Caccioppoli, R., 95, *214*
Caligo, D., 95, 168, 185, *214*
Caljuk, Z. B., 149, 164, 170(6), 175, 176, *213*
Čaplygin, S. A., 7, 15, *214*
Červen, J., 164, *214*
Cesari, L., 95, 168, 185, *214*
Čičkin, E. S., 149, 168(32), 169, 172, 176, *214*
Cimmino, G., 114, 149, *214*
Clark, C., 186, *214*
Coddington, E. A., 3(35), 33(35), 37(35), 63(35), 104(35), 105(35), 114(35), 129(35), 153(35), 165(35), 171(35), 175(35), 187(35), *214*
Collatz, L., 203, *214*
Constantinescu, F., *214*
Courant, R., 21, 28, 103, 104(39), 113, 209, *215*

D

de La Vallée Poussin, C., 169, 215
Duff, G. F. D., 210(41), 215

E

El'šin, M. I., 168(42), 176, 215
Erdélyi, A., 20(43, 44), 40(44), 41 (44), 42(44), 43(44), 215

F

Fite, W. B., 45, 120, 173, 215
Friedrichs, K. O., 113, 215

G

Gantmacher, F. R., 11(48), 191, 215
Gårding, L., 104(49), 215
Glazman, I. M., 104(50), 168, 174, 167, 205(50), 207, 208, 215
Greguš, M., 149, 160, 163, 164, 215
Gusarov, L. A., 95, 215

H

Haar, A., 7, 202, 215
Halanay, A., 168(60), 176, 215
Hanan, M., 149, 150, 151, 152, 153(61), 156, 157, 160, 215
Hartman, P., 33, 45, 63, 65, 66, 80, 88, 89, 90(76), 92, 94, 187, 216
Headley, V. B., 81(194), 221
Hilbert, D., 21(39), 28, 103, 104(39), 113, 209(39), 215
Hille, E., 33, 45, 60, 69, 85, 109, 111, 177, 216
Hopf, E., 194, 216
Howard, H., 55, 58, 114, 136, 139, 145, 147, 216
Hukuhara, M., 95, 168(86), 176, 216, 217
Hustý, Z., 176, 217

I

Ikebe, T., 203, 204(89), 217
Ince, E. L., 2(90), 6(90), 23(90), 165(90), 175, 217

J

Jentzsch, R., 134, 210, 217

K

Kalafati, P. D., 164, 176, 217
Kamke, E., 7, 217
Kato, T., 203, 204(89), 217
Kiguradze, I. T., 149, 168, 173, 176, 217
Kneser, A., 45, 175, 217
Komlenko, Ju. V., 149, 168, 175, 217
Kondrat'ev, V. A., 149, 154, 163, 164, 167(101), 168, 170, 173, 176, 217
Kreith, K., 114, 134, 194, 205, 206, 217
Kuks, L. M., 191, 207, 211(108), 217

L

Langenhop, C. E., 7, 217
Lax, P. D., 7, 218
Lazer, A. C., 149, 155, 158, 160, 163, 164, 218
Leighton, W., 2, 4, 5, 8, 9, 45, 48, 74, 112, 114, 121, 128, 142, 150, 177, 218, 219
Levin, A. Ju., 33, 149, 168, 169, 171, 172, 176, 218
Levinson, N., 3(35), 33(35), 37(35), 45, 63(35), 104(35), 105(35), 114 (35), 129(35), 153(35), 165(35), 168, 171(35), 175(35), 177, 185, 187(35), 214, 218
London, D., 109, 218
Lorch, L., 38, 218

M

Mammana, G., 149, 152, 157, 218
Mařík, J., 95, 218
Mikhlin, S. G., 21(130), 24, 28, 104 (131), 134, 218
Mikusiński, J., 168(132), 176, 218
Miller, J. C. P., 218
Moore, R. A., 45, 73, 104, 106, 107, 109, 112, 219
Morse, M., 38, 177, 219

N

Nagumo, M., 95, 202, 216, 219
Nehari, Z., 45, 46, 52, 56(143), 96,
  103(143), 109, 110, 114, 121, 128,
  142, 150, 218, 219
Nemyckii, V. V., 7, 219
Newman, J. D., 38, 218
Nikolenko, L. D., 219

O

Omel'čenko, O. K., 219
Osserman, R., 202, 203, 219

P

Pavlyuk, I. A., 176, 219
Picone, M., 2, 219
Pleijel, Åke, 113, 219
Pokornyi, V. V., 111, 219
Potter, R. L., 45, 76(152), 96, 99, 112,
  219
Protter, M. H., 191, 194, 203, 204(154),
  219
Putnam, C. R., 176, 219

R

Ráb, M., 31, 95, 149, 160, 164, 177,
  218, 220
Redheffer, R., 7, 202, 203, 220
Reid, W. T., 31, 150, 177, 178, 179,
  180, 181, 182, 220
Reynolds, C. N., Jr., 114, 149, 165, 166,
  220
Rus, I. A., 220

S

Samsone, G., 149, 152, 220
Schiff, L. I., 20(176), 28, 68(176),
  220
Schoenberg, I. J., 177, 214
Schröder, J., 7, 167(179), 202, 203,
  220

Shandar, Sh., 168(60), 176, 215
Skorobogat'ko, V. Ja., 220
Śliwiński, E., 207, 220
Stepanov, V. V., 7, 219
Sternberg, H. M., 129, 220
Sternberg, R. L., 114, 129, 150, 177,
  178, 220
Sturm, C., 1, 2, 221
Švec, M., 114, 149, 160, 164, 221
Swanson, C. A., 18(192), 81(194),
  114, 210(191), 186, 214, 221
Szarski, J., 7(205), 167(197), 202,
  221
Szegö, P., 218

T

Taam, C. -T, 62(199, 200), 160, 221
Teterev, A. G., 221
Toni, S., 221

V

Villari, G., 149, 160, 164, 221

W

Ważewski, T., 7, 221
Weinberger, H. F., 32, 203, 204, 219,
  221
Wend, D. V. V., 112, 221
Westphal, H., 7, 202, 221
Weyl, H., 168, 185, 222
Whyburn, W. M., 114, 150, 183, 222
Wiman, A., 95, 222
Wintner, A., 33(69–74), 45, 48, 60, 63,
  65, 66, 67, 80, 88, 89, 90(76), 92,
  94, 177, 187, 216, 222

Y

Yakubovič, V. A., 183, 222

Z

Zlamal, M., 149, 160, 222
Zoobawa, A. F., 176, 222

Subject Index

Airy equation, 7
  generalized, 81
Bessel function, 40, 41, 81
Bessel's equation, 7, 40, 76
Completely monotone function, 90
Confluent hypergeometric function, 42
Conjugate point
  of fourth order equations, 119–128, 131, 132, 135, 136, 140, 142
  of third order equations, 149–159
  of nth order equations, 168–171
  of systems of equations, 177, 184
Convex boundary, 106
Convex set, 105
Coulomb wave functions, 42
Courant's minimum principle, 21, 26, 27, 47, 53, 57, 103, 104, 114, 123, 132, 136, 150, 177, 208–211
Differential equation
  of class I, 151–157
    II, 151–157
  conditionally oscillatory, 52–55
  elliptic, 186–212
  nonoscillatory of second order, 40, 44–56, 60–95, 104–107, 109–112
    of third order, 150–152, 158–165, 171
    of fourth order, 115, 119–121, 126, 129, 134–148, 171–172
    of nth order, 172–175
    elliptic, 207
  oscillatory of second order, 44–46, 52–62, 67–81, 84–88, 95, 97, 101, 104, 106, 207
    of third order, 149–165
    of fourth order, 113–115, 119–121, 127, 128, 143–148
    of nth order, 173–175
  singular, 16, 63
  strongly nonoscillatory, 52, 56
  strongly oscillatory, 52, 56

Differential inequality, 6, 7, 14, 167, 202, 203
Disconjugacy criteria, 95, 184, 185
Disconjugate equation, 109–112, 185
Domain
  of differential operator, 1, 16, 21, 133, 198, 203
  of quadratic functional, 3, 4, 11, 17–22, 25, 188, 191–200, 209
Eigenfunction
  of second order equations, 20–28, 33, 47, 53, 57
  of fourth order equations, 103, 113, 122, 123, 132–134, 146
  orthogonal, 22, 28, 103, 113, 114, 134, 210
  of partial differential equations, 187, 204–211
Eigenvalue
  of second order equations, 21–28, 32, 33, 46, 47, 53–60, 96, 98, 103, 104
  of fourth order equations, 113, 114, 122–124, 132–137, 145–147
  of even order equations, 150, 177
  nondegenerate, 22
  of partial differential equations, 187, 203–211
  of systems of differential equations, 181, 182
Eigensolution, 67–68
Elliptic differential equation, 186–212
  nonoscillatory, 207
  oscillatory, 205, 206
  separable, 205–207
Focal condition, 129
Focal point, 29–32
  for systems, 177
Green's formula, 3, 6, 13, 18, 23, 187–210
Harmonic oscillator, 20, 205
Hermite equation, 76

226

Hermite polynomial, 20, 43
Hill's equation, 104–109
  nonoscillatory, 104–107
Homogeneous boundary condition, 21, 23,
  114, 134–137, 208–210
Hypergeometric function, 42
Integral equation, 34, 36, 68, 69, 113, 166,
  179, 210
Interval of nonoscillation, 168, 170
Interval of oscillation, 168–170
  of even (odd) oscillation type, 169–170
Laguerre function, 43
Laguerre's equation, 76
Legendre polynomial, 42–43
Limit cylindrical domain, 206
Mathieu equation, 108
Matrix, 177–182, 185–210
  negative semidefinite, 178
  positive definite, 178, 181, 182, 186–193,
    197, 204, 208, 210
  positive semidefinite, 178–182, 187, 189,
    193, 197, 198, 202, 206, 210
  symplectic, 183
Nodal domain, 205–208
Nodal property, 205–208
Nonoscillation criteria, *see* Oscillation criteria
Number of zeros, asymptotic formula for,
  95–104
Operator
  boundary, 21, 25, 133, 208–211
  differential, 1, 4, 6, 7, 21, 25, 74, 132–134,
    171–173, 187, 188, 197, 200, 203, 208,
    210
  inverse positive, 7
  Laplacian, 189, 207
Oscillation constant, 52–55
Oscillation criteria
  for second order equations, 15, 33, 45–56,
    63–88, 95
  for third order equations, 149, 156–165
  for fourth order equations, 135–148, 172
  for nth order equations, 168–177
  for complex equations, 109–112

for elliptic equations, 187, 205–208
for Hill's equation, 104–109
for systems of equations, 150, 177–184
Osgood's theorem, 76
Periodic function, 104–109
Periodic solution, 104
Quadratic form, 11, 191, 198
  positive definite, 193, 196, 211
  positive semidefinite, 11, 12, 17, 191, 192,
    195, 199, 211
Quadratic functional, 2, 4, 11, 13, 17, 18,
  21, 22, 25, 46, 101, 132, 133, 188,
  191–200, 208–211
Rayleigh quotient, 114, 123, 137, 146
Riccati equation, 33, 34, 60, 69, 82, 92,
  178
Riccati's inequality, 93
Schrödinger operator, 202, 203, 205, 207
Separation theorems
  for second order equations, 5, 8, 166
  for third order equations, 149–155, 166
  for fourth order equations, 114–122
  for nth order equations, 165–167
  for systems, 150, 177, 183
Solution, 1, 11, 16, 186
  principal, 120–122, 127, 152
  trivial, 2
  zero-maximal, 39–43
Stability criteria, 95, 168, 185
Stability theory, 7, 95, 168, 185
Strict Sturmian majorant, 5, 10, 14, 16, 19,
  187, 189, 193, 194, 197, 198, 202, 206
Subsolution, 7, 8, 15, 20, 187, 198–202
Supersolution, 7, 8, 15, 20, 198–202, 205
System of differential equations, 150, 168,
  177–185
  nonoscillatory, 177–184
  oscillation criteria for, 177–184
  oscillatory, 182, 184
Variation, 4, 6, 18, 26, 29, 133, 135, 186,
  189, 192, 196, 200, 209
Wiman's asymptotic formula, 95–99, 101,
  104
  extension of, 99

Mathematics in Science and Engineering

A Series of Monographs and Textbooks

Edited by RICHARD BELLMAN, *University of Southern California*

1. TRACY Y. THOMAS. Concepts from Tensor Analysis and Differential Geometry. Second Edition. 1965
2. TRACY Y. THOMAS. Plastic Flow and Fracture in Solids. 1961
3. RUTHERFORD ARIS. The Optimal Design of Chemical Reactors: A Study in Dynamic Programming. 1961
4. JOSEPH LaSALLE and SOLOMON LEFSCHETZ. Stability by Liapunov's Direct Method with Applications. 1961
5. GEORGE LEITMANN (ed.). Optimization Techniques: With Applications to Aerospace Systems. 1962
6. RICHARD BELLMAN and KENNETH L. COOKE. Differential-Difference Equations. 1963
7. FRANK A. HAIGHT. Mathematical Theories of Traffic Flow. 1963
8. F. V. ATKINSON. Discrete and Continuous Boundary Problems. 1964
9. A. JEFFREY and T. TANIUTI. Non-Linear Wave Propagation: With Applications to Physics and Magnetohydrodynamics. 1964
10. JULIUS T. TOU. Optimum Design of Digital Control Systems. 1963
11. HARLEY FLANDERS. Differential Forms: With Applications to the Physical Sciences. 1963
12. SANFORD M. ROBERTS. Dynamic Programming in Chemical Engineering and Process Control. 1964
13. SOLOMON LEFSCHETZ. Stability of Nonlinear Control Systems. 1965
14. DIMITRIS N. CHORAFAS. Systems and Simulation. 1965
15. A. A. PERVOZVANSKII. Random Processes in Nonlinear Control Systems. 1965
16. MARSHALL C. PEASE, III. Methods of Matrix Algebra. 1965
17. V. E. BENES. Mathematical Theory of Connecting Networks and Telephone Traffic. 1965
18. WILLIAM F. AMES. Nonlinear Partial Differential Equations in Engineering. 1965
19. J. ACZEL. Lectures on Functional Equations and Their Applications. 1966
20. R. E. MURPHY. Adaptive Processes in Economic Systems. 1965
21. S. E. DREYFUS. Dynamic Programming and the Calculus of Variations. 1965
22. A. A. FEL'DBAUM. Optimal Control Systems. 1965
23. A. HALANAY. Differential Equations: Stability, Oscillations, Time Lags. 1966
24. M. NAMIK OGUZTORELI. Time-Lag Control Systems. 1966
25. DAVID SWORDER. Optimal Adaptive Control Systems. 1966
26. MILTON ASH. Optimal Shutdown Control of Nuclear Reactors. 1966
27. DIMITRIS N. CHORAFAS. Control System Functions and Programming Approaches (In Two Volumes). 1966
28. N. P. ERUGIN. Linear Systems of Ordinary Differential Equations. 1966
29. SOLOMON MARCUS. Algebraic Linguistics; Analytical Models. 1967
30. A. M. LIAPUNOV. Stability of Motion. 1966

31. GEORGE LEITMANN (ed.). Topics in Optimization. 1967
32. MASANAO AOKI. Optimization of Stochastic Systems. 1967
33. HAROLD J. KUSHNER. Stochastic Stability and Control. 1967
34. MINORU URABE. Nonlinear Autonomous Oscillations. 1967
35. F. CALOGERO. Variable Phase Approach to Potential Scattering. 1967
36. A. KAUFMANN. Graphs, Dynamic Programming, and Finite Games. 1967
37. A. KAUFMANN and R. CRUON. Dynamic Programming: Sequential Scientific Management. 1967
38. J. H. AHLBERG, E. N. NILSON, and J. L. WALSH. The Theory of Splines and Their Applications. 1967
39. Y. SAWARAGI, Y. SUNAHARA, and T. NAKAMIZO. Statistical Decision Theory in Adaptive Control Systems. 1967
40. RICHARD BELLMAN. Introduction to the Mathematical Theory of Control Processes Volume I. 1967 (Volumes II and III in preparation)
41. E. STANLEY LEE. Quasilinearization and Invariant Imbedding. 1968
42. WILLIAM AMES. Nonlinear Ordinary Differential Equations in Transport Processes. 1968
43. WILLARD MILLER, JR. Lie Theory and Special Functions. 1968
44. PAUL B. BAILEY, LAWRENCE F. SHAMPINE, and PAUL E. WALTMAN. Nonlinear Two Point Boundary Value Problems. 1968
45. IU. P. PETROV. Variational Methods in Optimum Control Theory. 1968
46. O. A. LADYZHENSKAYA and N. N. URAL'TSEVA. Linear and Quasilinear Elliptic Equations. 1968
47. A. KAUFMANN and R. FAURE. Introduction to Operations Research. 1968
48. C. A. SWANSON. Comparison and Oscillation Theory of Linear Differential Equations. 1968
49. ROBERT HERMANN. Differential Geometry and the Calculus of Variations. 1968
50. N. K. JAISWAL. Priority Queues. 1968

In preparation

ROBERT P. GILBERT. Function Theoretic Methods in the Theory of Partial Differential Equations
YUDELL LUKE. The Special Functions and Their Approximations (In Two Volumes)
HUKUKANE NIKAIDO. Convex Structures and Economic Theory
V. LAKSHMIKANTHAM and S. LEELA. Differential and Integral Inequalities
KING-SUN FU. Sequential Methods in Pattern Recognition and Machine Learning